CLEARING PATHS

CONSULTANTS

Mildred Bailey

Rose Barragan

Barbara Burke

Barbara B. Cramer

Wilma J. Farmer

Teresa Flores

Charles Hacker

P. J. Hutchins

George Jurata

Nancy Mayeda

Kenneth Smith

Lydia Stack

Mary Wigner

Executive Editor: *Sandra Maccarone*

Senior Editors: *Gary W. Bargar, Ronne Kaufman*

Project Editors: *Pamela P. Clark, Eleanor Franklin*

Editorial Consultants: *Editorial Options, Inc.*

Design Director: *Leslie Bauman*

Assistant Design Director: *Kay Wanous*

Designers: *Craven Graphics, Thomasina Webb*

Production Director: *Barbara Arkin*

Production Manager: *Trudy Pisciotti*

D.C. HEATH AND COMPANY

Lexington, Massachusetts/Toronto, Ontario

Cover, Front Matter, Unit Openers designed by: *Thomas Vroman Associates, Inc.* Illustrators: Melanie Arwin, pp. 140-154; Kris Boyd, pp. 97-106; Walter Brooks, pp. 452-464; Adriene Burk, p. 119, pp. 136-137; Llynne Buschman, pp. 286-287; Shirley Chan, pp. 296-307; James Crowell, pp. 439-447; Pat Cummings, p. 124, pp. 318-330; Phyllis Demchick, pp. 216-217, pp. 309-314; Michael Esposito, pp. 554-577; Margie Frem, pp. 412, pp. 489-491; Paulette Giguere, pp. 384-385; June Grammer, pp. 49-51, pp. 52-60, pp. 218-227; Steve Henry, pp. 156-157; Carol Inouye, pp. 478-479; Greg Jones, pp. 24-32, p. 118, p. 121; Paul Kirschner, pp. 238-254; Joseph Lemonier, pp. 184-185, pp. 384-385; Morissa Lipstein, pp. 159-164, pp. 230-236; Ken Longtemps, pp. 368-373; Brian McCarty, pp. 41-47; Barbara McClintock, pp. 466-477; Lady McCrady, pp. 492-516; Barbara Moore, pp. 366-367; Jan Naimo, pp. 52-60; Ann Neumann, pp. 480-487; Louis Pappas, pp. 449-451; Susan G. Parnell, pp. 14-22; Marc Phelan, pp. 346-349; Albert John Pucci, pp. 168-182, pp. 271-284; Tim Raglan, pp. 126-134; Scott Reynolds, pp. 108-116; Amy Rowen, pp. 186-198; Jerry Smath, pp. 414-437; Joel Snyder, pp. 80-92, pp. 202-214; pp. 350-364; David Stone, p. 229; Freya Tanz, pp. 166-167, pp. 334-344; Marc Tauss, pp. 309-314; Lydia Viscardi, p. 158; Garth Williams, pp. 386-408.

Photo Credits: Dennis Hallinan, F.P.G., cover and p. 1; Hy Simon, Photo Trends, pp. 8-9; Freda Leinwand, Monkmeyer, p. 11; Michal Heron, p. 12; Chris Springmann, Black Star, p. 13; Alan Philiba, pp. 36-39; Cliff Fuelner, Image Bank, pp. 78-79; Aline Amon, courtesy Lauren Goodrich, p. 122; Dennis Cipnic, Photo Researchers, pp. 138-139; Fraunces Tavern Museum, p. 182; Lowell Georgia, Photo Researchers, pp. 200-201; Dennis Milon, p. 256; courtesy of The American Museum of Natural History, pp. 257-260; Josef Muench, p. 262; Simon Cherpitel, Magnum, pp. 266-267; Laura Ingalls Wilder Memorial Society, DeSmet, South Dakota, p. 269 and p. 270 (top left, bottom left); from the Ingalls Family Album, p. 270 (top right); courtesy of the Dance Theatre of Harlem, pp. 291-294; Geri Vartanian, Photo Researchers, pp. 332-333; Jane Burton, Bruce Coleman, Inc., p. 374; Alan Blank, Bruce Coleman, Inc., p. 375; David Overcash, Bruce Coleman, Inc., p. 377 (left); J. Shaw, Bruce Coleman, Inc., p. 377 (right) and p. 378; Dr. E. R. Degginger, Bruce Coleman, Inc., p. 379; Peter Ward, Bruce Coleman, Inc., p. 381 (top); Lynn M. Stone, Bruce Coleman, Inc., p. 381 (bottom); D. J. Lyons, Bruce Coleman, Inc., p. 382; Hubert Schreibl, pp. 410-411; Bernard Wolf, pp. 466-477.

ACKNOWLEDGMENTS

Every reasonable effort has been made to trace the owners of copyright materials in this book, but in some instances this has proven impossible. The publishers will be glad to receive information leading to more complete acknowledgments in subsequent printings of the book, and in the meantime extend their apologies for any omissions.

To Abingdon Press for "7 Silly Simons" by Bernice Wells Carlson. Adapted from "Seven Simons," from *Funny-Bone Dramatics* by Bernice Wells Carlson. Copyright © 1974 by Abingdon Press. Used by permission.

To Isaac Asimov for "The Fun They Had" from *The Magazine of Fantasy and Science Fiction.* Copyright 1951 by Newspaper Enterprises Association, Inc. Copyright 1954 by Fantasy House, Inc. Reprinted by permission of the author.

To Atheneum Publishers for "A Chimp Learns to 'Talk' " by Aline Amon, copyright © 1975 by Aline Amon Goodrich from *Reading, Writing, Chattering Chimps;* for "Encounter" by Lilian Moore, text copyright © 1973 by Lilian Moore from *Sam's Place Poems from the Country;* and for "Metaphor" by Eve Merriam, copyright © 1964 from *It Doesn't Always Have to Rhyme.* All used by permission of Atheneum Publishers.

To Will Barker for "Keep It a Secret" from *Codes, Cyphers, and Cryptograms* by Will Barker. Copyright © 1963 by Will Barker. Reprinted by permission of Will Barker and the American Red Cross *News.*

To Curtis Brown, Ltd., for "Spelling Bee Blues" by Laurene Chambers Chinn, copyright 1949 by Laurene Chambers Chinn, published in *Collier's;* reprinted by permission of Curtis Brown, Ltd.

To Coward, McCann & Geoghegan, Inc., for "Phoebe and the General" by Judith Berry Griffin from *Phoebe and the General* by Judith Berry Griffin, text copyright © 1977 by Judith Berry Griffin; for "The Street of the Flower Boxes" from *The Street of the Flower Boxes* by Peggy Mann, copyright © 1976 by Peggy Mann; and for "Two Months from Alice Yazzie's Year" by Ramona Maher from *Alice Yazzie's Year* by Ramona Maher, copyright © 1977 by Ramona Maher. All adapted and reprinted by permission of Coward, McCann & Geoghegan, Inc.

To Thomas Y. Crowell for abridged and adapted text of *The March of the Lemmings* by James R. Newton, copyright © 1976 by James R. Newton, A Let's Read and Find Out Book; and for the adapted text of *The Seeing Stick* by Jane Yolen, copyright © 1977 by Jane Yolen. Both by permission of Thomas Y. Crowell.

To Dodd, Mead & Company, Inc., for "Meteorites: Stones from the Sky" by R. V. Fodor from *Meteorites; Stones from the Sky* by R. V. Fodor. Copyright © 1976 by Ronald V. Fodor. Reprinted and adapted by permission of Dodd, Mead & Company, Inc.

To E. P. Dutton for "Mr. and Mrs. Juicy-O" from *Tales of a Fourth Grade Nothing* by Judy Blume. Copyright © 1972 by Judy Blume. Reprinted by permission of E. P. Dutton.

To Elsevier/Nelson Books for "Encyclopedia Brown Solves a Case" by Donald J. Sobol. Adapted from "The Case of Bugs Meany's Revenge" from *Encyclopedia Brown Keeps the Peace* by Donald J. Sobol. Copyright © 1969 by Donald J. Sobol. Reprinted by permission of the Publisher, Elsevier/Nelson Books.

To Don and Betty Emblen for "Moonlight—A Horse with a Mind of His Own" from *Palomino Boy* by Don and Betty Emblen. Copyright 1948. Used by permission.

(Continued on page 592)

Contents

one

two

three

four

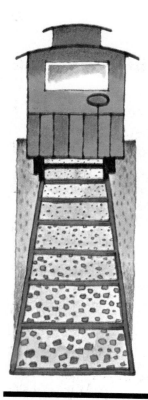

five

six

seven

Pocket Park

This is our special place—
a green pocket sewn on a grey street.
This is our place—our so special place—
the place we touch the earth
and the earth touches us.
This is our spring place for digging and planting.
This is our summer place for growing and weeding.
This is our fall place for gathering and remembering.
Even in winter we will come to this place.
We will speak quietly
while our garden sleeps under the snow.

Bobbi Katz

11

ENCYCLOPEDIA BROWN SOLVES A CASE

Bugs Meany divided his life in two. Bugs spent half his time making mischief. The rest of his time was spent trying to get even with Encyclopedia Brown.

Bugs resented having Encyclopedia outsmart him all the time. He longed to knock the boy detective colder than the paint on an icehouse floor, and twice as flat.

Bugs didn't dare throw a punch, however. It wasn't because Encyclopedia's father was chief of police. It was because of Sally Kimball.

Bugs had never dreamed that a ten-year-old *girl* could scare him. But then it happened. Sally caught him bullying a Cub Scout. Bugs had laughed when Sally told him to pick on someone his own size. But he roared in surprise when Sally dropped him with her first punch.

Because of Sally, Bugs never threatened Encyclopedia with his muscles. Sally was the boy detective's partner.

"Bugs doesn't like me. And he won't ever live down the licking you gave him," warned Encyclopedia.

"We'd better keep on our guard," agreed Sally. "He's dangerous. Like a spinning restaurant— always trying to turn the tables."

"I suppose we ought to thank him," said Encyclopedia. "His troublemaking brings in business."

"That reminds me," said Sally. "I came by around noon and saw Duke Kelly, one of Bugs's Tigers, sneaking out of the detective agency. Where were you?"

"Out," said Encyclopedia. "I received a telephone call from a boy who called himself Mike Gaither. He asked me to meet him out by the old lighthouse right away. I was feeling adventurous, so I went. I waited there an hour. He never showed up."

"A phony telephone call . . . Then, while you were gone, Duke Kelly . . ." Sally frowned. "I'll bet Bugs Meany is up to something."

"I doubt that Bugs will bother us for a while," said Encyclopedia. "He's too busy building himself into Mr. Junior Idaville."

"Mr. Junior Idaville?" asked Sally.

"The Y.M.C.A. is holding a body-building contest next week," said Encyclopedia. "The man with the best build will be crowned Mr. Idaville. The title Mr. Junior Idaville will go to the boy with the biggest muscles."

"If Bugs takes off his hat, he's a cinch to win," said Sally.

Just then a police car stopped in the Browns' driveway. Officer Friedman got out, followed by

Bugs Meany. The Tiger leader wore a bathing suit and a beautiful suntan.

"I've said all summer this detective business isn't on the level. It's just a front for passing stolen goods!" exclaimed Bugs.

"Take it easy, Bugs," said Officer Friedman. And to Encyclopedia she said, "Bugs claims you have his wristwatch."

"I don't know what you're talking about," said Encyclopedia.

"Oh, yes, you do!" bellowed Bugs. "Those two gorillas gave it to you!"

"Huh?" said Encyclopedia.

"Don't look so sweet and innocent," growled Bugs. "Those two big guys came up to me while I was lying on the beach at noon today. They took the watch right off my wrist. I followed them to the road. I saw them give the watch to you."

"Where were you at noon today?" Officer Friedman asked Encyclopedia.

"I was out at the old lighthouse," answered Encyclopedia. Then he explained about the mysterious telephone call.

"Did anyone see you at the lighthouse?" asked Officer Friedman.

"No one saw me. I waited an hour and then came home," said Encyclopedia.

"He was out at the lighthouse, but no one saw him!" jeered Bugs. "Boy, if I couldn't think up a better alibi, I'd eat my hat!"

"Your mouth is big enough," snapped Sally. "What were you doing on the beach, anyway?"

Bugs strutted in the doorway. "I was getting this suntan," he said. "Meet the next Mr. Junior Idaville."

He lifted his arm and made a muscle.

"A suntan makes your muscles stand out better," Bugs went on. "You can't just lie down to bake. You've got to keep turning so you don't burn too much on one side."

Encyclopedia had to agree that Bugs had done a good job of tanning himself. There wasn't a spot that was too light or too dark on his arms, legs, or body.

"I'll bet this little crook has my wristwatch right here," said Bugs. "He's planning to sell it when things cool down."

"Search the place," Encyclopedia invited. "You won't find your wristwatch."

"Oh, yeah?" sneered Bugs.

Bugs began searching the shelves at the back of the garage.

"Getting a suntan is a real art," he boasted. "I'd been tanning myself on the beach three hours when those two big guys jumped me. One more hour and I'd have been ready to walk off with the Mr. Junior Idaville title."

As he talked, his smoothly tanned hands and wrists dipped into the boxes on the top shelf. Suddenly, his face lighted up. He pulled out a wristwatch.

"Here it is!" he cried joyously. He waved the wristwatch about for all to see.

"Stop acting, Bugs," said Encyclopedia calmly. "You're only trying to get even. It won't work. Your wristwatch was never stolen."

WHAT WAS ENCYCLOPEDIA'S PROOF?

(To find out, turn the page.)

The Solution to the Case

Bugs said he had been tanning himself for three hours when the two men took the watch off his wrist. Yet, there wasn't a spot that was too light or too dark on Bugs's arms, legs, or body. Furthermore, his hands and *wrists* were smoothly tanned.

If Bugs had really been robbed as he claimed, there would have been a white, untanned mark around his wrist where the watch had been worn for three hours in the sun!

Bugs confessed. He had sent Encyclopedia on a wild-goose chase with the telephone call. Then Duke Kelly, one of his Tigers, had slipped into the Browns' garage and hidden the watch in the box for Bugs to find.

1. Who was Encyclopedia Brown? Who was Sally Kimball?

2. Why did Bugs Meany want to "get even" with Encyclopedia Brown?

3. What did the boy who called himself Mike Gaither tell Encyclopedia Brown?

4. Where had Bugs Meany been for three hours? Why was he there?

5. What did Bugs Meany claim Encyclopedia Brown had taken? How did Encyclopedia Brown prove that Bugs Meany had NOT been robbed?

6. What kind of person was Bugs Meany? Think about the licking that Sally Kimball gave Bugs. Do you think that had anything to do with the fact that Bugs wanted to be Mr. Junior Idaville? Explain your answer.

7. Why do you think Encyclopedia Brown got the nickname "Encyclopedia"?

8. Have you ever solved a mystery on your own? What was the mystery? How did you solve it?

THE FUN THEY HAD

That night, Margie talked about it into her personal tape diary. In the "take" for May 17, 2155, she said, "Today Tommy found a real book!"

It was a very old book, printed on paper. Margie remembered her grandfather saying that *his* grandfather had talked about real books printed on paper.

Margie and Tommy turned the old pages. They were yellow and crinkly. It was comical to read words that stood still instead of moving like on a book screen. Then, when they turned back to the page before, the same words were still on it. That was comical, too, because book screens kept moving on to other words.

"This kind of book seems like such a waste," said Tommy. "I guess you just throw it away when you're through reading it. My book screen must have at least a thousand books on it, and it's good for plenty more. I'd never throw *it* away."

"Me neither," said Margie. She had seen a lot of book screens but none like Tommy's. He was two years older than Margie.

"Where did you find this book?" she asked.

"In my house."

"What's the book about?"

"School."

Margie was surprised. "School? What's there to write about school?"

Margie had been having trouble in school. The mechanical teacher had been giving her test after test in geography. But Margie had been doing worse and worse. Her mother finally decided it was time to open up the teacher. The geography section might have a crossed wire or two. Her mother sent for the county inspector.

The inspector came with her box of tools and wires for the teacher. She smiled at Margie and then went straight to work. She took the teacher apart. Margie hoped she wouldn't know how to put it together again. But the inspector did know how. After an hour or so, there it was again—large, square, and ugly.

Margie hated the big screen which printed lessons and asked questions. However, the part she hated most was the slot for homework and test papers. Margie had to do all her work in a special punch code. After the punched card went into the slot, the teacher graded her work quickly.

The county inspector smiled after she was finished. She patted Margie's head and said to her mother, "It's not Margie's fault. The geography section was geared a little too quickly. That happens sometimes. I've slowed it down to the right level. I'm sure Margie will do fine, now. The rest of her work is quite all right."

Margie was disappointed. She had hoped the teacher would be taken away for good. Once Tommy's teacher was taken away for nearly a month. The spelling section had blanked out.

Feeling as she did about the mechanical teacher, Margie couldn't help exclaiming to Tommy, "*Why* would anyone write about school!"

Tommy said knowingly, "Because it's not our kind of school! This is the kind of school they had hundreds of years ago."

Margie was hurt. "Well, I don't know what kind of school they had then." She read the book over his shoulder for a while. Then she said, "Anyway, they still had a teacher."

"Sure, they had a teacher, but it wasn't a *regular* teacher. Not the kind we have. It was a person."

"A person? How could a person be a teacher?"

"Well, he or she taught pupils things and gave them lessons to take home."

"A person isn't smart enough to be a teacher."

"Why not? My parents know as much as my teacher."

"They can't. People can't know as much."

"They know almost as much, I bet."

Margie wasn't going to argue. She said, "Well, I wouldn't want a strange person in my house to teach me."

Tommy laughed. "You don't understand, Margie. The teachers didn't live in the house. They had a special building then. All the children were sent to a school building."

"And they all learned the same things?"

"Not exactly. But they were taught in groups."

"But a teacher has to be set so it'll fit the mind of each child it teaches."

"Well, they did things differently then. If you don't like it, you don't have to read the book."

"I didn't say I didn't like it," Margie said quickly. She didn't really want to argue. She wanted to read about those funny schools.

They weren't even half finished with the book when Margie's mother called her. "Margie! School!"

Margie looked up. "Not yet, Mama."

"Now," said Mrs. Jones. "It's probably time for Tommy, too, I expect."

Margie said to Tommy, "Can I read the book some more with you after school?"

"Yes," he said, "I guess I'll let you." He walked away whistling, the dusty old book tucked beneath his arm.

Margie went into the schoolroom. It was right next to her bedroom. The teacher was on and waiting for her. It was always on at the same time every day, except Saturday and Sunday.

The screen was lit up. It read: "Please insert in the slot yesterday's homework for all lessons. Then, prepare for the lesson on fractions."

Margie did so with a sigh. She was thinking about her grandfather's grandfather's school. She pictured children sitting together in the classroom. She thought of children learning lessons together. Margie smiled as she thought of the children leaving school together.

And the teachers were people!

The mechanical teacher was flashing on the screen: "When we add ½ and ¼. . . ."

Margie did not even see the screen. She was thinking about the children in the old schools. She was thinking about the fun they must have had.

THINK ABOUT IT

1. In what year does this story take place?

2. How was the old book that Tommy found different from the kind of "book" that he and Margie were used to reading?

3. How did Margie's mechanical teacher work? How did Margie turn in her homework and test papers to the mechanical teacher?

4. How did Margie feel about the old-fashioned school Tommy told her about? Why do you think she disliked her own type of school so much?

5. Why do you think the author picked "The Fun They Had" for the title of the story?

6. Would you like to be taught the way Margie and Tommy were taught? Why or why not?

PLAY SOCCER

What game is the most popular sport in the world? Is it football? Tennis? Baseball? No. It's soccer.

Perhaps you have already played soccer. If you haven't, try to imagine a ball game where you use your head, chest, or thighs to get the ball. Try to imagine yourself racing up a field moving the ball with your feet. Try to imagine the thrill of kicking the ball into the goal and scoring for your team. That's soccer. People say that once you play soccer, no other sport will match it for excitement.

There are eleven players on a soccer team. Ten players cover the field, and one player is goalie. Any player can block or pass or shoot. But each player also has a certain job to do on the field. The halfbacks' job is getting the ball away from the other team. The forwards' job is moving the ball down the field and shooting for goals. The job of the fullbacks is to protect their own goal. They also must stop the other team from scoring.

All you need to play soccer are a soccer ball
and some goal and field markers. The game can
be played in any open field or a lot. An official
playing field measures from 100 to 130 yards
long and from 50 to 100 yards wide.

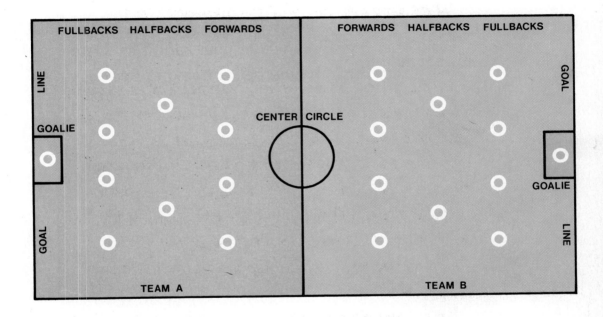

The chart above shows one of the ways that
players can line up to start a game. A soccer
game begins at the center of the field. There is
a coin toss between the captains of the two teams.
Whichever captain wins the toss begins the game
by kicking the ball to a teammate. The play then
continues without any time-outs for the full length
of the game.

Much of the action in soccer comes from dribbling. Dribbling means giving the ball short taps with the feet. You can try it. Using the inside or outside of your feet, try to move the ball as you walk. Then slowly increase your speed until you are running. Don't let the ball tell you where to go. Keep it a little in front of your feet at all times. Let it go only where you want it to. Here, the player dribbling the ball is trying to decide where to pass it.

Stopping the ball in soccer is called "trapping."
You are not allowed to trap a ball with your
hands. The pictures below show the four ways to
trap a soccer ball.

Trap with your head.

Trap with your foot.

Trap with your thigh.

Trap with your chest.

In soccer the ball is kicked either to make a goal or to pass it to another player. If a player is good at passing, the team has a better chance of winning the game. Never kick the ball with your toe. These pictures show how good kicks are made.

With the inside of the foot

With the outside of the foot

With the instep

In soccer there are only two times when it is all right to hold the ball with the hands. One time is when the ball goes out of play on the sideline. A player is then allowed to make a throw-in to another player. The other time holding the ball is allowed is when the goalie gets the ball. The goalie is the only player that can pick up the ball and throw it.

A good goalie uses every part of the body to stop the ball. If you want to be a goalie, you will have to learn how to dive, fall, and grab. If the goalie fails to stop the ball from going through the goal posts, the other team scores a point. The team scoring the most goals in the game (usually 60–90 minutes) wins.

Have the few pointers on these pages aroused your interest in soccer? If so, grab a soccer ball and a rule book. Then round up a few friends and play—soccer!

1. How many players are there on a soccer team? What do halfbacks specialize in doing? What do forwards do? What do fullbacks do?

2. About how big should a soccer field be?

3. What does "dribbling" mean?

4. What are four ways of "trapping" the ball in soccer?

5. Which of the following reasons did the author probably have for writing this article? Explain your answer.

   to make you laugh

   to give you information

   to get you to buy something

6. Why do you think soccer has become the most popular sport in the world?

7. Have you ever played soccer? Did you enjoy it? Is soccer a sport you would be interested in learning? Why or why not?

ODD JOBS

When we talk about odd jobs, we often mean simple house chores like mowing the lawn or drying the dishes. But there are many other jobs that are called "odd" because they are unusual or special.

Rattlesnake Milker

You've probably heard of people who milk dairy cows to earn a living. But did you know that some people milk rattlesnakes for a living? *That's* certainly an odd job. In fact, it's not only odd, it's dangerous!

Of course, the milk of a snake is not the same as the milk of a cow. In fact, it isn't milk at all—it's poison! Once the poison is taken from the snake's fangs, it can be used to treat snakebite. This medicine can save the lives of people who have been bitten by rattlesnakes.

A rattlesnake must be handled very carefully. The poison is inside glands just behind and on either side of the upper jaw. The snake must be held tightly, right behind the head, so that it cannot turn to bite.

Milkers first cover a clear jar with a thin sheet of rubber. Then, wearing heavy gloves, they hold the snake's head over the jar. They press behind the jaws to open them. The fangs then come forward. The snake, of course, is angry and frightened. It strikes at the closest thing, the jar. The fangs pierce the thin rubber sheet. The poison is then released and drips harmlessly into the jar.

Rattlesnake milkers have to be strong enough to handle snakes safely. They must also be able to stay calm at all times.

Ladybug Rancher

Being a rancher doesn't sound like such an odd job. Perhaps you've even met a cattle or sheep rancher. But have you ever met a ladybug rancher?

Ladybugs, those colorful little bugs with dots on their backs, aren't just pretty. They're useful, too! They eat plant lice and other garden pests.

Ladybug ranchers raise ladybugs in herds. Then they sell them by the gallon to farmers. Did you know that there are 75,000 ladybugs to a gallon? Of course, if you want to be a ladybug rancher, you'll have to know a lot about other bugs, too. You'll also have to like being around them!

Pearl Wearer

If snakes and bugs aren't for you, perhaps wearing pearls is. Though most people pay *to* wear pearls, some people are paid *for* wearing them!

Pearls are valued for their shine. Many jewels sparkle most when they are clean. However, pearls shine brightest when they are covered with a coating of oil. The kind of oil that makes pearls shine best is skin oil. The more pearls are worn against the skin, the more they shine. Some people have skin oils that are quite good for pearls. These people are paid to wear other people's pearls to make them shine.

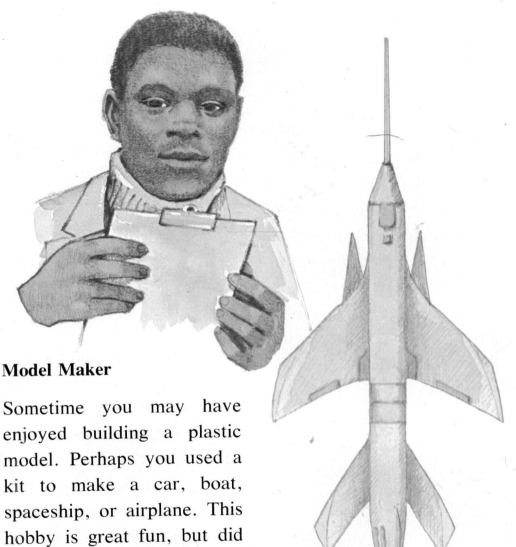

Model Maker

Sometime you may have enjoyed building a plastic model. Perhaps you used a kit to make a car, boat, spaceship, or airplane. This hobby is great fun, but did you know that some people are paid to make models?

People who earn their living making models don't use kits. Their models are always of things that aren't yet in use.

These models are called *prototypes*. People with ideas for new products make test models to see how well the finished products will look and work.

45

If you were to pay a visit to a manufacturing company, you might see prototypes. They might look like toys to you, but they are important in testing new ideas.

Prototypes are also important because they show how hard and costly something will be to make. If the test product doesn't work or look right, the company knows not to make the product in large numbers.

Earthquake Watcher

You know that there are scientists who study and forecast the weather. But did you know that there are people who study and forecast earthquakes?

These scientists, or "earthquake watchers," use special instruments that measure movement within the earth. Earthquake watchers can tell when and where an earthquake is taking place. They can also tell how strong an earthquake is. They then warn the people living in earthquake zones about when to expect an earthquake. Thus, an earthquake watcher provides an important public service.

Apartment-Sitter

Baby-sitting is not an odd job, but what about apartment-sitting? People who travel a lot sometimes hire someone to live in their apartment while they are away.

Apartment-sitters often are asked to feed and walk household pets and to water the plants. Apartment-sitting doesn't pay much, but the work is easy and the job can be fun.

Now you know what rattlesnake milkers, ladybug ranchers, pearl wearers, model makers, earthquake watchers, and apartment-sitters do. Can you think of any other odd jobs? Look through the want ads of your town newspaper and you may discover a few more. Who knows, you may even find the perfect odd job for you!

THINK ABOUT IT

1. What is the poison that is taken from a rattlesnake's fangs used for? Where is the rattlesnake poison found?

2. How are ladybugs useful to farmers?

3. Why are some people paid to wear other people's pearls?

4. What are the models made by professional model makers called? What are those models used for?

5. How do earthquake watchers help people?

6. Why might someone enjoy being an apartment sitter? What kind of person might enjoy being an earthquake watcher?

7. Which of the jobs described in this selection would you be interested in trying? Why?

ON THE LOOKOUT!

Meet Penny Evans. She's on the lookout.
Penny spends a few months each spring looking
out to sea. She may watch and wait for hours
or even days before spotting what she's looking
for—WHALES!

Penny watches whales so that scientists
will have up-to-date records on the movement
of whales within the world's oceans. The
information that Penny collects teaches us
more about the habits of whales.

Penny keeps records of the whales she spots.
She uses a special graph called a "line graph"
to keep track of the whale spottings.

The line graph below is one of Penny's graphs. It shows the number of whales Penny spotted each year during the month of May.

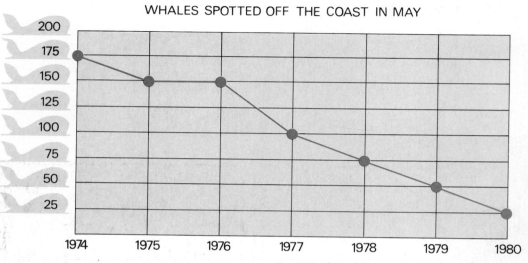

WHALES SPOTTED OFF THE COAST IN MAY

See how well you can read Penny's graph. Try answering these questions:

1. Which part of the graph gives the numbers of whales?

2. Which part of the graph gives the years?

3. Find the dot on the line for 1974. Look at the number of whales on the left. What number is the dot even with? That is the number of whales Penny spotted in May, 1974.

4. In which two years did Penny spot the same number of whales?

5. Look at the colored line that connects the dots. Has the number of whales Penny spotted off the coast increased or decreased since 1974?

Why not become a grapher, too? You can keep a record of all sorts of everyday things. Here are some line graphs you might enjoy copying and completing.

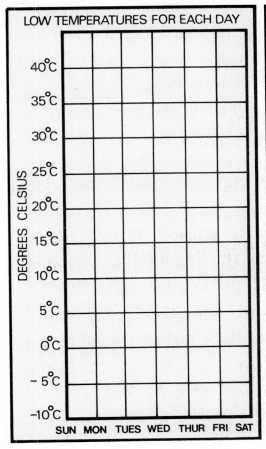

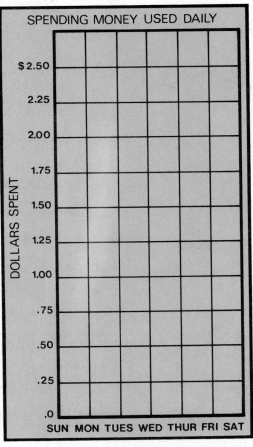

THE GIRL WHO SAVED THE TRAIN

As if pulled by a magnet, Kate Shelley kept near the window on that stormy July night in 1881. Her mother, pale and ill, sat nearby mending stockings. Three younger children lay sleeping in the next room.

"Sit down and try to rest," Mrs. Shelley begged for the tenth time. But neither Kate nor her mother would rest on that frightening night.

Kate pressed against the cold, wet window-pane and stared into the night. She was watching the strip of railroad tracks that lay between Moingona[1] and Boone, Iowa. Blinding lightning danced across the sky. It lit the

[1] **Moingona** (moin gō′nə)

52

railroad bridge that crossed the angry waters of the Des Moines[2] River.

It was near this bridge where Kate's father had been killed just three years ago. Mr. Shelley had worked on the railroad. It was also in this river that her brother, Michael, Jr., had drowned a few months later. Now, it was Kate who supported the family.

Kate pushed her hair from her face. Then she walked to the window on the other side of the room. From there, she could see another bridge. This second bridge crossed Honey Creek, a stream emptying into the Des Moines River.

The heavy rains of the past week had already filled the creek above its banks. Tonight's rain was sending the whirling water higher up the hillside. The family horse and cows were in a barn near the creek. They were in danger of being trapped.

"I'm going to let the animals out," Kate said as she grabbed her mother's old raincoat from behind the door. The coat was much too big, so she threw it over her head and ran

[2] **Des Moines** (di moin')

out into the storm. In knee-deep water, Kate made her way to the barn and opened the door. After the animals splashed up the hill to safer ground, she waded back to the house.

Kate was about to hang the wet coat behind the door when she heard a frightening sound. She dashed to the window and saw a steam engine pulling slowly onto the Des Moines River Bridge.

Flashes of lightning lit the countryside. Kate knew that this engine had been sent ahead of the passenger train to check for washouts. She remembered hearing her father tell how storms such as this could destroy roadbeds and bridges.

Slowly, the engine pushed across the first bridge. With her heart pounding like the angry storm, Kate ran to the other window. The engine was now inching across the swaying Honey Creek Bridge.

The engine was nearly halfway across when the bridge buckled. The hot engine pitched into twenty-five feet of swirling water. Kate heard a hissing sound and saw a billow of steam as the engine went under.

"They've gone down, Mother!" Kate cried.
Again she headed for the door. This time
she put the big coat on and tied the belt
about her waist.

"There's nothing you can do, child!" her
mother pleaded.

"I'm going to Moingona to stop the passenger train," Kate said firmly.

Taking her father's railroad lantern, Kate
ran into the terrible night. She stopped by the
wrecked Honey Creek Bridge long enough
to spot two crew members hanging on tree
branches in the frothy water. The rest of the
crew were not in sight. Kate knew that she
could be of no help here. She turned and
headed in the other direction.

Moingona Station lay one mile to the west.
To get there quickly, Kate would have
to cross the Des Moines River Bridge. Most
people stayed away from this bridge even
on quiet, sunny days. The bridge was built
only for trains.

The bridge was little more than two steel
rails stretched across widely spaced crossties. Some of the crossties were so far apart
that someone Kate's size could easily fall

through them. There were no handrails to hold
and no place to go if a train should come. She
hoped that tonight the train would be late.

Frightened as never before, Kate made her
way onto the shaky bridge. The roar of the
water was deafening, and the strong wind
shook the narrow bridge.

Suddenly, the wind blew out the flame in
her lantern. Kate was forced to go on in
blackness. She dropped to her hands and
knees and held on to the cold railroad track.

Kate began feeling her way, foot by foot. She shivered as the wind-driven rain almost took away her breath. Her legs burned from being scraped on the railroad ties. The lantern was a heavy load.

A sudden flash of lightning showed a huge tree heading beneath the spot where Kate was crawling. Holding her breath, she watched the tree crash up and down in the angry water. The limbs, cracking against the bridge, showered her with muddy water as the tree slipped beneath the bridge. Then it was out of sight as suddenly as it had appeared.

On she crept. After what seemed hours, she cried out with joy. Cold mud squished between her fingers! She had crossed the bridge and was on solid ground. Getting to her feet and still clutching the unlit lantern, she dashed down the track.

A few minutes later, soaking wet and tired, she opened the station-house door. "Honey Creek Bridge is out!" Kate gasped, sinking to the floor. She had done all a fifteen-year-old could do. The rest was up to the railroad agent.

The passenger train was not due to stop at Moingona. The agent rushed to the front of the station just in time to stop the train. Rescuers were sent to the washed-out bridge to help the crew members.

To Kate the frightening night seemed like a bad dream, a nightmare she wanted to forget. But the world wouldn't let her forget. Passengers on the train collected money for her education. She received a gold watch and chain from the Order of Railway Conductors.

The railroad gave her money, a half barrel of flour, a load of coal, and a lifetime pass to ride the trains. From across the country, letters of praise poured into the Shelley home. Children from a nearby school presented her with a medal.

Later Kate went to school and studied to become a teacher. For a time she taught at a school not far from her home. Then in 1903, she accepted a job as a station agent at Moingona Station.

The Honey Creek Bridge, of course, was rebuilt right after the flood. Later, the Des Moines River Bridge was replaced by a beautiful new bridge. Going to and from her new job, Kate crossed the Kate Shelley Bridge. The bridge had been named for the fifteen-year-old girl who saved the train.

THINK ABOUT IT

1. What happened to the steam engine as it crossed Honey Creek Bridge?

2. Why did Kate decide to go to Moingona? Why was it dangerous for Kate to cross the Des Moines River Bridge?

3. After Kate reached Moingona Station, what did the agent do?

4. How was Kate rewarded for her bravery?

5. Why do you think it was especially important to Kate that she save the passengers on the express train from plunging into Honey Creek?

6. Have you ever known anyone whose quick thinking saved another person's life? What happened?

Mr. and Mrs. JUICY-O

Part One

One night my father came home from the office all excited. He told us Mr. and Mrs. Yarby were coming to New York. Mr. Yarby's the president of the Juicy-O Company. He lives in Chicago. I wondered if he'd bring my father another crate of Juicy-O. If he did I'd probably be drinking it for the rest of my life. Just thinking about it was enough to make my stomach hurt.

My father said he invited Mr. and Mrs. Yarby to stay with us. My mother wanted to know why they couldn't stay at a hotel like most people who come to New York. My father said they could. But he didn't want them to. He thought they'd be more comfortable staying with us. My mother said that was about the silliest thing she'd ever heard.

The next day we fixed up Fudge's bedroom for our guests. Mom put fancy sheets and a brand-new blanket on the hide-a-bed. That's a sofa that opens up into a bed at night. It's in Fudge's room because that used to be our den. Before he was born we watched TV in there. And lots of times Grandma slept over on the hide-a-bed. Now we watch TV right in the living room. And Grandma doesn't sleep over very often.

My mother moved Fudge's crib into my room. He's going to get a regular bed when he's three, my mother says. There are a lot of reasons I don't like to sleep in the same room as Fudge. I found that out two months ago when my bedroom was being painted. I had to sleep in Fudge's room for three nights because the paint smell made me cough. For one thing, he talks in his sleep. And if a person didn't know better, a person could get scared. Another thing is that slurping noise he makes. It's true that I like to hear it when I'm awake, but when I'm trying to fall asleep I like things very quiet.

When I complained about having to sleep with Fudge my mother said, "It's just for two nights, Peter."

"I'll sleep in the living room," I suggested. "On the sofa . . . or even a chair."

"No," my mother said. "You will sleep in your bedroom. In your own bed!"

There was no point in arguing. Mom wasn't going to change her mind.

Right after lunch my mother opened
up the dinner table. We don't have a
separate dining room. When we have
company for dinner we eat in one end of
the living room. When we finished setting
the table Mom put a silver bowl filled
with flowers right in the middle. I said,
"Hey, Mom . . . it looks like you're
expecting the President or something."

"Very funny, Peter!" my mother
answered.

Sometimes my mother laughs like crazy at my jokes. Other times she pretends not to get them. And then, there are times when I know she gets them but she doesn't seem to like them. This was one of those times. So I decided no more jokes until after dinner.

I went to Jimmy Fargo's for the afternoon. I came home at four o'clock. I found my mother standing over the dinner table mumbling. Fudge was on the floor playing with my father's socks. I'm not sure why he likes socks so much, but if you give him a few pairs he'll play quietly for an hour.

I said, "Hi, Mom. I'm home."

"I'm missing two flowers," my mother said.

I don't know how she noticed that two flowers were missing from her silver bowl. There were at least a dozen of them left. But sure enough, when I checked, I saw two stems with nothing on them.

"Don't look at me, Mom," I said. "What would I do with two measly flowers?"

So we both looked at Fudge. "Did you take Mommy's pretty flowers?" my mother asked him.

"No take," Fudge said. He was chewing on something.

"What's in your mouth?" my mother asked.

Fudge didn't answer.

"Show Mommy!"

"No show," Fudge said.

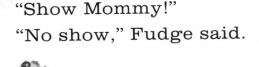

"Oh yes!" My mother picked him up and forced his mouth open. She fished out a rose petal.

"What did you do with Mommy's flowers?" She raised her voice. She was really getting upset.

Fudge laughed.

"Tell Mommy!"

"Yum!" Fudge said. "Yummy yummy yummy!"

"Oh no!" my mother cried, rushing to the telephone.

She called Dr. Cone. She told him that Fudge ate two flowers. Dr. Cone must have asked what kind, because my mother said, "Roses, I think. But I can't be sure. One might have been a daisy."

There was a long pause while my mother listened to whatever Dr. Cone had to say. Then Mom said, "Thank you, Dr. Cone." She hung up.

"No more flowers!" she told Fudge. "You understand?"

"No more," Fudge repeated. "No more . . . no more . . . no more."

My mother gave him a spoonful of peppermint-flavored medicine. The kind I take when I have stomach pains. Then she carried Fudge off to have his bath.

Leave it to my brother to eat flowers! I wondered how they tasted. *Maybe they're delicious and I don't know it because I've never tasted one,* I thought. I decided to find out. I picked off one petal from a pink rose. I put it in my mouth and tried to chew it up. But I couldn't do it. It tasted awful. I spit it out in the garbage. Well, at least now I knew I wasn't missing anything great!

Part Two

Fudge ate his supper in the kitchen before our company arrived. While he was eating I heard my mother remind him, "Fudge's going to be a good boy tonight."

"Good," Fudge said. "Good boy."

"That's right!" my mother told him.

I changed and scrubbed up while Fudge finished his supper. I was going to eat with the company. Being nine has its advantages!

My mother was all dressed up by the time my father got home with the Yarbys. You'd never have guessed that Fudge ate two flowers. He was feeling fine. He even smelled nice—like baby powder.

Mrs. Yarby picked him up right away. She walked into the living room cuddling him. Then she sat down on the sofa and bounced Fudge around on her lap.

"Isn't he the cutest little boy!" Mrs. Yarby said. "I just love babies." She gave him a big kiss on the top of his head. I kept waiting for somebody to tell her Fudge was no baby. But no one did.

My father carried the Yarbys' suitcase into Fudge's room. When he came back he introduced me to our company.

"This is our older son, Peter," he said to the Yarbys.

"I'm nine and in fourth grade," I told them.

"How do, Peter," Mr. Yarby said.

Mrs. Yarby just gave me a nod. She was still busy with Fudge. "I have a surprise for this dear little boy!" she said. "It's in my suitcase. Should I go get it?"

"Yes," Fudge shouted. "Go get . . . go get!"

Mrs. Yarby laughed, as if that was the best joke she ever heard. "I'll be right back," she told Fudge. She put him down and ran off to find her suitcase.

She came back carrying a present tied up with a red ribbon.

"Ohhhh!" Fudge cried, opening his eyes wide. "Goody!" He clapped his hands.

Mrs. Yarby helped him unwrap his surprise. It was a windup train that made a lot of noise. Every time it bumped into something it turned around and went the other way. Fudge liked it a lot. He likes anything that's noisy.

I said, "That's a nice train."

Mrs. Yarby turned to me. "Oh, I have something for you too uh . . . uh . . . ."

"Peter," I reminded her. "My name is Peter."

"Yes. Well, I'll go get it."

Mrs. Yarby left the room again. This time she came back with a flat package. It was wrapped up too—red ribbon and all. She handed it to me. Fudge stopped playing with his train long enough to come over and see what I got. I took off the paper very carefully in case my mother wanted to save it. And also to show Mrs. Yarby that I'm a lot more careful about things than my brother. I'm not sure she noticed. My present turned out to be a big picture dictionary. The kind I liked when I was about four years old. My old one is in Fudge's bookcase now.

"I don't know much about big boys," Mrs. Yarby said. "So the clerk in the store said a nice book would be a good idea."

A nice book would have been a good idea, I thought. *But a picture dictionary! That's for babies!* I've had my own regular dictionary since I was eight. But I knew I had to be polite so I said, "Thank you very much. It's just what I've always wanted."

"I'm so glad!" Mrs. Yarby said. She let out a long sigh and sat back on the sofa.

My father offered the Yarbys something to drink.

"Good idea . . . good idea," Mr. Yarby said.

"What'll it be?" my father asked.

"What'll it be?" Mr. Yarby repeated, laughing. "What do you think, Hatcher? It'll be Juicy-O! That's all we ever drink. Good for your health!" Mr. Yarby pounded his chest.

"Of course!" my father said, like he knew it all along. "Juicy-O for everyone!"

While my father and Mr. Yarby were discussing Juicy-O, Fudge disappeared. Just when everyone had a glass of Mr. Yarby's favorite drink, he came back. He was carrying a book—my old, worn-out picture dictionary. The same as the one the Yarbys just gave me.

"See," Fudge said, climbing up on Mrs. Yarby's lap. "See book."

I wanted to vanish. I think my mother and father did, too.

"See book!" Now Fudge held it up over his head.

"I can use another one," I explained. "I really can. That old one is falling apart." I tried to laugh.

"It's returnable," Mrs. Yarby said. "It's silly to keep it if you already have one." She sounded insulted. Like it was my fault she brought me something I already had.

"MINE!" Fudge said. He closed the book and held it tight against his chest. "MINE . . . MINE . . . MINE. . . ."

"It's the thought that counts," my mother said. "It was so nice of you to think of our boys." Then she turned to Fudge. "Put the book away now, Fudgie."

"Goodnight Fudgie!" my brother said, waving at us.

Fudge was supposed to fall asleep before we sat down to dinner. But just in case, my mother put a million toys in his crib to keep him busy. I don't know who my mother thought she was fooling. Because we all know that Fudge can climb out of his crib any old time he wants to.

And you're fooling yourself if you think Fudge stayed in his crib and went to sleep. Read *Tales of a Fourth Grade Nothing* by Judy Blume and find out why Mr. and Mrs. Yarby move to a hotel the next day and whether Mr. Hatcher keeps the Juicy-O account.

1. Who was Mr. Yarby? Why were Mr. and Mrs. Yarby staying at the Hatchers' house?

2. How did Peter's mother feel about the Yarbys' visit?

3. Why didn't Peter like to sleep in Fudge's room?

4. What did Fudge do with two of the flowers in his mother's silver bowl?

5. What present did Mrs. Yarby bring for Fudge? What did she bring for Peter? How did Peter feel about his present?

6. Why was Peter so embarrassed when Fudge brought out his old dictionary? How do you think Mr. and Mrs. Hatcher felt then?

7. After Fudge was put in his crib, what do you think he did?

8. Do you have younger brothers or sisters? How do they act when company comes? Do they ever say or do things that embarrass you? What do they do?

two

Rococo Skates

Ten pairs of students clattered along the floor inside the museum. Ms. Ryan was taking the class to see some paintings. She walked beside the line, looking forward and back along the double row of girls and boys.

Mary Ann was at the very end of the line, behind Frances, the girl with whom she was supposed to be walking. Ms. Ryan looked back and saw that Mary Ann was lagging behind the rest of the class.

"Please close up the line, Mary Ann," said Ms. Ryan. "We have to stay together. This museum is huge."

Mary Ann stepped up but dropped back again. She noticed that the floors were of hardwood and that today most of the galleries were empty. "This would be a good place to roller-skate," she thought. "I could go shooting down the galleries and around corners, yelling like anything. I could stop myself against statues so big and heavy they wouldn't fall. I could go

swinging around a statue, just holding with one hand, and then take off again, rolling and yelling. If only I had a pair of skates, I could have a great time."

Mary Ann didn't have any skates. She had wanted a pair for as long as she could remember. It seemed as if everyone she knew had skates.

If she had skates—she wouldn't just roll along. She'd swing, she'd glide, almost like a dancer. She would play tag with Frances and the other boys and

girls who had skates. Maybe she'd get some for her birthday. But that was still a long way off—almost six months from now.

The ten pairs of students clattered along the galleries. Here and there Ms. Ryan would hold up her hand, signaling the class to stop, and she would tell the class about this painting or that. Ms. Ryan seemed to enjoy the museum trip, and that made the class enjoy it even more.

Ms. Ryan stopped before a framed picture of a table with a bottle, a loaf of bread, a knife, and a basket of fruit. Mary Ann began to think more about the painting and less about roller-skating. "It isn't bad," she thought. On an easel nearby was another painting of a table with a bottle, a loaf of bread, a knife, and a basket of fruit. It was, in fact, an exact copy of the picture on the wall. Except for the frame around the original, it was difficult to tell the paintings apart.

"Why are there two the same?" asked Mary Ann.

"Art students are allowed to come in and copy famous paintings," said Ms. Ryan. "This one is a particular favorite with artists."

"I'd never copy," said Mary Ann. "I'd rather do my own, even if it was bad."

Mary Ann lagged behind the class, standing before the easel and looking from the copy to the original. "I wonder if the paint is still wet on the copy," she thought. It would be easy enough to find out. She knew she shouldn't touch it, but she reached out her right hand and pressed her finger against the painting. It *was* wet. She felt the paint slide a little under her finger. Frightened by what she had done, Mary Ann hurriedly caught up with Frances and the rest of the class.

"I saw you," whispered Frances. "You're just lucky no one else saw you. Did you leave a mark on it?"

Mary Ann didn't answer. She walked alongside Frances, breathing rather fast.

Ms. Ryan walked on, with ten pairs of students clopping behind her. They walked and stopped, walked and stopped.

"The paintings seem like magic windows," Mary Ann thought. Through them she could see people, places, and objects as she had never seen them before.

Then the class went through rooms full of furniture. The boys and girls saw sewing tables, old chair desks, and beds that people used over two centuries before. There was one very large bed with a canopy over it. The canopy of rose silk was held up with carved, golden figures leaping through the air and holding wreaths of flowers.

"This is rococo furniture," said Ms. Ryan.

"Rococo. What a nice word," Mary Ann thought to herself. "It sounds like the name of a game to play, or a pigeon cooing, or something you shout.

"Rococo," Mary Ann said out loud, and Frances looked at her and repeated it after her.

"Rococo," said Frances.

"Rococo," said Mary Ann, trying to sound like a pigeon.

Mary Ann and Frances began to laugh. They bumped against each other as they repeated, "Rococo!"

They walked and looked, walked and looked. Mary Ann and some of the other children began to get tired.

"All right, class," Ms. Ryan said at last, "I think that's enough for today. Let's turn around and find our way out."

The double row turned, and Mary Ann and Frances were at the head of the line. They walked along, past the furniture. "Rococo!" said Mary Ann and Frances, swaying against each other. They walked past pictures and more pictures. Now they were in the room where the painting on the easel had been.

"Look!" said Frances. "The copy's gone!"

Mary Ann was next to the wall. She leaned over as she came to the framed picture of the table with the bottle, the loaf of bread, the knife, and the basket of fruit. Then she gave such a loud cry that everyone stopped. "No!" cried Mary Ann. "It's the other one. The real one's been stolen!"

"How can you tell?" said Frances.

"Quick!" cried Mary Ann. "We've got to tell someone important."

Ms. Ryan stepped between Mary Ann and Frances.

"What's wrong?" she said.

"The painting!" cried Mary Ann. "The real one's been stolen. This is the copy that was on the easel!"

"What *are* you talking about?" Ms. Ryan asked.

"Trust me!" cried Mary Ann. "We must tell the head of the museum right away."

"Come on, Mary Ann," said Ms. Ryan. "Stop joking. It's time to leave."

By this time one or two people in other galleries had heard the racket and were standing about trying to find out what had happened. A guard in a uniform walked by hurriedly, announcing that the museum would be closing soon.

Mary Ann knew that the original painting was gone. She had to do something about the theft before the museum closed.

"I must tell someone," cried Mary Ann. She spun about, not knowing where to go. She began to run back along the way she had come. She ran past pictures and statues, dodging people or bumping against them. Everyone turned to look, and then came the rest of the class rushing along the galleries after her.

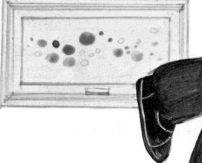

Mary Ann came to the rococo furniture room, and there were two guards coming toward her, one from each doorway. She ran around two chairs and a desk, and slipped past the guards. She could hear the other students behind her.

Mary Ann ran out into a marble hall, and at her left she saw a door marked Office of the Director. The Office of the Director! She turned about and pushed open the heavy door and dashed inside, just as some guards caught up with her.

"A picture's been stolen!" gasped Mary Ann to the people in the office. "I *know* it's been stolen. You just come with me and I'll show you. Please believe me. I can prove it, but you'll have to come and see for yourselves. Only, hurry!"

While she was talking, the director came out of an inner office. At the same time, Ms. Ryan, Frances, and three guards arrived through the outer door.

"Let's just go along and have a look to make sure," said the director. "It's pretty hard to steal a painting here. But let's make sure."

Back to the gallery they went, all of them.

When they got to the picture, the director put on a pair of glasses with a black ribbon attached to them. He looked at the picture very carefully. After quite a while, he turned to Mary Ann.

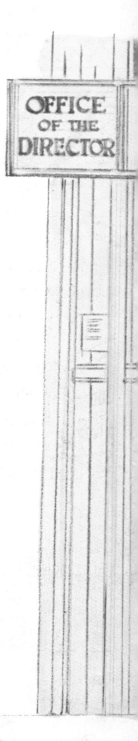

OFFICE
OF THE
DIRECTOR

"This is a very good copy," he said. "But it *is* a copy. The real painting has been stolen. I'm going back to my office now. Please wait for me in the outside office."

Ms. Ryan and Frances, along with Mary Ann and the director, marched over to the offices. They waited, as the director had asked. When the director came out, he had a great blue leather book in his arms.

"This is for you, Mary Ann," he said. "It has pictures of most of the paintings in this museum. It even has one of the stolen painting. If it hadn't been for your sharp eyes, the theft might not have been noticed until the picture was out of the country. You have done a very fine thing. Most people would have been fooled by that copy."

"I guess *I* couldn't be fooled," said Mary Ann.

"Here's the book then, Mary Ann," he said.

Mary Ann took the great book, bound in blue leather, and said thank you, politely. The director watched her.

"Maybe there is something you'd especially like, Mary Ann," he said, "besides the book."

"Oh, no," said Mary Ann quickly. "The book is fine!"

But Frances burst out, "She wants roller skates!"

"Roller skates it is," said the director, and he called to an aide. In a few minutes, Mary Ann and Frances and the aide were going down the steps outside the museum. The rest of the class and Ms. Ryan stood and watched the three of them climb into an automobile.

"How did you know about that copy, Mary Ann?" asked the aide as they drove along.

"I touched the copy lightly with my finger, and it left a tiny mark," she said. "Right in the middle of the basket."

"Oh, so that was how you knew the original was missing," said Frances. "But don't worry! I won't tell."

"Neither will I," said the friendly aide. "What do you say, Mary Ann and Frances, skates first or sodas first?"

"Sodas," said Frances.

"Skates!" said Mary Ann.

"Oh, all right," said Frances.

"I've just made up a new game," said Mary Ann. "We could call it Rococo Skates."

"What's that?" asked the aide.

"Something like tag on skates," Mary Ann said with a smile. "But this would be a special game."

THINK ABOUT IT

1. What had Mary Ann wanted for a long time?

2. Why did one of the galleries have two paintings that were alike?

3. What happened when Mary Ann touched the copy of the painting on the easel? How did Mary Ann tell the copy from the original later?

4. Why do you think the author titled this story "Rococo Skates"?

5. Have you ever been to a museum? What part of the museum did you like best?

6. Why do you think museum visitors are asked not to touch the paintings? If you were in Mary Ann's place, would you have told the museum director that you had touched the copy and left a mark on it? Why or why not?

WHAT'S SO FUNNY?

What's funny about this cartoon?

"Sorry, Wags. Ranch houses are out. Rococo is in."

Reading cartoons is different from reading a story. When you read a story, you depend on words to get the idea. When you read a cartoon, you must put together words and pictures to get the point.

The words that go under a cartoon or in speech "balloons" are called *captions*. Some cartoons don't need captions. The pictures alone tell the whole story. More often, though, you need to read the caption *and* look at the picture to unlock the humor.

Look at the cartoon on this page. Now that you have read the story "Rococo Skates" you know what the word *rococo* means. So you can unlock all the humor in this cartoon.

MARMADUKE

"But that's not the stick I told you to fetch!"

Now look at the cartoons on pages 95 and 96.
Try to answer these questions:

1. Which picture(s) would be funny even without a caption?
2. Would any of the captions be funny without pictures? Why?
3. At the end of the *Peanuts* cartoon, is the look on Charlie Brown's face funny to you? What could he be thinking?
4. Compare the *Peanuts* and *Wee Pals* cartoons. What makes each funny? How are the jokes alike? How are the jokes different?

5. The pictures in *Peanuts* and *Wee Pals* could be funny with different captions. Pick one of these cartoons and try to make up your own captions for it.

© 1961 United Feature Syndicate. Inc.

From Wee Pals by Morrie Turner. Reprinted by permission.

You probably have favorite cartoons. Why not find some you like and share them with your teacher and classmates? Together you can decide what makes each cartoon funny.

7 SILLY SIMONS

CHARACTERS

Susie Simon

Sonny Simon

Sammy Simon

Other Simons: Sidney, Sally, Sissy, Soupy

Stranger

SETTING

*The play takes place along the banks of a make-believe river. Each **Simon** wears a hat and has a fishing pole. The fishing pole should be a long stick with a line attached to one end. A weight or cork is on the end of each line.*

*As the play begins, all the **Simons** are sitting along the left side of the river bank. They pretend to fish. **Susie** sits closest to the audience. **Sonny** sits next to her. **Susie** looks up at the sky and sees that it is getting late. She then gets up with her pole and wades across the river. The other **Simons** continue fishing.*

Susie steps out of the river on the other side. She dries the soles of her feet on the grass. *Susie* feels her feet to see if they are dry. She seems satisfied. Then she looks back at the other **Simons** and calls to them.

Susie Simon: Yo, ho! Simons! It's time to call it a day. *(Motions to other **Simons** to join her. The other **Simons** stop fishing and stand up. They shoulder their fishing poles, ready to go home. **Sonny** then leads the other **Simons** across the river. One by one they step out of the river and join **Susie** on the other side.)*

98

Susie Simon: Ah, here we are!

Other Simons (*They look all around them.*):
Yes, indeed! We are surely here.

Susie Simon: Wasn't it a great day for fishing?

Sonny Simon: I didn't catch one fish.

Sammy Simon: I didn't catch any fish either.

Other Simons: Nor I. Nor I. Nor I. Nor I.

Susie Simon: Don't get all fired up. I just said, "It was a great day for fishing." Nothing wrong with the day.

Other Simons: No, no. Nothing wrong with the day.

Susie Simon: Well, now I think it's time to hit the road.

Other Simons (*They look at each other and nod. Then they get down and start hitting the road.*): Yes, yes. Time to hit the road.

99

Susie Simon (*Shaking her head*):　Simons!
　　Hold your horses!

Other Simons:　Whose horses? Where?

Susie Simon:　What I really meant was that it's
　　time to go home. But before we head off,
　　we'd better think.

Other Simons (*Walking around in small circles,
　　pretending to be thinking*):　Better think,
　　better think.

Susie Simon: It was a great day for fishing, but fishing can be very dangerous.

Other Simons: Very dangerous.

Susie Simon: In fact, one of us might have drowned.

Other Simons (*Upset and shouting*):   Drowned? One of us drowned? Who? Who? Who drowned?

Susie Simon (*Yelling*):   Quiet! Don't lose your heads. (*Other **Simons** look at each other. They drop fishing poles and quickly hold onto their heads with their hands.*) I said, ''Someone MIGHT have drowned.'' We'd better think.

Other Simons (*Walking around in circles again, pretending to think*):   Better think, better think.

Susie Simon: We know that there were seven Simons when we left this morning—Sammy, Sonny, Sidney, Sally, Sissy, Soupy, and Susie, of course.

Other Simons: Of course, of course.

Susie Simon: If we count seven Simons here, we'll know that not one of us has drowned. Stand in a straight line, and I'll count.

*(Other **Simons** form a line. **Susie** counts out loud as she points to each **Simon**, forgetting to count herself.)* One, two, three, four, five, six. Six Simons! Oh no! One Simon has drowned?

Sammy Simon: Let me count, maybe you missed someone. *(**Susie** gets in line. **Sammy** counts out loud as he points to each **Simon**, forgetting to count himself.)* One, two, three, four, five, six—six Simons! Oh no! One Simon HAS drowned.

*(**Other Simons** take turns getting out of line and counting. Each **Simon** forgets to count himself or herself. Each yells, "Six Simons! Oh no! One Simon has drowned!" The **Simons** work themselves into a frenzy. They run back and forth along the river, calling, "Simon! Simon!"*

Stranger enters. Stands to the side, looking puzzled by all the screaming **Simons**. **Susie** finally notices the stranger and runs up to him.)

Susie Simon: Sir! Sir! (*Other **Simons** rush with **Susie** downstage.*)

Stranger: What's wrong?

Susie Simon: We think one of us drowned. Did you run across a Simon?

Other Simons (*Together*): We lost a Simon! One Simon's missing! One Simon drowned!

Stranger: Just a minute. Calm down. How do you know one Simon drowned?

Susie Simon: There are seven Simons— Sammy, Sonny, Sidney, Sally, Sissy, Soupy, and Susie. That's me. This morning we all came fishing. (*After each sentence, **Other Simons** nod in agreement. **Stranger** nods that he understands.*) We fished until it was time to go home. Fishing can be dangerous.

A person can drown. So we lined up and counted ourselves. Each time we counted, we found only six Simons.

Other Simons (*Together*):   Six Simons. I counted. I counted.

Susie Simon: There were seven Simons this morning. Now we count six Simons. So one Simon must have drowned.

(*Stranger* *looks at* *Simons*. *Points to each one.* *Quickly counts silently.*)

Stranger: You're sure that you counted.

Simons: Yes, yes, we counted.

Stranger: Everyone counted six Simons.

Simons: Yes, yes! Six Simons.

Stranger: Are you sure one Simon drowned? Did you see anyone fall into the water?

Susie Simon: No! No! Nothing like that. But we know that one Simon is missing. This morning we were seven Simons. Now we count six Simons. One Simon must be missing!

Stranger: Maybe I can help you find your missing Simon.

Simons *(Together)*:   How? Tell us!

Stranger: All right. Line up. *(Simons line up.)* Everyone, put your hat on the ground in front of you. *(Each Simon does so.)* Now, we'll count hats. All together. *(Stranger points to each hat as he and Simons count together.)* One, two, three, four, five, six, seven!

Simons: Seven hats!

Stranger: Now! Everyone, pick up your hat. *(Each does so.)* Put your hat on your head. *(Each does so.)* We'll count again. All together.

Stranger and all Simons: One, two, three, four, five, six, seven!

Stranger: There are seven hats on seven heads. There must be seven Simons!

Simons *(Yelling)*:   Seven Simons! Seven Simons!

*(They crowd around **Stranger**, but do not get in front of him. **Susie** extends her right hand to **Stranger** and pumps his arm up and down as she thanks him.)*

Susie Simon: Thank you! Thank you! Thank you! You found our missing Simon! Thank you!

Stranger: You are welcome. Very welcome! *(He gets weary with the handshaking.)*

Susie Simon: If you ever need help, remember the seven Simons.

Stranger: Oh, how could I ever forget the seven Simons! Now, I must say good-bye and be on my way. *(Exits.)*

Simons (*Calling and waving as **Stranger** exits*):
Good-bye, our friend. Good-bye. (*They pick up their fishing poles, form a line behind **Susie**, and march off the stage counting.*)

Simons: One, two, three, four, five, six, seven. One, two ——————

THINK ABOUT IT

1. Where does this play take place? Who are the characters in the play? Where did you find this information?

2. What were all the Simons doing at the beginning of the play?

3. What did Susie Simon think had happened to one of the Simons?

4. Why had all the Simons miscounted?

5. What did the stranger do to straighten out the confusion?

6. Why do you think this play is called "7 Silly Simons"? Make up another good title.

7. At first the Simons thought that something terrible had happened. But then they discovered that everything was all right. Have you ever been in such a situation? What happened?

Two Months from Alice Yazzie's Year

Alice Yazzie's Year is a wonderful month-to-month story about a Navajo girl. In the story, there is a poem for each month of Alice's year. Here, you will read two of those poems. Before you read each poem, I will tell you something about Alice's life and our Navajo culture.

The poems on these pages are about Alice Yazzie's life during January and September.

Navajos call January *Yas Nilt'ees.*[1] This means "crusted snow." It gets very cold in January. When you walk on frozen snow, you can hear it crunch under your feet. Very long ago, our language was young and we had fewer words. Then *Yas Nilt'ees* may have meant "boiling or thawing snow for water."

[1] **Yas Nilt'ees** (yäs' nilt ās')

108

September is called *Bini'ant'aatsoh.*[2] This is the time when the last crops of the year grow ripe. *Bini'ant'aatsoh* means "maturing of the late crops."

Alice's name, Yazzie, means "little" or "tiny" in Navajo. Her grandfather's name, Tsosie, means "slim." These names are heard a lot in Navajoland.

Navajos raise sheep, and children often herd them. They raise sheep for wool. They shear their sheep in the spring when the weather gets warm. Some of the wool they sell. Some they save to weave beautiful Navajo rugs. Navajos also raise goats and cattle. The sheep and cattle are sometimes sold for meat. Lambs are sold in the fall. Lamb is the Navajos' favorite meat.

[2] **Bini'ant'aatsoh** (be nē'änt ä'tsō)

JANUARY   YAS NILT'EES

The snow slowed the world,
the Navajo world.
"Go see if the sheep are fine,"
Grandfather Tsosie tells Alice Yazzie.
"The hay is frozen
and so is the ground," says Alice, returning.
"The horses look like they blame me
for causing this cold."

Her nose red, her chin buried in sheepskin,
she carries the smallest lamb
into the hogan.
"Just for the night," says Alice Yazzie
holding the lamb.
"He's all new and starry.
He's too new to be cold."
Grandfather grunts.
He doesn't say no.

Alice heats milk in a bottle
over burning pinyon.
Grandfather watches.
The new lamb sucks.
The pinyon burns low.
The lamb goes to sleep.
His nose is a black star.

"It *is* cold out there," Alice tells Grandfather
as she goes to bed.
Grandfather nods.
He wears a red flannel shirt
    Alice gave him for Christmas.
He looks at the low fire.
He looks at the lamb.
Grandfather says
to Alice Yazzie,
to Alice Ben Yazzie,
"It was almost this cold
the night you were born."

Schools in Navajo country are often a long bus ride from home. Some schools are such a long ride away that children live at the school instead of coming home each day. These are called boarding schools. Many of the schools are run by the United States government. They are called Indian schools. Sometimes the teachers take students on trips. The trips are fun. The children see and learn about life in the cities and other places away from Navajo country.

SEPTEMBER BINI'ANT'AATSOH

Alice pulls her hair back into one long braid.
Last year's gym shorts are too short. She's grown.
Her toes won't even wiggle
in last year's tennies.
It's a mile through the dust
to the yellow bus stop. In winter: through mud.
The pup seems to beg with his eyes:
"Stay home. Let's us play, Alice Yazzie.
The two of us."

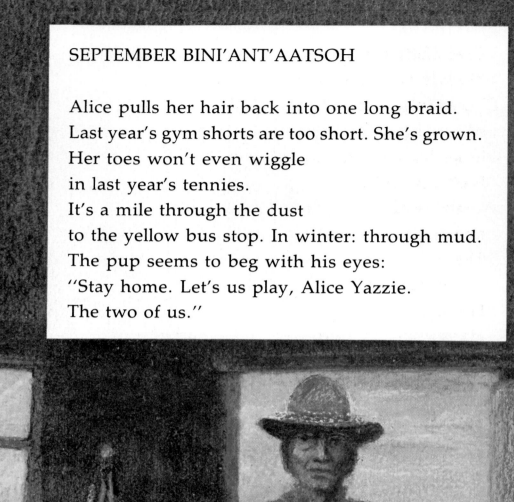

Grandfather frowns.
"We do what we must.
I see you must go to school. This year—
not so many hot dogs in the cafeteria.
More books in the learning center.
We'll see to that."
Grandfather sits on the school board
and helps decide about classes and buildings.
The oldest school board man, he sees change
    happening.
He says it must come.
He even voted for girls to play football
if they want to. And study mechanical drawing.

Alice starts off in her tie-dyed T-shirt
and a denim skirt faded canyon blue.
Grandfather calls. He gives Alice a ride
behind him, on his horse,
to the bus stop shelter.
Alice is surprised.
"Remember," says Grandfather,
nudging the old mare until she faces around.
"You don't have to take mechanical drawing
if you don't want to."
"Thank you, Grandfather."
As they move off, old man on old horse,
Alice feels winter coming.

Alice Yazzie is a true Navajo. She knows that Beauty is before her. Beauty is behind her. Beauty is below her. Beauty is above her. Beauty is all around her. And Beauty is Happiness.

THINK ABOUT IT

1. What do the Navajo words for "January" and "September" mean? What do *Yazzie* and *Tsosie* mean?

2. Why are sheep important in Navajo culture?

3. Why did Alice bring the smallest lamb into the hogan?

4. What does the cold night remind Grandfather of?

5. Why does the author say that Alice Yazzie is a true Navajo?

6. What do you think Grandfather means when he says "We do what we must"?

7. How do you think Alice and Grandfather feel about each other?

8. In what way is Beauty "all around" Alice Yazzie? In what way is Beauty in your life?

A Chimp Learns to "Talk"

How do animals learn and communicate? How do their minds work? In what ways do people's minds work differently? How does someone learn a language? In 1966 two scientists—Doctors Beatrice and Allen Gardner—were asking these questions. To answer them, the Gardners wanted to teach a baby chimp to use Ameslan, the sign language of the deaf.

The Gardners worked at the University of Nevada in Washoe County, Nevada. So when their baby chimp arrived from Africa, they named her Washoe. Washoe was about the same age as a one-year-old child when she came.

The Gardners hoped to compare Washoe's growth with that of hearing children and with deaf children who were learning Ameslan.

Children usually grow up in homes around objects they learn to name. They have toys, pets, books, bottles, blankets, food, and flowers. They hear people's voices and see their movements all the time.

They do not live in bare cages. Any baby brought up alone behind bars would grow much more slowly than other children. It might never speak at all. It would have no one to talk to and nothing to say.

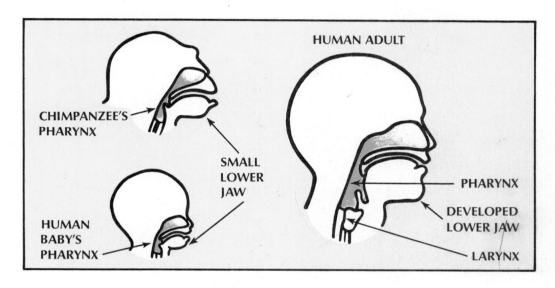

CHIMPANZEE'S PHARYNX

HUMAN ADULT

HUMAN BABY'S PHARYNX

SMALL LOWER JAW

PHARYNX

DEVELOPED LOWER JAW

LARYNX

The pharynx helps people speak.

The *pharynx* is the air space in the back of the throat. In older children and adults, the pharynx is long. It also bends very easily. Sound waves travel from the *larynx,* or "voice box," through the pharynx to the mouth. The mouth then forms the sounds into words. The pharynx helps "mold" the sound waves into word sounds we learn. It does this by changing shape quickly, but very slightly, as the sound waves pass through it. Both a human baby and a chimpanzee have a small lower jaw and a short, stiff pharynx. A baby's lower jaw and pharynx change as it grows. The pharynx gets longer as the lower jaw develops. As the pharynx gets longer, it also gets flexible. A chimpanzee's lower jaw and pharynx never change like this. This is one big reason why people can speak but chimpanzees can't.

If Washoe was going to be compared with children, she needed as interesting a life as possible. So Washoe had her own trailer behind the Gardners' home. The trailer had a living room, kitchen, bedroom, and bath. Outside, Washoe had a large yard with a jungle gym, flowers, trees, and gardening tools. She liked to play with the watering hose and sometimes sprayed her friends. Inside were all the cleaning tools needed in every home. Washoe had clothes, blankets, brushes, toys, and even a full refrigerator!

Washoe had no chimp friends. Students from the university helped the Gardners. They became Washoe's caretakers, friends, and teachers. With burglar alarms and boat horns they also kept Washoe from places that might hurt her.

Washoe liked picture books and magazines. At first the pictures seemed real to her. She tried to pick flowers off the pages. The students put together scrapbooks of her favorite pictures. Washoe looked through them alone and with her friends.

The students took Washoe on trips so she could learn about the world outside her home. She played in country fields. She romped in the university nursery school and playgrounds. But she went there only on weekends, when there were no children to excite her. And no children to be excited by a visiting chimp!

When Washoe came to Washoe County, she was very little with big, round eyes in a small, wrinkled face. She climbed trees and hung from branches by just one arm. On the ground she acted more like a baby. She crawled, often tugging a blanket behind her. She used her hands like a baby and slept a lot.

When Washoe was awake, her friends made signs with her. Washoe began to "speak" slowly, as a child does. She learned only four signs during her first seven months of training—**come-gimme, more, up,** and **sweet.**

After seven more months, she knew nine more signs. Then she began to learn more quickly. When she was about three, Washoe could make thirty-four signs. This was much less than a three-year-old child would know, but it made history. An animal was "talking" with people at last!

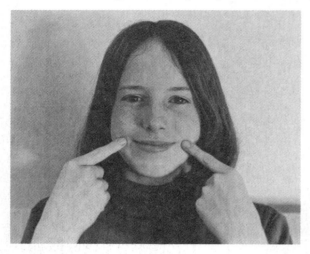

This girl is showing the Ameslan sign for *smile*.

Here is Washoe's version of the same sign.

From *Science Year, The World Book Science Annual.*
© 1973 Field Enterprises Educational Corporation.

From *Science Year, The World Book Science Annual.* © 1973 Field Enterprises Educational Corporation.

In this picture Washoe and her friend Roger are having a conversation. Washoe and her friends had many conversations. Here is one of them.

> Roger: What you want?
> Washoe: Tickle
> Roger: Who tickle?
> Washoe: Dr. Gardner
> Roger: Dr. Gardner not here
> Washoe: Roger tickle

Compare these signs in Ameslan with some that Washoe made.

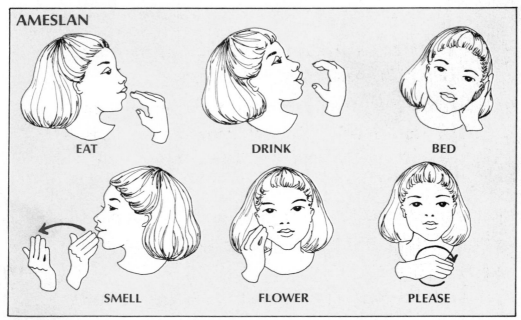

AMESLAN

EAT   DRINK   BED

SMELL   FLOWER   PLEASE

"WASHOESE"

EAT (FOOD)   DRINK (CUP)   BED

SMELL   FLOWER   PLEASE

1. What is Ameslan? Why did the Gardners want to teach Ameslan to a baby chimp?

2. What did the Gardners name the chimp whom they were teaching? Why? How old was the chimp when she came to live with the Gardners?

3. With what did the Gardners want to compare the chimp's growth? Why was it important that the chimp lead an interesting life?

4. Why did the chimp's ability to learn signs make history?

5. Do you know of any other animals that have learned to communicate with people? Tell about them.

6. Why do you think scientists are so eager to find out about how animals learn?

7. Do you think that you would enjoy working with animals? Which animal would you most like to teach?

A Voice from Below

A cricket talking to a boy. Impossible, you say? What could they talk about? How would they do it? This is a story about the impossible and how it happened.

It snowed again for a whole day and a night. The paths that Mr. Silvanus had dug to the road, and out to the garbage cans, and to the garage, were quite covered again. Schools were closed. It was not an unwelcome holiday for Simms Silvanus, although he missed his school friends. But, if the truth were known, it was a relief, for a change, to be free of the sound of his teacher's voice—dotted with *i*'s, crossed with *t*'s, and sprinkled with commas and semicolons.

Simms had a good deal of time to do what he wished. First, he helped his parents by sweeping up the kitchen. Next, he sorted out all the old nails and screws and put them in separate boxes. Then he put together a jigsaw puzzle. He read three chapters in *Swiss Family Robinson*. That made him think a warm climate might be nicer after all, even if there wasn't any snow to roll in. Then he lay on his back on the bed and stared out the window. Through the looped white organdy curtains he saw a glaring white patch of world. It was beautiful, but it just wasn't enough. Simms got up and went to his telegraph key.

He did a few trial runs of letters and punctuation marks, just for practice. Then he decided that he was ready for words. That wasn't so easy, but he went at it slowly.

"Hello," tapped Simms. "Hello."

He thought that was a good way to start a message. So he practiced several times. "Hello. My name is Simms."

Very good!

"My name is Simms," he tapped again. "I am a boy. I am a boy of nine." He thought that he was doing quite well for a beginner. It was slow, but it was right.

"What a shame this isn't hooked up," Simms thought. "It's too bad someone doesn't have a set I could send messages to. When this snow stops, I'm going to see if I can get one of my friends to learn." And then he tapped again.

"Hello. My name is Simms." He was really getting the hang of it. "Hello. My name is Simms. I am a boy of nine."

And then, in the pause that followed, *there came an answer!*

"Hello," came a piping sound in Morse code. Simms's hand hung in the air over the telegraph key. It was hard to believe, and yet it *did* seem to be an answer.

"But it's not connected to anything! There's no one receiving the message," he mused. "How could it be? I must have imagined it, or maybe it was just an echo." But he tried again. "Hello!" he tapped.

"Hello," came the creaky answer.

Simms's hand was unsteady, but he rushed as much as he could. "I'm Simms," tapped Simms.

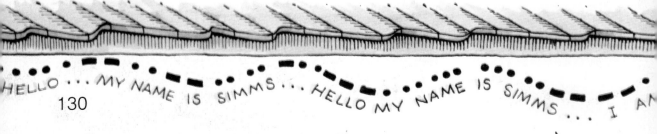

There was a pause. Then came the chirped reply. "I'm *Orthoptera Grylidae*."

Simms's mind churned. As quickly as he could, he tapped out, "Who did you say you are? And where are you, anyhow?"

Slowly, too, but gaining in skill, the reply was chirped. *"Orthoptera Grylidae*. Cricket." And then again. *"Orthoptera Grylidae*. Cricket. Under the floor. Under the floor."

Simms found that it was even harder to listen to a message than to send one. He worked hard and fast to try and understand. When he had thought it out, he still couldn't believe it. He mulled it over in his mind for a bit. After a few moments he came to a conclusion that was partly true.

"For heaven's sake!" he thought. "Crickets understand Morse code! I wonder if anyone knows that? My word! This may be a great discovery. Dots and dashes—that must be what crickets do all the time out in the fields all summer!" He got back to the key.

A BOY OF NINE...

"Hello," he tapped, because he could do that very fast by now.

"Hello," chirped Cricket.

"How are things?" tapped Simms.

"What things?" asked the cricket.

Simms thought about this. Then he tapped, "The things that have to do with your life. How are they?"

"That will take a lot of thought to answer, but I will think about it," chirped the cricket. "How are your things?"

Simms would have been able to answer this question a minute ago by saying "Just great." Now he answered slowly. "I will think about it, too." And so he asked another important question. "Are you alone?"

"No," chirped Cricket. "And yes," it added. "I am alone as a cricket, but as a creature I am not alone."

"Who is with you?" tapped Simms. He tapped very slowly. The cricket could chirp quickly, but it used the language slowly. So they were quite an even match.

"Right here, I am by myself," chirped Cricket. "However, on the other side of the house there are quite a few very pleasant folk. There's a mouse family, quite charming—he, she, and three young Mus children."

Simms was interested. "Mice!" he said. "My parents would be wild. Do you know anything about a rat?"

"Yes," said Cricket. "There is one rat."

"Just one?"

"Just one."

"Big?"

"Enormous!"

"Who else is there?" asked Simms.

"There's a mole, a spider, and a very large group of ants."

"All in our house?" tapped Simms. "All these creatures live in our house?"

"All under the house," chirped Cricket.

"Tell me about them," tapped Simms.

"I've just met them," chirped Cricket. "I don't know them well, but the mice seem a bit worried."

"About what?" tapped Simms. And at that moment a voice could be heard by both boy and cricket. It was a parent's voice saying, "Bedtime, Simms."

"I'll have to go now," tapped Simms hurriedly. "But tell me tomorrow. Good night."

"A very good night," chirped Cricket.

Generally speaking, crickets don't get excited. But this cricket now sensed an unusual feeling under his crisp coat of chitin. It was excitement!

Of course, Simms was excited, too. His discovery that cold and snowy winter was to make a big difference to both him and the cricket. It was also to have an effect on the Mus family and all the other creatures that lived under the Silvanus home. To find out how, read The Cricket Winter *by Felice Holman.*

134

1. Why wasn't Simms Silvanus in school?

2. What was Simms doing with his telegraph key? Why didn't Simms think he could receive a return message?

3. Who returned Simms's message? What code was used to send the messages?

4. In addition to the cricket, who else was living under Simms's house?

5. What do you think the mice were so worried about?

6. Why was the cricket so excited? Do you think that Simms felt excited, too?

7. Have you ever used a secret code to send messages? What kind of code did you use? To whom did you send messages?

The Friendly Cricket

El Amigo Grillo

This story-song is from Costa Rica.

1. As I was a-walk-ing, a-long streets a-far,___
1. U-na ves pa-sean-do por la ca-lle-cit-ta,
Oo-nah behs pah-seh-ahn-doh pohr lah kah-yeh-see-tah

There I met a crick-et, strum-ming his gui-tar;___
me en-con-tré un gri-lli-to con su gui-ta-rri-ta.
meh-ehn-kohn-treh-oon gree-yee-toh kohn soo gee-tah-ree-tah

I went to pass him; he sang out "Good day,"
Y vol-ví a pa-sar y aún es-ta-ba a-llí,
Ee bohl-bee-ah pah-sahr ee-ah-oon ehs-tah-bah-ah-yee,

We shook hands to-geth-er, and went on our way.
le ten-dí la ma-no y el ha-ci-a a-sí.
leh tehn-dee lah mah-noh ee-ehl ah-see ah-ah-see.

136

2. *As I was awalking, along Union street,*
   A cricket playing songs, there I chanced to meet,
   I went to pass him; he sang out "Good day,"
   We shook hands together, and went on our way.

2. Una vez paseando por la calle Unión,
   Me encontré al grillito con el acordéon,
   Y volvía pasar y aun estaba alli;
   Le tendí la mano y el hacía así.

2. Oo-nah behs pah-seh-ahn-doh pohr lah kah-yeh oo-nyohn,
   meh-ehn-kohn-treh-ahl gree-yee-toh kohn ehl ah-kohr-dyohn,
   ee bohl-bee-ah pah-sahr ee-ah-oon ehs-tah-bah-ah-yee.
   leh tehn-dee lah mah-noh ee-ehl ah-see-ah-ah-see.

3. *As I was awalking Europe Promenade,*
   I met little cricket, with a lemonade.
   I went to pass him; he sang out "Good day,"
   We shook hands together, and went on our way.

3. Una vez paseando por la calle Europa,
   Me encontré al grillito tomando unas copas.
   Y volvía pasar y aun estaba allí;
   Le tendí la mano y el hacía así.

3. Oo-nah behs pah-seh-ahn-doh pohr lah kay-yeh eh-oo-roh-pah,
   meh ehn-kohn-treh ahl gree-yee-toh toh-mahn-doh oo-nahs koh-pah
   ee bohl-bee-ah pah-sahr ee-ah-oon ehs-tah-bah-ah-yee.
   leh tehn-dee lah mah-noh ee-ehl ah-see-ah-ah-see.

three

Moonlight

A Horse with a Mind of His Own

Juan Morena was born and grew up in Palomino Valley near San Diego in southern California. His parents had moved to the valley from Mexico some years before, but then one day a tragedy occurred. A fire destroyed the dairy that Juan's parents owned. Both of Juan's parents were killed in the fire. Left alone, Juan went to live with friends of his family—three sisters who ran the Sherman Grove Store. Behind the store were some small cabins that the sisters rented to summer visitors. It was in Sherman Grove that Juan got to know and trust his horse Moonlight.

Juan's horse, Moonlight, was not really a white horse. He was a dappled horse. He looked more gray than white because there were so many little spots of black hair scattered among the white hairs of his hide.

In fact, most people laughed when Juan told them his horse's name was Moonlight. But Juan had spent many evenings looking up at the moon. He knew that the moon looked as much gray as white. At least it looked that way to him. So, he thought, he had a right to call his gray horse Moonlight if he wanted to.

Juan had to admit, though, that his horse did not look calm and peaceful like the light of the moon. His eyes looked a little red, and they rolled around a lot, and often looked wild. But this was easy to understand because Moonlight was once a wild horse.

Juan's father, Mr. Morena, had trained Moonlight for Juan. At first, Juan used a saddle whenever he rode Moonlight. But then Juan's father taught him to ride Moonlight bareback. Juan learned to take a long run and jump on Moonlight's gray back. Then he would lean far down over Moonlight's neck and catch the rope looped around Moonlight's black mane.

When Juan wanted to stop his horse, he pulled hard at the rope. But when he wanted to guide Moonlight to one side or the other, Juan pressed his knee into Moonlight's right or left side. When he wanted Moonlight to go faster, Juan slapped Moonlight's flanks with the palm of his hand.

Most of the visitors at Sherman Grove, of course, rode with a saddle. They always seemed surprised that Juan could stay on his horse without a saddle. But Juan liked to feel Moonlight's smooth, fat sides under his legs. And when Moonlight galloped across the brown hills, it seemed as if Juan were a part of the horse.

The summer visitors watched this slender boy riding about on the gray horse. It seemed to them that it was hard to tell where the horse began and the boy left off. For Juan had learned to make his body follow every move of Moonlight's body.

They understood each other so well that Juan hardly had to press Moonlight's sides to guide him. He could just call out the way he wanted the horse to go.

The summer visitors did not know that it had not always been this way. It was a long time before Juan had really learned to understand his horse.

When Juan first got his horse, his father had told him one thing. "If you want to be a real friend of Moonlight," he had said, "you must learn never to be afraid of him."

That had sounded easy. But Moonlight still had such a wild look in his eyes and so many of his wild ways. For many months, Juan feared that Moonlight would someday kick up his heels, pitch Juan off, and run back to the hills. That was because Moonlight had a stubborn streak. And, every time Moonlight got stubborn, it made Juan afraid. And every time he became afraid, Moonlight seemed to know it and to grow more and more stubborn.

If Moonlight wanted to turn in at a house or a path, he always turned in. It didn't matter how fast he was going. It didn't matter how hard Juan pulled at the rope about his neck. And there were times, riding across big, flat mesas behind the Grove, when Moonlight insisted on going around a bush one way. It didn't matter how hard Juan pressed his knee into the horse's side to go the other way.

Little by little, Juan came to understand that Moonlight often had good reasons for going the other way. Sometimes, Juan would look back. Then he would see that Moonlight had noticed a gopher hole in the path, or a snake, or a sharp rock. He also learned that it helped to sing a song to Moonlight when he seemed jittery.

But there were other times when Moonlight seemed "just plain ornery." He would run when he wanted to. He would go in whatever way he liked.

For a long time, Juan did not think this was right. He tried in every way he could to make his horse obey. But the more he pulled at the rope, the more stubborn Moonlight became. The more he pressed his knee into Moonlight's right side, the harder Moonlight pulled to the left.

Then Moonlight snorted and tossed his head back so that he looked at Juan with one wild eye. It was almost as if he were saying, "Look out, boy! One day you'll push me too hard. And that will be the last of you!"

Juan sat very straight and proud on Moonlight's back. He tried to show that he wasn't afraid, really. But if there were no people about, Juan bent over his horse's neck. Then Juan whispered softly into his ear, "Ah, Moonlight, *amigo*.[1] Let's be friends. Why do you not want to be friends?"

Moonlight only twitched his ears, as if the sound of Juan's voice annoyed him. Then the boy felt sad and very small on Moonlight's broad back.

How did Juan finally become friends with Moonlight? Well, it happened in a strange sort of

---

[1] **amigo** (ə mē′gō) friend

way. It happened in a way that people sometimes make friends.

Early one morning, Juan went out to the small corral down by the river. That was where Dave Plummer kept the young calves from his herd. The corral was a small, rickety pen made from willow branches. Dave had gathered the willows from along the river bank. Then he ran them through holes in fence posts.

This morning, Dave looked red in the face and worried. He was patching up a hole in one side of the corral. He looked up and saw Juan coming.

"Just the person I want to see," he called to Juan. "I'm looking for somebody big enough to go across the canyon and round up that pesky brown calf that broke out of here last night.

"I'd go myself," Dave added, scratching his long chin. "But I've got to fix this fence 'fore any others wander off to the hills."

Juan's stomach felt as if it had suddenly caved in. The canyon was one place he avoided as much as possible since getting his horse. The canyon had steep walls, higher than a house in places. True, there was a dirt road which went down the side of the cliff. Then it went through the sandy river bottom and up again on the other side. But

Juan had never been quite sure that he could keep his horse away from the steep banks. What if Moonlight became stubborn!

It might have been that Dave Plummer suspected this. He stopped his work for a moment and looked sharply at the boy.

"Think you're big enough for the job?" he asked. He seemed to size up Juan from head to toe.

As soon as Dave said this, Juan knew what he had to do. He stood very straight and answered, "Yes sir, Mr. Plummer."

"Well, you might be at that," Dave Plummer grunted. He pounded a nail in the fence post. Then he turned quickly back to Juan. "What about that hoss of yours? Think you can manage him?"

Juan wanted with all his heart to say no. He didn't want to go near that canyon. But he just said, "Yes sir, I think I can." Then he turned and ran as fast as he could down to the river. There Moonlight was grazing. He threw a rope over the horse's neck and jumped on his back.

As he rode past Dave, Juan even swaggered a bit to show that he was not afraid. But, as he rode out of sight behind the willows, Juan began to feel nervous again.

Juan watched Moonlight carefully. Everything seemed all right today. And so Juan rode his horse down the little dirt road into the bottom of the canyon. He rode up again on the other side.

Juan found the calf eating alfalfa in the meadow on the far side of the canyon. It was easy to catch him. He happened to be standing in the corner of the fence under a tree. Juan slipped quietly off his horse. He threw a rope about the calf's neck before the animal knew what had happened. Then the boy climbed back on Moonlight. Leading the calf by the rope, he started back for the corral.

It was on the way back that it happened. Juan had ridden down the road on the far side of the canyon. He crossed the sandy bottom and started up the homeward side. Things were going so nicely. He dug his heels into Moonlight's sides and slapped his flank as he headed up the winding, narrow road.

Moonlight's ears twitched warningly. Juan's elation vanished immediately. His stomach suddenly felt empty. The old feeling of fear crept over him. He could almost feel that fear running down his body and into his horse. He could remember his father's voice telling him, "As soon as you are afraid, son, your horse will always know it."

And, sure enough, Moonlight shook slightly and started balking.

151

It all happened before Juan had much time to think of anything. At this point in the road, the bank of the canyon sloped up above the road a little less sharply than it did anywhere else. Moonlight suddenly jerked his head. Then he started to climb up the side of the steep canyon wall.

Juan tugged and tugged at the horse's neck rope. He pressed hard with his knee into Moonlight's side. But the horse kept right on going up the canyon wall. Then, before Juan had time to think, he found himself sitting in the soft dust of the canyon road. His body made a "plop" of a sound as he landed. Little clouds of brown dust billowed up around his head.

At first Juan was merely angry. When he looked about, the calf was gone off down the canyon. He wondered what Mr. Plummer would say. Then he felt foolish as he thought how people would laugh and call him a *niño*[2] if they found out his horse had thrown him and run away.

It was only then that Juan had a curious thought. He had not been hurt at all in the fall! The dust was soft. The distance he had fallen was a hundred times shorter than it had always looked from on top of Moonlight's back.

[2] *niño* (nē′nyō) child

Juan sometimes thought about it afterward, and he was not quite sure how it happened. But when he looked up that day and saw Moonlight standing on top of the cliff, watching him, he knew he would never again be afraid of his horse. Moonlight had not run away at all. Instead, he stood there looking like a small boy who had done something he had been told not to, but had to do anyway.

Juan made his way up the soft bank. He placed a sure, strong hand on his horse's neck.

"I understand, *amigo*," he said softly. "I guess you just had to show me you had a right to go up that bank if you wanted to. Next time I'll go with you.

"Yes," Juan said to himself. "Next time I'll go with you."

Then he climbed on his horse, and they went off in search of the calf again.

1. Why did Juan call his horse Moonlight? Why did some people laugh when Juan told them his horse's name?

2. What advice had Juan's father given to him when he first got his horse? Why did Juan find it difficult to follow his father's advice?

3. How did Juan finally become friends with Moonlight?

4. Did Juan understand why his horse had insisted on climbing up the canyon wall? Why *had* the horse done this?

5. Do you think Juan understood animals? Why or why not?

6. What kind of horse was Moonlight? Would you like to have such a horse?

7. Have you ever had a pet? Was there ever a time when you were afraid of your pet for some reason? Do you think that animals can sense when you are afraid of them? Explain your answer.

Try Your Tongue on These!

A flea and a fly in a flue
Were imprisoned, so what could they do?
   Said the fly, "Let us flee,"
   Said the flea, "Let us fly,"
So they flew through a flaw in the flue.

Anonymous

One day I went out to the zoo,
For I wanted to see the old gnu,
   But the old gnu was dead
   And the new gnu they said
Was too new a new gnu to view.

Anonymous

ELETELEPHONY

Once there was an elephant,
Who tried to use the telephant—
No! no! I mean an elephone
Who tried to use the telephone—
(Dear me! I am not certain quite
That even now I've got it right.)

Howe'er it was, he got his trunk
Entangled in the telephunk;
The more he tried to get it free,
The louder buzzed the telephee—
(I fear I'd better drop the song
Of elephop and telephong!)

Laura E. Richards

157

ANIMAL RIDDLES

Which takes less time to get ready for a trip—an elephant or a rooster?

A rooster. He takes only his comb, while the elephant has to take a whole trunk.

Why are elephants so wrinkled?

Did you ever try to iron one?

What's white outside, green inside, and hops?

A frog sandwich.

What did the porcupine say to the cactus plant?

"Is that you, Mama?"

What's the best way to catch a squirrel?

Climb a tree and act like a nut.

The March of the Lemmings

High in the mountains of the Far North, lacy snow-flakes drift slowly down. They settle onto the white blanket that covers the earth.

In a tunnel beneath the snow, two small animals touch noses. Then they go along their underground tunnel in opposite directions. One is headed for its snug little nest lined with grass and hair. The other is searching for a meal of roots or moss.

The tunnel is one of the many passages that criss-cross each other. Each one ends in a nest. This is a colony of lemmings. Lemmings are little animals that are shaped like hamsters.

Thousands of lemmings wander through the hallways of their underground city. Still more lemmings rest in their nests. They are eating roots or seeds, or nursing their litters of young. The colony has grown very large during the past few years. That's because there was plenty of food and plenty of room to grow.

Lemmings have soft, fluffy fur that is long and thick. It protects them against the cold, cold winters. In summer the fur is yellowish brown, with darker spots along the back, and grayish on the underside. Full-grown lemmings weigh only three or four ounces, but their heavy coats and short, stocky legs make them look plump. From the tip of its stubby tail to the end of its nose, a lemming measures about five inches. It has small ears and little black eyes. Its head seems rather large for the rest of its body.

During the winter, family after family is born into the lemming colony. Each mother lemming has several litters. There may be as many as eleven babies in a litter. In only a few weeks, these young lemmings start having babies of their own.

Then summer comes. The lemmings feast on grasses and leaves. More and more lemmings are born. In only a year or two, the colony becomes crowded. The food supply becomes scarce.

Now the lemmings in the colony are hungry all the time. The little rodents are no longer friendly. They quarrel and fight over what little food and space are left.

Then, as if by a signal, a few lemmings leave the colony. Others join them, and soon there are hundreds—and then thousands. A few stay behind, but most of the colony heads down the mountainside. Some scientists think they start their journey looking for food.

As they move along, the lemmings pass other colonies. More lemmings join them. Soon there are millions of marchers. They swarm down into the valleys.

The march continues. The lemmings move through farms, eating the crops as they go. They nibble their way across the land, climbing hills and crossing fields and meadows.

When the lemmings come to a stream or a lake, they jump in and swim across it. Some are eaten by fish. Others become tired and drown. Many die of hunger or disease. But the rest keep going. Nothing stops the march. On and on they go.

A year or two may pass before the lemming army finally reaches the sea. Still they do not stop. Plunging into the icy salt water, they swim and swim—until they can swim no more. Then they sink beneath the waves and are gone. The march is over.

Those lemmings that stayed behind in their homes in the mountains are enjoying a good life. Since most of their neighbors are gone, they have plenty of room. Now there is enough food for all of them. They are busy having large families. And their children are having large families. The colony is growing very quickly again.

Everything will go well for a few years. But some-day there will be too many lemmings again. There will not be enough food to feed all of them. Then most of the lemmings will band together and march to the sea.

Why do the lemmings go into the ocean? Do they think they can swim across it? Do they think it is just another lake or stream? Some scientists believe this is the reason.

Maybe the lemmings still follow the same route that their ancestors took long ago. Millions of years ago there may have been dry land where the ocean is now.

Some scientists think that the lemmings start to march because changes occur in their bodies or in their brains. The changes force them to keep moving until they die. Nobody really knows.

1. What do lemmings look like?

2. Where do lemmings live? What do they eat? What happens when their food supply becomes scarce?

3. When do the lemmings begin their march to the sea? How long does the march take? What do the lemmings do when they reach the sea?

4. What explanation do scientists give for the lemmings' march to the sea?

5. What might happen to the lemmings if they didn't march to the sea?

6. Do you know of any other animals that behave in ways that seem strange to people? What do these animals do? Do you know a scientific explanation for what they do?

IN TIME OF SILVER RAIN

In time of silver rain
The earth
Puts forth new life again,
Green grasses grow
And flowers lift their heads,
And over all the plain
The wonder spreads
Of life, of life, of life!

In time of silver rain
The butterflies lift silken wings
To catch a rainbow cry,
And trees put forth
New leaves to sing
In joy beneath the sky
As down the roadway passing boys
And girls go singing, too,
In time of silver rain
When spring
And life are new.

Langston Hughes

PHOEBE AND THE GENERAL

In 1776, the year Phoebe Fraunces was thirteen years old, her father gave her a very dangerous job. Phoebe was going to be a spy. At that time most black people in America were slaves. But Phoebe and her father had always been free.

Phoebe's father, Samuel Fraunces, owned the Queen's Head Tavern, an eating house in New York City. Many Patriots, including General George Washington, met there because they knew it was a safe place to talk. They knew that Samuel Fraunces could be trusted.

One day, Samuel Fraunces overheard a conversation that he thought was a plot against the life of General Washington. But he had no proof. He asked his daughter Phoebe to go to Washington's headquarters at Mortier House to live as a housekeeper. Samuel Fraunces and Phoebe knew that General Washington was leading the American army in a war for freedom. But even as they made plans to save his life, they thought how strange it was for a man to fight for freedom if he himself owned slaves. For General Washington did own slaves. And it was even stranger that Phoebe and Samuel Fraunces would save the general, but others like them would not share in the freedom Washington was fighting for.

While Phoebe was at Mortier House, her real job would be to find out if someone was planning to kill General Washington, and, if so, how. Samuel Fraunces warned his daughter to watch for a member of General Washington's body-guard—someone whose name began with *T*.

Part One

Phoebe was a good housekeeper. But she did not forget why she was there. Day after day she watched, and waited, and listened. General Washington came and went. The house was full of people all the time—officers of the Army, friends, members of the bodyguard. Phoebe slipped among them silent as a shadow, as her father had taught her. Whenever she saw anyone talking softly, she stopped to poke the fire, fill their glasses, light new candles. But still she saw nothing, heard nothing.

Each day at noon she took a basket and went down to the waterfront to do the day's marketing. When she was finished, she would make her way to the edge of the harbor and stand looking out over the ocean. No one took any notice of her, in her clean white apron and cap, a shawl thrown across her shoulders. Nor did anyone particularly notice the man who always came to stand beside her.

Phoebe never had anything to report to her father. She was particularly careful to watch every member of the general's bodyguard who came to the house. None was called by a name starting with *T*. They all seemed truly fond of the general and laughed and joked with him.

Two members of the bodyguard did stand out from the others. One was especially nice. Mr. Hickey was his name. He smiled at Phoebe while she was serving and often came into the kitchen to joke with her. Hickey seemed much younger than the other men. Like Phoebe, he seemed not to have many friends. Phoebe often saw him sitting by himself.

Mr. Green was another member of General Washington's bodyguard who kept to himself. But he was not like Hickey. Phoebe would always say, "Evening, sir," but he never so much as looked at her. From what she could tell, Green didn't say much to anyone. Though his name didn't begin with *T*, Phoebe made up her mind to watch him very carefully. There was something about him she didn't like.

Part Two

One day, when Hickey came to the kitchen,
he had a small cloth bag with him. He handed it
to Phoebe. "Here," he said. "It's some seed for
your precious chickens."

Phoebe was surprised. Mortier House had its
own hen house and a yard where several chickens pecked and scratched contentedly. Phoebe
didn't know anyone had noticed that she fed
them. She opened the bag. "But it's good seed,
sir!" she protested. "It's too good to feed the
chickens!"

Hickey laughed. "It's only the king's true men
who'll be missing it," he said.

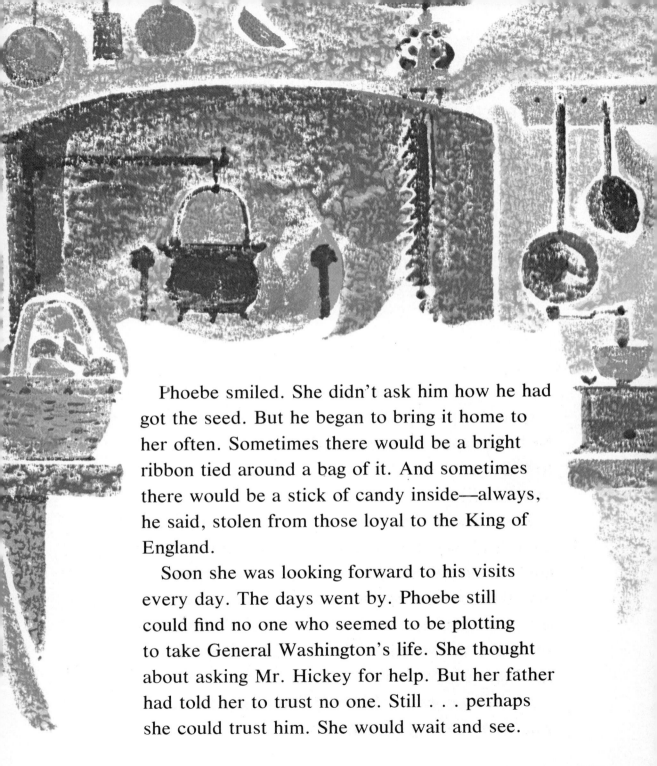

Phoebe smiled. She didn't ask him how he had
got the seed. But he began to bring it home to
her often. Sometimes there would be a bright
ribbon tied around a bag of it. And sometimes
there would be a stick of candy inside—always,
he said, stolen from those loyal to the King of
England.

Soon she was looking forward to his visits
every day. The days went by. Phoebe still
could find no one who seemed to be plotting
to take General Washington's life. She thought
about asking Mr. Hickey for help. But her father
had told her to trust no one. Still . . . perhaps
she could trust him. She would wait and see.

Weeks went by. The beautiful house, once so strange to Phoebe, was now like a good friend. She knew she was there to save General Washington's life. But she began to wonder if perhaps her father was mistaken.

Then one day, when she went to the market, her father wasn't there. Phoebe stood by the water a long time, waiting and wondering. Should she go to the Queen's Head? Or back to Mortier House? As she was trying to decide, she saw her father hurrying toward her. He looked very worried.

"Phoebe," he said urgently. "I have heard that General Washington will be leaving Mortier House in a very few days. The person known as *T* will act before that time. You must find out who it is!"

Phoebe's mind was whirling as she hurried back toward the house. She was frightened, but she was also determined. She *would* save General Washington! She had long ago figured that he would likely be shot. During dinner he always sat in a chair by the window. He would make an easy target for anyone waiting outside. If only she could get him to change his place!

As she reached the kitchen door, Phoebe saw Hickey sitting on the steps. "Why are you so solemn, pretty Phoebe?" he asked.

"Oh, Mr. Hickey, sir," said Phoebe breathlessly. "I'm so worried. . . ." She paused. She did need help! Should she tell him? But her father's words came back to her. "Trust no one," he had said. "No one." She sighed. She'd have to keep trying alone.

"Well," said Hickey after a moment. "I've something to bring a smile back to that pretty face. Fresh June peas for the general's dinner— first of the season! His favorite and mine—and enough for us both! Some friends of the king will be mighty hungry tonight!" He handed her a large sack, filled to the brim with pea pods. Phoebe smiled in spite of herself. "I'll be here to fill my plate at dinnertime," Hickey promised.

All afternoon, as she went about her chores, Phoebe worried. *How* could she get the general's chair away from that window? By dinnertime she was almost sick with fear. She was in the kitchen with Pompey, the cook's young son, getting ready to serve the plates when a voice behind her made her jump. It was Hickey.

"I've come for my peas," he said softly.

"Oh! Mr. Hickey, sir!" she said. "You gave me such a start! I was—" She stopped and looked at him, even more startled. He looked ill? frightened? She couldn't tell which.

"Which is my plate, and which is General Washington's?" he said. "It wouldn't do for him to have more than me." He spoke quickly, without smiling this time.

"I never heard of such carryings on over a pile of peas!" Phoebe said. "This is the general's plate, and this is yours!" She turned away to fill Pompey's salt cellar and turned back just in time to see Hickey's hand move quickly away from General Washington's plate and slide into his pocket. Something winked for a second in the light—something shiny, like glass.

"What are you doing to General Washington's plate?" she said. "I told you yours is here!" She picked up the plate. Was it her imagination, or was there something grainy, like sugar, on the peas? Phoebe looked more closely, but as she looked, whatever it was seemed to have disappeared. An instant later she wasn't sure—had she seen anything at all? She thought of the window again and forgot about the peas. She had to serve General Washington.

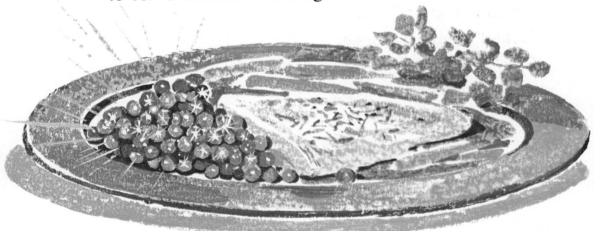

Part Three

Leaving Hickey standing in the kitchen, Phoebe nervously entered the dining room. As she walked toward the general, she noticed the empty chair. Who was missing? But even as she asked herself the question, she knew. It was Mr. Green. Was he outside the house, with a gun, waiting? General Washington was sitting by the window, as she had feared. The window was open! As she went past, Phoebe looked outside anxiously. There was not a sound, not a shadow, not a movement.

"Well, Phoebe!" General Washington exclaimed as she stopped beside his chair. "June peas! How did you get them so early in the season?"

"It wasn't me, sir," replied Phoebe, looking past him out the window. "It was your Mr. Hickey brought them in, fresh today. He said they're your favorite."

"And mine as well!" said Washington's friend General Gates. "Where is Mr. Thomas Hickey? I want to thank him!"

Phoebe started to put the plate down in front of General Washington. Then, in a flash, it came to her who she was looking for. Mr. Green was

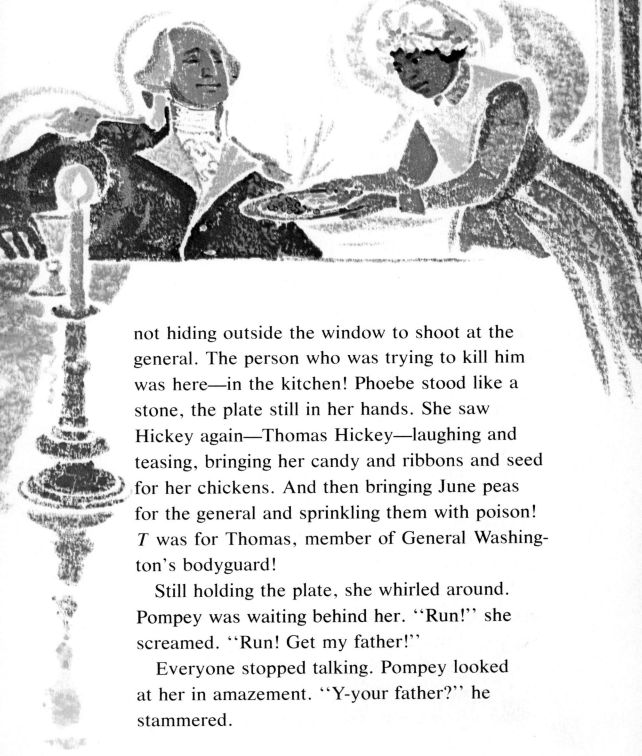

not hiding outside the window to shoot at the
general. The person who was trying to kill him
was here—in the kitchen! Phoebe stood like a
stone, the plate still in her hands. She saw
Hickey again—Thomas Hickey—laughing and
teasing, bringing her candy and ribbons and seed
for her chickens. And then bringing June peas
for the general and sprinkling them with poison!
T was for Thomas, member of General Washington's bodyguard!

Still holding the plate, she whirled around.
Pompey was waiting behind her. "Run!" she
screamed. "Run! Get my father!"

Everyone stopped talking. Pompey looked
at her in amazement. "Y-your father?" he
stammered.

"Sam Fraunces! At the Queen's Head! Go!"
And she stamped her foot. Pompey had never heard Phoebe sound like that before. He dropped the salt cellar and ran through the kitchen door.

Everyone in the dining room sat frozen. All eyes were on Phoebe. "General Washington!" she cried. "Mr. Hickey has put poison in your dinner! I saw him!" There was a gasp from the table.

"What jest is this?" roared General Gates, getting up from his place and reaching for the plate. But before he could take it from her, Phoebe ran to the open window and threw the whole plate out into the yard.

Now the dining room was in an uproar. Food spilled. Chairs overturned; the men jumped to their feet in confusion. No one knew what to do.

It was General Gates who first noticed the chickens in the yard. "Look!" he shouted, pointing out the window.

Three of Phoebe's chickens had come to peck at the peas she had thrown outside. Two had already fallen dead. The third was still moving its wings, but as they watched, it, too, grew still. The poison, meant for General Washington, had killed the chickens instead.

"Get Hickey!" bellowed General Gates, and members of the bodyguard rushed to obey. Minutes later Thomas Hickey was dragged in from the yard, his face white with terror. He had not been able to escape. Minutes after that, Sam Fraunces burst into the room. Phoebe was still standing by the window, shaking. He ran to her and held her tightly. Phoebe clung to him, burying her face in his shoulder.

"Well done, daughter," Samuel Fraunces said quietly. "Well done."

After the excitement had died down and Hickey had been taken away, General Washington came to speak to Phoebe and her father. "It's nice to know people whom I can trust," he said simply. "Thank you."

Postscript from the Author

The story of Phoebe Fraunces is based on historical facts. Samuel Fraunces did allow his restaurant to serve as a meeting place for the Patriots. He was so loyal to the revolutionary cause that after the war ended he was rewarded by the Congress. Soon after that Fraunces changed the name of the Queen's Head to the name by which it is still known today—Fraunces Tavern. The tavern is still standing, at the corner of Broad and Pearl Streets in New York City. Part of it is a museum, but the bottom floor is still a restaurant. It looks very much as it did when Samuel Fraunces and his family lived there, except that it no longer has its red-tiled roof.

1. Who was Samuel Fraunces? Why did he send his daughter Phoebe to live as a housekeeper at Mortier House?

2. Which two members of General Washington's bodyguard stood out from the others? Why?

3. Where did Mr. Hickey say he got the chicken seed and other things he brought to Phoebe?

4. Why didn't Phoebe ask Mr. Hickey for help in finding out who was plotting against the general? Was it good that she didn't? Why?

5. How did Phoebe save the general's life?

6. Why do you think Mr. Hickey was so nice to Phoebe?

7. Phoebe did not suspect the real villain at first. Were there any clues that should have made her suspicious?

8. What kind of person was Phoebe Fraunces? What did she do that makes you think this?

9. Why did Phoebe and her father choose to help General Washington? Why might they have chosen differently? What would you have done in their place? Why?

IT'S ABOUT TIME

Time lines can help you understand history. They show you the order in which important events happened. Here is a time line of important events around the time of the American Revolution. You can see that the Revolutionary War itself takes up only part of the time on the time line.

Events on a time line are arranged *chronologically. Chronological* means "in the order in which events take place in time." To read this time line, begin at the far left end of the line. Read toward the far right end of the line. On this time line, which event happened first? Yes, Crispus Attucks died at the Boston Massacre. Which events happened last?

Use the time line to answer these questions.

1. What happened in 1776?
2. When was the Boston Tea Party?

IMPORTANT EVENTS OF THE AMERICAN REVOLUTION

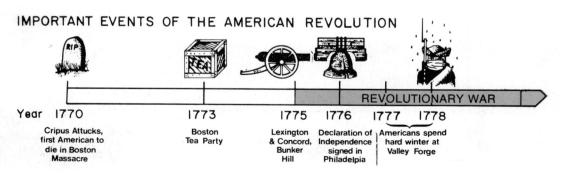

Year	1770	1773	1775	1776	1777	1778
	Cripus Attucks, first American to die in Boston Massacre	Boston Tea Party	Lexington & Concord, Bunker Hill	Declaration of Independence signed in Philadelpia	Americans spend hard winter at Valley Forge	

REVOLUTIONARY WAR

184

3. Which events came before the war? Which came after?

4. Did the Battle of Bunker Hill take place before or after the Declaration of Independence was signed?

5. What other important event took place the same year our Constitution was signed?

6. In 1783 General Washington gave a party for his soldiers at Fraunces Tavern. Why do you think they had a party?

7. Which happened first: Americans *became* independent or Americans *declared* their independence?

Time lines do not tell you *where, why,* or *how* history happened. They only tell you *when* events took place. Find some time lines in a social studies book. Look for time lines in the history books you borrow from the library, too. You can walk through history in your mind as your eyes read a time line.

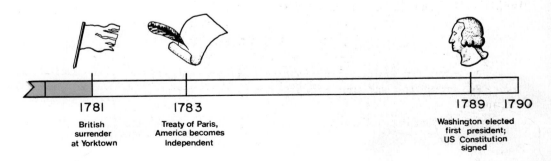

| 1781 | 1783 | | 1789 | 1790 |
| British surrender at Yorktown | Treaty of Paris, America becomes Independent | | Washington elected first president; US Constitution signed | |

Beneath the Saddle

Nathan Cathcart sat up in bed. His heart pounded. A pistol shot had awakened him. From the frozen road at the base of the hill came the clatter of hoofbeats. Then a heavy object struck the front door. It made the whole house tremble.

"Open in the King's name!" came a voice.

Nathan felt his throat tighten. He was alone in the little farmhouse. He thought of his mother and wished she were there. The men at the door were British soldiers. There could be little doubt of that.

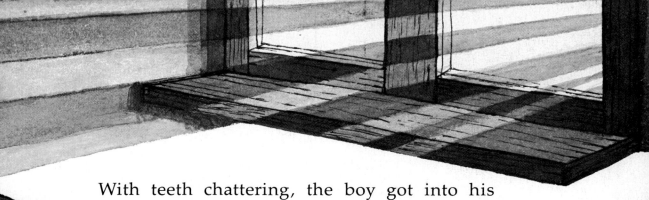

With teeth chattering, the boy got into his clothes. He made his way down the steep, narrow stairway.

"Who is there?" he called.

"You will soon find out if you keep us waiting any longer!" a voice yelled back.

Nathan drew aside the heavy oak bar and lifted the latch. With a rush of cold air, the door swung back. In front of him stood two British dragoons in scarlet uniforms. Beyond them he could see others, on their way up the hill, leading their horses.

"Whose house is this?" demanded one of the soldiers. The two dragoons strode inside.

"I live here with my mother," Nathan replied. "Tonight I'm alone. My mother had to go to Norfolk* to take care of my aunt, who is ill."

"Well, young rebel," the dragoon ordered, "go and fetch candles, for we mean to have a look about. Mind you, lose no time!"

*Norfolk (nôr'fək)

Nathan hesitated. Then he went into the kitchen. Why did these people wish to search the house? What could they expect to find?

In a few minutes he was back in the hallway with two lighted candles. By that time, the rest of the party had reached the house. They strode noisily inside and then closed the door.

"You wait right here, young puppy," one dragoon said to Nathan. Shivering with cold and excitement, Nathan stood silently beside the door. There were almost a dozen soldiers in the house. Some were upstairs. Some were downstairs.

Nathan could hear parts of their talk. He found out that they were searching for someone. But he could not figure out whom they wanted.

188

At last, those on the second floor came clumping down the stairs. "We are wasting our time here!" one of them shouted. Then the whole party went outside. Nathan saw them mount their horses and start down the hillside.

Closing the door, he went upstairs. On the floor of his own room, a candle was burning. It was dangerously close to the bed covering. He carried it downstairs. He placed it upon the high mantelpiece above the fireplace, where the soldiers had left the second one.

For some time he stood before the hearth. His head was bowed. His forehead was wrinkled. Who was it the dragoons were seeking? He remembered the pistol shot that had awakened him. What did it all mean?

Outside the wind was rising. He heard the mournful sound of it in the chimney and among the pines. Now and again a beam cracked with the cold. The boy hunched his shoulders and thought of his bed with its warm blankets. He snuffed out the candles and started upstairs.

Then a gentle knock at the door made him stiffen and catch his breath. "Who is there?" he asked.

"A friend," said a low voice.

Nathan swung the door open. Then he uttered a little cry of surprise. There in the moonlight stood a man in the uniform of the Continental Army. A bloodstained kerchief was around his head.

Nathan understood. This was the person the British wanted!

"Thank ye, lad," said the stranger as he entered the house. "The night is cold. . . ."

"And they've wounded you!" said Nathan.

"Aye, that is true, but 'tis not a bad wound." The stranger laughed mirthlessly. "So they thought to find me in the house, eh? Little did they know I was outside! You are alone here, lad?"

"Yes," said Nathan. "My mother is at Norfolk."

In the living room, the stranger dropped wearily upon a bench before the hearth. He covered his face with his hands. "A sorry mess I've made of things!" he muttered.

Nathan watched him uneasily. "What has happened, sir? I would like to be of help if there is anything I can do!"

The stranger lifted his head. "Lad," he said, "I have made a sorry mess of an important job. My name is Dawson. I am a dispatch rider. I was carrying important papers from General Washington at White Plains. Dragoons laid an ambush for me yonder. I sought to escape by riding away. They fired, and a pistol ball grazed the side of my head. It made me lose control of my horse. The creature raced up the road and bolted into the woods. A branch swept me to the ground. They found my horse but could not find me!"

"Oh," exclaimed Nathan, "then 'tis not so bad after all!"

"Not so bad?" repeated Dawson. "In truth, affairs could hardly be worse!"

Nathan looked at him wonderingly.

"The papers I carried were on the horse," Dawson added bitterly. "I had thrust the packet between saddle and blanket. I thought it would be safe—and now the British have my horse!"

Suddenly he rose to his feet. From the road came the ring and clatter of hoofbeats and the sound of voices. The dragoons were returning.

"Come!" cried Nathan. "You must hide!"

"Where?" Dawson glanced wildly about.

Nathan strode to the great fireplace and stepped inside. With his shoulders he pressed against the wooden wall at one end. The wall moved. There was an opening perhaps half a foot wide.

"Squeeze in there!" he ordered. "Then push the wall back into place. You will be safe if you make no sound. Quick!" He thrust Dawson inside.

When the panel closed again, Nathan ran to the window. He saw the dragoons coming at a fast pace up the hillside. What should he do?

Suddenly Nathan ran to the door. He slid back the bar so the door would open at a touch. Then he went swiftly up the stairway to his room. The cords of his bed creaked loudly as he flung himself into it.

A few seconds later he heard the soldiers in the hall, then in the lower rooms. He lay with thumping heart while the stairs creaked under the tread of heavy boots. Now the soldiers were on the second floor. Now they were in his room! One of them flashed his tinderbox. The light showed the boy sitting up, wide-eyed, in bed with the blankets about his shoulders.

"Where is the rebel rider? Where is he hiding?"

Nathan swallowed hard and remained silent.

"Have you no tongue in your head?"

Before the boy could answer, a dragoon caught hold of him and threw him onto the floor. They searched the bedroom to see if anyone was hiding there.

Bruised and shaken, Nathan rose and made his way downstairs. He planned to flee to the nearby woods. As he went outside, he almost ran into a dragoon who was holding the bridles of half a dozen horses.

"Wait a bit, lad!" the soldier exclaimed, and his voice sounded kindly. "Wait a bit, I say. We mean ye no harm and that be the truth!"

Nathan hesitated.

" 'Tis a cold night!" observed the soldier, blowing on his hands. "The horses feel it, too!"

Steam from the horses' nostrils rose white and sparkling in the moonlight. The frozen earth resounded under their restlessly stamping hooves.

"They are fine-looking horses, sir," Nathan remarked, with an effort.

"Aye, fine animals they are indeed!"

The boy was studying them carefully. Which was the dispatch rider's horse? He singled out a sleek black mare. She looked more tired than the others. Then he saw that her saddle was different from the other saddles!

Slowly he walked over to her and patted her nose. At that moment one of the soldiers stepped to the doorway and began to talk to the man who held the bridles. Nathan heard no word of what they were saying. His fingers were upon the mare's blanket. They inched up under the saddle. At last his fingers touched something that felt like paper.

Just then one of the other horses moved against the black mare. She backed away, almost knocking the boy over.

"Steady, there!" yelled the soldier, and then kept talking with the dragoon in the doorway.

As Nathan thrust his fingers under the saddle again, he heard the dragoons coming down the stairs. He guessed that the search was ended and that they were about to ride off! Again his hand was touching something beneath the saddle. With his fingers upon a corner of the object, he drew it slowly down. For a moment, moonlight flashed on a white packet as he jerked it forth and thrust it beneath his shirt.

Nathan was nowhere in sight when the British rode off. He had retreated to the shelter of a brush heap at the north of the house. He stood ready to retreat farther into the woods if the soldiers should decide to hunt for him, but they were not interested in a young boy. They had searched the house twice. They were satisfied that the rebel rider was not within.

At least a quarter of an hour went by. Then Nathan entered the house and thrust his shoulder against the panel by the fireplace. Dawson stepped forth, blinking in the candlelight.

"Eh?" he demanded, gazing hard at something in the boy's hand. "What's that?"

"I took it from beneath the saddle," said Nathan.

"You—you—what?" With a strained cry Dawson seized the packet and examined it. Then his legs shook under him, and he sat down hard upon the bench.

"Lad!" he muttered. "You—you tricked them!" Suddenly he sprang to his feet and threw his arms around Nathan. "You've done me a service! Aye, you've done your country a service. I'll never forget it as long as I live! Tell me your name, lad!"

"Nathan Cathcart, sir."

"Cathcart, eh? I'll not be likely to forget that name! I had a friend, Jack Cathcart, who fell at Bunker Hill."

"He was my father," Nathan said in a low voice.

For several seconds Dawson and Nathan stood facing each other in silence. . . .

"Well, lad," the soldier said at last, "I must be off. The Blue Fox Tavern lies but a few miles up the road, and there I can obtain another horse. Your hand, Nathan, and I promise you that General Washington shall hear of what has happened this night!"

Nathan watched him as he made his way down the slope in the moonlight. Then Nathan climbed the stairs once more to his room, this time to sleep undisturbed.

1. Why did the British soldiers come to Nathan Cathcart's house? Did they find what they were looking for?

2. What was the important mission that Dawson, the dispatch rider, had been given? Why did Dawson think that he had made a "sorry mess" of his job?

3. How did Nathan Cathcart help Dawson? How did he know which horse belonged to the wounded dispatch rider?

4. Why was Nathan so eager to help Dawson? How do you think Nathan's father would have felt about what Nathan did?

5. How is this story like "Phoebe and the General"? How is it different?

6. Do you know of any other young people who have acted bravely to save someone or something? What did they do?

four

MR. BUSINESS TYCOON

"Paul, what's that in your hand?" Tony looked down at the young boy and his sister from his high perch on the stool.

"It's an apple," Paul said. "Mrs. Stern gave it to me when I delivered the groceries."

"Well, OK," Tony said. "Just remember the rules of my business. Any money a customer gives you when you're working for me is half mine. Fifty-fifty. That was our agreement. OK?"

"OK," Paul answered. He reached for his sister's hand.

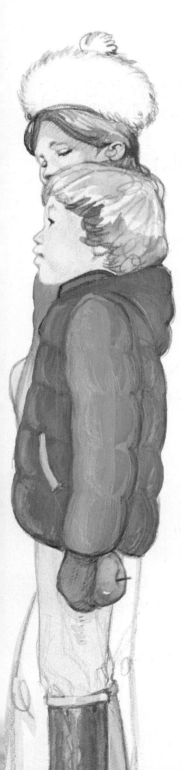

"Just don't forget it, Paul," Tony said. "Ernestine, what did you do to those magazines? They look as if somebody walked on them!"

"It's still snowing," Ernestine said. "They must have got wet."

"Well, you'd better hurry and get them delivered," Tony said. "I have to get my snow-shoveling business going."

Tony watched them go out hand in hand. Then he took a pencil and checked off the two names on an old tablet.

"A kid really has to work hard to find work—and then to find someone to *do* the work. It's a tough life being a boss," he thought.

He heard shuffling feet on the stairs. That should be Stevie Reynolds, who took care of Tony's dog-walking service. But along with the shuffling were heavier, firmer steps. Tony put the money can in a drawer. He closed the drawer and waited.

Stevie came through the door, followed by Mrs. Reynolds. She stood there for a few moments, glaring and breathing heavily from climbing the four flights of stairs. She half dragged Stevie across the floor.

Mrs. Reynolds marched up to Tony with Stevie in hand. "So, Mr. Business Tycoon," she said. "You think you're so smart getting younger children to do your work. Just look at this!"

She ran her hand through a jagged hole in Stevie's trouser leg. "One of those mean dogs on Christopher Street did this," she said.

Stevie's lower lip quivered. "Balder did it," Stevie blubbered. "He got into a fight with Toto."

"Toto?" Tony said. "I told you not to walk Toto and that Great Dane at the same time. A little dog like Toto will tackle another dog ten times his size. I told you that the very first day."

"I had to get home," Stevie said. "I did it the quickest way."

"That isn't my fault," Tony said.

"Well, it's somebody's fault," Stevie's mother said. "If I have to, I'll go straight to Balder's owner. Somebody's going to pay for these pants."

Tony looked at the jagged hole. "Did they cost very much?" he asked.

"Eight dollars," Mrs. Reynolds said, more calmly. "Somebody's got to pay for these pants."

Tony hesitated. He opened the drawer and brought out the money can. He fished around for the coins. He counted them out slowly and handed the coins to Mrs. Reynolds. Now there were only three coins left in the can.

Stevie's mother put the money into her purse. "From now on," she said, "you can walk those dogs yourself. Stevie will not be walking them for you." She dragged Stevie sniffling out the door.

Tony drew a line through Stevie's name on the tablet. He took the three coins out of the can and juggled them in his hand. "That isn't much to run a business on," he said to himself.

Tony went into the next room. He stood by the other window in the apartment. The window looked out onto a smoke-blackened brick wall. Snowflakes filtered down the narrow space between the buildings. The snow was piling up on the ledge outside the window.

Tony went into the kitchen and took a coat from the doorknob. He pulled a knitted cap down over his ears. He looked at the clock. His mother would not be home from work for nearly two more hours.

Tony went back into the next room. He reached under the bed and brought out a snow shovel. He slung the shovel over his shoulder and started out.

On the sidewalk the snow crunched under Tony's feet. It was a dry snow. Good. That might mean a heavy snow. The yellow light from Mr. Levy's tailor shop shone on the falling flakes. Tony knew that Mr. Levy did not like snow piling up outside his shop.

"Yes. Shovel the snow," Mr. Levy said, before Tony could finish asking for the job. "I will pay you. Shovel the snow." Mr. Levy made a gesture as if brushing away all the snow and all the cares of the world.

"There are others who don't like the snow," Tony thought. He began scraping the shovel over the walk. "I will shovel the snow for them, too. I can earn back the money I had to give Stevie's mother."

There was Mrs. Dudley at the bakeshop. There were Mr. Tanner at the movie theater and Mr. Emil at the meat market. Tony bought bread from Mrs. Dudley twice a week, with his own money. The bread was his responsibility, now that there were only Tony and his mother in the family.

Once a week he and his mother went to the movies, where Mr. Tanner worked. They both loved the movies.

"Yes," Tony told himself, "I'm sure Mr. Tanner will want me to shovel. And Mr. Emil, too."

Last year people had said he was too little, but they wouldn't say that now. He'd grown two inches since last winter. He was big enough to shovel lots of snow.

Several pairs of feet trooped by on the sidewalk. Tony held the shovel and waited. But some of the feet did not go on by. They stopped by Tony.

Paul and Ernestine stood stiffly, holding their mother's hand. Tony had a strange feeling in his stomach. Paul and Ernestine—what could they want?

"The furnace broke," Paul said. "We don't have any heat at home. We have to go to the settlement house. I can't get Mrs. Volchek's groceries for you today."

Their mother pulled Ernestine a step closer to Tony. "I can't deliver the magazines either," Ernestine said, looking down. She held out a large soggy envelope.

Tony took the envelope from Ernestine. After studying it a moment, he tucked it inside his jacket. "A boss's job is not an easy one," Tony thought as he pushed the shovel along the walk.

"Hey, Tony!"

The piping voice came from high above him. It was Alberto Ravelo. He was the youngest worker Tony had. Alberto leaned out of a top-floor window. "My father says I have to stay inside today," he said. "I can't go over and sweep the hallway for Mrs. Gonzales."

Tony went on shoveling snow. There was a numbness in his hands now and in his mind.

"Ha! Did Mr. Business Tycoon bite off more than he can chew?" someone shouted.

Tony heard the words before he knew they were meant for him. Then he recognized the voice and looked up, scowling.

Anna Marie stood glaring down at him. She had grown twice as fast as Tony in the past several years.

"Where are all your helpers now?" she teased.

"Aw," he said. "I don't need them, and I don't need you." He threw the snow in the gutter. "I already gave you your chance. I gave you the chance to be practically a partner with me. You turned it down."

"Ha! A *chance!*" Anna Marie said in a ringing voice. "A chance to be one of your helpers! Some offer!" She ran away laughing. After she had disappeared into the falling flakes, Tony could still hear her laughing.

209

"I don't need her," Tony told himself. "I'll take care of all the jobs myself. I'll show her."

"The snow is still falling," Mr. Levy growled, as he gave Tony the money.

It was not easy for Tony to walk past Mrs. Dudley's bakeshop. He was thinking about all the snow. And the money that could be earned shoveling it! But he still had to deliver the magazines that were in the soggy envelope under his jacket. He also had letters to mail for Mrs. Radzinsky, and Mrs. Gonzales's hall to sweep. Also soon it would be time to walk Toto and Balder.

Snow or no snow, Tony was determined to go to the movies Saturday night with his mother. He was determined to buy the bread whether snow fell or not.

Tony took one long look at the snow piled in front of Mr. Emil's meat market. Then he turned and ran toward the building where Toto and Balder were waiting to be walked.

On the way, Tony made a stop to get Mrs. Volchek's grocery list. He took it without a word and ran out. He left the list at the quiet grocery store where he knew the owner, Miss Adams. She agreed to have Mrs. Volchek's order ready when Tony returned.

Tony remembered his own words when he picked up the dogs. *Don't ever walk Toto and Balder together.* Today he would have to.

Toto and Balder pulled at the leashes and sniffed at the cold air. Balder scooped up the snow with his nose. Toto barked and snapped at the falling flakes. Balder's leash was a long one. That was good. Tony wound Toto's leash around his arm to make it as short as possible. With Balder up ahead and Toto held back, Tony was sure they would not fight.

At the grocery store, Mrs. Volchek's order was ready. With the bag of groceries in one arm, and the two leashes tight in the other hand, Tony started back toward Mrs. Volchek's house.

The dogs pulled Tony along. But then his feet slipped on the hard-packed path along the center of the walk. He jumped to the side into the soft snowdrifts.

"Balder! Wait!" Tony cried. He shifted the sack of groceries.

Balder did not wait! He bounded ahead. Tony's feet churned. He pitched forward, face down in the snow. Cans of groceries tumbled from the bag. Toto licked the snow from Tony's face. The long leash slipped from Tony's hand. "Balder! Balder! Here, Balder! Come back!" he called.

At first Tony did not know who it was that rushed past him. He caught a glimpse of someone disappearing through the falling snow. Anna Marie came back in a few moments with Balder. She held the dog's leash firmly.

There was no expression on Anna Marie's face as she handed the leash to Tony. "Here," she said, "you take care of Balder. I'll carry the groceries. You can't do everything at once."

"Anna Marie, I'll . . . ." Tony began, as they trudged through the snow. "I'll pay you . . . ."

"Don't get the idea I'm one of your *paid* helpers," she said. "Keep your money. I'm just helping you. When we've delivered the groceries and returned the dogs, we can sweep the hallway for Mrs. Gonzales. With two of us working, we should get all the work done today."

Later when they had finished the chores, Anna Marie suggested that they go shovel the snow for Mrs. Dudley and Mr. Emil. Tony agreed and soon those chores were done too.

Then Anna Marie helped Tony count the money he had received for doing the chores.

"Tony, why do you want so many jobs? Are you saving up to buy something?" she asked.

"Yes," he answered. "I was saving to buy movie tickets for Mom and me. I thought it would be nice for *me* to treat for a change."

Tony looked at Anna Marie for a moment. Then he counted the money in his pocket. He smiled warmly and added, "If you would like to, why don't you come to the movies with Mom and me? You earned more than enough to pay your way."

They walked slowly down the street toward Tony's house. They were both smiling.

THINK ABOUT IT

1. Why did Tony think that being a boss was hard work?

2. Why was Mrs. Reynolds angry? What did she ask Tony to do?

3. Why didn't Anna Marie want to work with Tony when he gave her the chance?

4. What did Tony buy each week with the money he earned? What else was Tony earning money for?

5. What is a business tycoon? Do you think Tony was a successful business tycoon? Give reasons for your answers.

6. Why do you think Anna Marie decided to help Tony?

7. Have you ever earned money helping someone else? What did you do? How did you use the money?

8. What do you think of Tony's business? If you were in his place, would you run the business differently? How?

A TYCOON'S MAP

When Tony started his neighborhood business, he decided to give a map of the area to each of his workers. Tony hoped the maps would help them find their jobs faster and get their work done quicker. Here's a copy of Tony's map. As you can see, the map includes street names, a scale to show distance, and a legend. The legend shows the symbols used on the map and what they mean. Direction arrows on the map show north, south, east, and west.

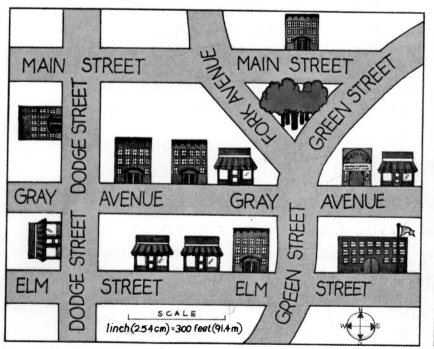

How good are you at map reading? Use the map, scale, and legend to answer these questions:

1. Tony's apartment house is on the corner of Elm and Green Streets. Point to it on the map.
2. What street is the movie house on?
3. How far is it from Tony's apartment to the movie house? Use the scale to answer.
4. How many stores are there on Gray Avenue?
5. What street is the school on? Is it east or west of Green Street?
6. Miss Adams's Grocery Store is the only store east of Green Street on the map. What street is the store on?
7. Mr. Emil's Meat Market is on Dodge Street just north of Elm Street. What street is north of the market?
8. Which three streets surround the park?

Now that you've read Tony's map, try reading a map of your neighborhood. First find a map that shows all the streets around your home. Then see if you can locate your home, school, and local food store. Look to see if the map shows any other important buildings.

Spelling Bee Blues

Ellen closed the front door behind her. She had just left one world—home—and was about to enter another—school. It was not always easy for her to balance these two worlds. For example, in her home world, Ellen spoke mostly Chinese. And in her school world, she always spoke English. Sometimes she'd forget and speak Chinese at school. Then her friends would tease her good-naturedly about it.

Ellen's mother told her many times that, being Chinese-American, she had the best of both worlds. Many of her friends were not able to speak a second language. Ellen should be proud that she could.

Ellen was proud. But now she wished that she had more confidence in herself. Today after school was the countywide spelling bee. Ellen was one of the finalists. The winner of the county finals would go on to the statewide finals at the capital.

All that day at school, Ellen could not keep her mind on her lessons. She thought mostly about the spelling bee—not the contest itself, but the audience.

"How can I spell in front of all those people?" she wondered. "Especially with Mother not there!"

Ellen was sure that her brother Henry would be in the audience. And maybe Henry's friend Jane would be there, too. But Ellen's mother had shown no interest in coming.

"It ought to be enough that my brother is in the audience," Ellen told herself. "Only it isn't. A brother isn't your mother."

In the afternoon, the thirty-five spelling finalists from all over the county were ushered onto the stage of Ellen's school auditorium. Ellen moved slowly to her assigned seat. Minutes later the curtains onstage parted, showing the audience to the boys and girls onstage. It was a big audience, fathers and mothers, aunts and uncles, teachers and friends, all eager to watch the contest.

"Thirty-five boys and girls onstage!" thought Ellen. "And almost twice as many parents in the audience." She looked around nervously, hoping to spot her brother—and maybe even her mother.

Then the contest began. Soon it was Ellen's turn to spell. The teacher said the word clearly, and Ellen repeated it before spelling: *"Pheasant, p-h-e-a-s-a-n-t."*

They finished with the fourth-grade spelling book and started on Book Five. Twenty-eight finalists were still on the stage. Ellen was one of them.

The teacher—Ms. Kinsman—was pronouncing the word for a girl down the line from Ellen. "Science." That was a word with a special meaning for Ellen. Her mother was a scientist. Her father had been one, too. Her parents had shown her how to do all kinds of experiments with chemicals and test tubes. Ellen had always enjoyed working with her parents. Now Ellen missed her father a lot.

Ellen heard Ms. Kinsman's voice and a boy's voice replying, spelling the word *confidence*. Ellen's mind wandered again, her thoughts playing with the word *confidence*, too.

Confidence was such an important thing for a person to have. It was one of those things you couldn't see or touch, but only felt inside yourself. If only her father had not died so suddenly. If only her mother had more free time to spend with her. Then maybe Ellen would have more confidence. Then she would not be so shy and unsure of herself. Then she would not be so concerned about what others thought of her.

Ellen searched the audience again for her mother and brother. But Ms. Kinsman was looking at her, ready to pronounce the next word. They were spelling sixth-grade words now, and twenty finalists remained.

"*Foreign,*" Ms. Kinsman said.

"*Foreign,*" Ellen repeated softly, smiling at Ms. Kinsman. "*F-o-r-e-i-g-n.*" That was an easy one.

Spelling had always come easily to Ellen. Even so, she had worked hard for this contest. When she became class champion, her own teacher, Mr. Diller, had begun helping her. They had practiced spelling every day after school. They had doubled their work after Ellen won the school spelling bee.

It was then that Mr. Diller had said, "I think you might even win the county contest and go on to the big one at the capital."

Ellen's mind came back to the contest. Ms. Kinsman was using seventh-grade spelling words now. The finalists had been on the stage two hours. Only ten of them were still in the contest. Ellen was beginning to think Mr. Diller might be right. She knew that she could win this contest. Only she wasn't sure she really *wanted* to win it. She wasn't sure she really *wanted* to go to the capital.

Suddenly one of the judges rose. "Perhaps it is time to go into a much higher list, Ms. Kinsman. Let's try tenth grade."

A sigh rippled among the finalists. Ellen did not join in the sigh. Mr. Diller had taken her all the way through the high-school lists.

SCENT CENT

The girl next to Ellen had just spelled *strait*. Ellen recalled the very list on which she and Mr. Diller had worked—a group of words that had what Mr. Diller liked to call "silent letters."

Now Ms. Kinsman was smiling at Ellen. *"Scent."*

Ellen took a deep breath and spelled, *"C-e-n-t."* She knew perfectly well that it was *not* the word Ms. Kinsman wanted.

Assuming that she had made a mistake, Ellen turned to leave the stage. She had let Mr. Diller down. She had let Henry down, too. And she had betrayed herself and her gift for spelling.

"Just a minute!" Ms. Kinsman said. "I wanted you to spell *scent,* meaning 'smell.' I should have defined the word I wanted, since the two words sound alike."

"Oo-o-o-h," sighed Ellen. "It's a fine thing when you try to miss a word and can't," she thought. Then she spelled the word. *"S-c-e-n-t."*

One of the judges said, "We will take a break. Recess until the bell rings."

223

With a whoop the remaining finalists scattered to visit in the audience. Ellen hurried toward the door at the back of the auditorium. She was not planning on returning to the spelling bee.

"I always knew you were a good speller," said a voice behind her.

"Mr. Diller!" shouted Ellen.

"We'd be very proud to see you win."

Ellen spun around and saw Henry and Jane smiling proudly at her. "I don't want to win!" she blurted out.

Suddenly she knew why. She put her feelings into a rush of words, speaking in Chinese. "I don't want to go to the capital without my mother. She says I should be proud to be Chinese-American. But *she* isn't proud of me. She isn't even here!"

Henry's face changed. His eyes turned from Ellen's and met Jane's. Ellen rushed into the hall. She wished the tears would stop coming into her eyes. She knew what she would do, now. She wouldn't win—but she would stay in the contest as long as she could without winning.

After three rounds in the tenth-grade list, six finalists remained. Ms. Kinsman turned to a list titled "Words Tricky to Spell."

"*Ache*," she said.

Already . . . All right . . . Disappointment . . . Eighth . . . Forty . . .

"Words make language," Ellen thought. "Language is a highway, linking all peoples and all ages. My mother is right about my having the best of both worlds—knowing both Chinese and English. Why, I didn't even get the two languages confused today! If my mother knew more English, maybe she would be here. Maybe it isn't that she doesn't care . . ."

Freight . . . Receive . . . Whether . . .

Three finalists remained. Ellen saw Henry alone at the back of the audience. Where could Jane have gone? Maybe she had got tired of listening to words being spelled and had gone home. So now Henry sat alone.

Many parents had come here this afternoon from all over the county, some from a long way off. Ellen's mother worked only six blocks away from school. But perhaps there was a very good reason why her mother hadn't come.

"*Patiently,*" said Ms. Kinsman.

Patiently was a lonely word, and being patient could be a lonely job. Ellen wished she could be more patient and trusting. Perhaps it wasn't too late to try.

"*Undefeatable,*" said Ms. Kinsman, looking at Ellen.

Ellen had risen, but she wasn't listening. Two people had just come in at the back. They went to sit beside Henry. Ellen saw Jane. And then she saw her mother smiling at her. Ellen had lived all her life with that loving smile.

"*Undefeatable,*" repeated Ms. Kinsman.

Suddenly Ellen realized that Ms. Kinsman was waiting for *her.*

"I'm sorry. I didn't hear the word," Ellen said. She raised her voice for the proud announcement: "My mother just came in."

"Undefeatable," Ms. Kinsman said.

Ellen spelled the word clearly, proud of her spelling and proud of her mother. This was a beginning. This was a beginning of a new understanding between Ellen and her mother. Her mother had realized how important her being there was to Ellen. Ellen now felt new courage.

"When you can find the courage you need, nothing can really defeat you anymore. You are undefeatable," Ellen thought. "I have to win, now. I have to win and go to the capital. Even if Mother is too busy to come with me. But maybe she will!"

Mother would watch the contest, and together she and Ellen would look at all the state buildings. Together they could grow to understand each other. After such a trip, they could go anywhere!

1. What did Ellen's mother mean when she said that Ellen had the best of both worlds?

2. Why was Ellen concerned about being in the spelling bee?

3. What would happen to the winner of the county spelling finals?

4. Why did Ellen say that she didn't want to win the contest?

5. Why did Jane leave the hall?

6. Why did Ellen change her mind about wanting to win the contest?

7. Why do you think Ellen's mother had finally decided to come to the contest?

8. How do you think Ellen's relationship with her mother will change in the future?

9. Have you ever been in a situation in which you felt shy and unsure of yourself? What happened?

Metaphor

Morning is
a new sheet of paper
for you to write on.

Whatever you want to say,
all day,
until night
folds it up
and files it away.

The bright words and the dark words
are gone
until dawn
and a new day
to write on.

Eve Merriam

229

TALK

In most places around the world, there is usually great respect for anyone in high office. However, there are also people everywhere who are ready to poke fun at their officials. One of the most common ways of doing this is through stories.

"Talk" is based on a tale from West Africa. In West Africa, a specially carved and decorated stool is the symbol of a chief's wisdom and power. A wise and patient chief is made fun of when his stool does a most remarkable thing!

Once, not far from the city of Accra[1] on the
Gulf of Guinea,[2] a farmer went out to his garden
to dig up some yams to take to market. While he
was digging, one of the yams said to him:

"Well, you picked a fine time to show up. You
never weeded me; you never watered me. Now
when you are hungry, you come around with
your digging stick. Go away and leave me
alone!"

The farmer turned around and looked at his
cow in amazement. The cow was chewing her
cud and looking at him. "Did you say something?" the farmer asked.

---

[1] **Accra** (ə krä′)   [2] **Guinea** (gin′ē)

The cow kept on chewing and said nothing, but the man's dog spoke up.

"It wasn't the cow who spoke to you," the dog said. "It was the yam. Listen to what the yam says!"

The farmer became angry, because his dog had never talked before; besides he didn't like his tone. So the man took his knife and cut a branch from a palm tree to whip his dog. Just then the palm tree said, "Put that branch down!"

The farmer was getting very upset. He started to throw the palm branch away, but the palm branch said, "Farmer, put me down softly!"

The farmer put the branch down gently on a stone, and the stone said, "Hey, take that thing off me!"

This was too much for the frightened farmer to bear. He started to run for his village. On the way he met a fisherman carrying a fish trap on his head.

"What's the hurry?" the fisherman asked.

"My yam said, 'Go away and leave me alone!' Then my dog said, 'Listen to what the yam says!' When I went to whip the dog with a palm branch, the tree said, 'Put that branch down!' The palm branch said, 'Put me down softly!' Then the stone on which I rested the branch said, 'Take that thing off me!'"

"Is that all?" the fisherman asked. "Is that so frightening?"

"Well," said the fisherman's trap, "did he take it off the stone?"

"Wow!" the fisherman shouted. He threw the fish trap on the ground and began to run with the farmer. On the trail they met a weaver with a bundle of cloth on his head.

"Where are you going in such a rush?" the weaver asked them.

"My yam said, 'Leave me alone!' " the farmer said. "My dog said, 'Listen to what the yam says!' The tree said, 'Put that branch down!' The branch said, 'Do it softly!' And the stone said, 'Take that thing off me!' "

"And then," the fisherman continued, "the fish trap said, 'Did he take it off?' "

"That's nothing to get excited about," the weaver said. "That's no reason at all."

"Oh, yes, it is!" the weaver's bundle of cloth said. "If it happened to you, you'd run too!"

"Wow!" the weaver shouted. He threw his bundle on the trail and started running with the other men. They came to a ford in the river and found a man bathing.

"What are you running away from?" the man asked.

The farmer said breathlessly, "My yam talked to me and said, 'Leave me alone!' My dog

said, 'Listen to what the yam says!' When I cut myself a branch, the tree said, 'Put that branch down!' The branch said, 'Put me down softly!' The stone said, 'Take that thing off me!' "

"And my trap said, 'Did he?' " the fisherman panted.

"And my bundle of cloth said," the weaver wheezed, " 'You'd run too!' "

"Is that why you're running?" the man in the river asked.

"Well, wouldn't you run if you were in their position?" the river said.

The man jumped out of the water and began to run with the others. They ran down the main street of the village to the house of the chief. The chief's servants brought his stool out, and he came and sat on it to listen to their complaints. The men began to recite all their troubles.

"I went out to my garden to dig yams," the farmer said, waving his arms. "Then everything began to talk! My yam said, 'Leave me alone!' My dog said, 'Listen to what the yam says!' The tree said, 'Put that branch down!' The branch said, 'Put me down softly!' The stone said, 'Take that thing off me!' "

"And my fish trap said, 'Well, did he take it off?'" the fisherman said.

"And my cloth said, 'You'd run too!'" the weaver said.

"And the river said, 'Wouldn't you run?'" the bather said hoarsely, his eyes bulging.

The chief listened to them patiently, but he couldn't keep from scowling.

"Now this is really a wild story," he said at last. "You'd better all go back to your work before I punish you for disturbing the peace."

So the men went away, and the chief shook his head and mumbled to himself, "Nonsense like that upsets the community."

"Fantastic, isn't it?" the chief's stool said. "Imagine, a talking yam!"

THINK ABOUT IT

1. Where does this story take place?
2. In West Africa, what does the chief's carved and decorated stool stand for?
3. Why did the farmer become frightened?
4. Why did the fisherman become frightened?
5. Why did the weaver become frightened?
6. Why did the bather jump out of the river?
7. How do you think the chief felt when he heard his stool speak?
8. Do you think the chief was a wise leader? Why or why not?
9. If you were the chief, what would you have said to the excited men?
10. What are some ways in which people poke fun at their leaders here and now?

Part One

"For the last time, no."

Outside, there was cold and limitless space. It was warm inside the skipper's quarters aboard the *Lotus,* but Randy Blanchard was not comfortable.

"I don't doubt your ability," Captain Williams went on. "I know that half the gear you brought from Earth contains facts on space navigation. And I know that Shannon has let you chart our position and course daily. But I still can't let you pilot this craft! Don't you understand?"

Randy could feel the redness creeping up his neck and face.

"But, captain," Randy said, as he tried to keep his voice level. "Shannon's whole crew is sick now, and there's only Shannon left. If something happens to him, there won't be a backup pilot, and . . ."

"That's a chance we have to take," the skipper interrupted.

"I know I can do it," Randy went on. "My charts are just as dependable as the ones that Shannon drafts. In fact, Shannon helped me with mine. I know the instrument panel perfectly, and I know that I could get us back to Earth on time."

"I'm sure you could," Captain Williams said, "but I just can't let you. For one thing, this is a freighter, and you signed on as a passenger— the only passenger aboard, in fact. Think of the trouble I'd be in if I let a passenger pilot this craft. You don't even have a space navigator's license. The government, the pilots' union—everyone would be down my throat. I'm sorry, Randy, but I just can't do it."

Randy Blanchard sighed and turned to go.

"Don't forget," the skipper reminded him, "that there's an epidemic of Centaurian* fever on Earth. We have to get this cargo of serum there on time. That's another reason I can't take any chances. I'm sorry."

Captain Williams nodded in dismissal, and Randy left the cabin.

"Still, it has been a good journey," Randy thought as he moved down the narrow corridor to his bunk. He had traveled in the Alpha Centauri solar system. That would always be something to remember and talk about.

He turned in at a small door and sat down on his bunk. On a nearby table were his tapes, films, and books on space navigation. Neatly piled beside them were the charts that he had worked on since they blasted off. "They are of no value now," Randy thought bitterly. "No value at all."

A slight sound caused him to look up. A tall man with a friendly face covered with freckles stooped to enter the door.

* **Centaurian** (sen tôr′ē ən)

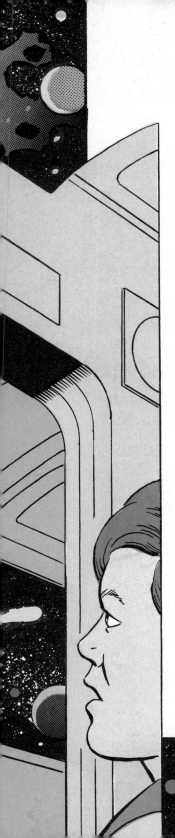

"Hi, Randy," he said. "How'd your talk with the skipper go?"

Randy looked at him with a grin. "Not so good, Mr. Shannon. Here, sit down if you can find a place. Not good at all. Captain Williams says it's not a matter of my ability. It's against the rules of the union and the government for me to try my hand at space navigation. And since I don't have a license, it's out of the question."

Shannon eased himself down on the bunk beside Randy and crossed his arms. "It's not so bad as all that," he said. "You're young yet. You'll get your chance."

"Yes, but when?" Randy flared. "Why not give me the chance now—in case you need a backup?"

"You don't have a license, remember?"

Randy shrugged. "I'm years too young to get a space navigator's license." Then he paused and studied Mr. Shannon closely. "Your crew is in sick bay, isn't it? Suppose something happened to you —could Captain Williams get the *Lotus* back home?"

"I think so," Shannon answered. "At least she has a workable background in space navigation. She has to to hold her job. As long as nothing unusual happened, she could put the spacecraft on automatic—like it is now—and coast on in."

Shannon stood up. Randy was looking at the stack of charts.

"Well," Shannon said. "I've got to keep my eye on things. By the way, you haven't charted our position once today. Want to come along?"

Randy shook his head.

"Listen, Randy," Shannon said. "There was a big meteor coming our way last time I looked. If it comes where I think it will, we may have some excitement dodging it. Want to see how I do it?"

"I know how to do it," Randy answered. He was still looking at the charts. "Useless! Might as well get rid of them."

"Well, if you don't want to come, I can't make you," Shannon said. "After all, you are a passenger and not a crew member. See you later."

The freckled navigator took a step toward the door. But suddenly he turned back and sat on the bunk beside Randy again. Randy looked at him closely. There was an odd expression on Shannon's face.

"What's the matter?" Randy asked.

Shannon shook his head. "I just feel a little dizzy," he explained. "I'll be all right in a minute." He got up from the bunk again and went to stand in the doorway. "Sure you won't come along?"

"Not now," Randy said.

The navigator grinned and left.

Randy picked up one of the charts. "Useless!" he repeated. Then he gathered up all the charts. There was a disposal chute right there beside the table. Once the charts were in the chute, they would be pulled outside and shredded to nothing by the vacuum of outer space. Randy was convinced now that he had wasted his time on the charts.

The loudspeaker suddenly blasted.

"Dr. Curry. Calling Dr. Curry." It was the voice of Captain Williams. "Dr. Curry. Report to the captain's quarters at once."

The loudspeaker was silent now. Suddenly the skipper popped her head through the doorway. "Have you seen Dr. Curry?" she asked.

"No, ma'am," Randy replied.

"There's another person down with what looks like Centaurian fever," the captain said.

It was an odd situation. On Centauri IV, the crew had been exposed to the disease that never bothered the Centaurians themselves. Now, a third of the crew of the *Lotus* were in sick bay. So far as he knew, Randy was one of the lucky Earth people not affected by the disease. He had been exposed many times with no ill effects. Otherwise, he could never have convinced his parents to let him travel on the *Lotus.* Also, he had pointed out, with the epidemic on Earth, he was in no more danger on Centauri IV than on Earth.

"Who is it this time?" he called after the skipper.

Captain Williams was hurrying down the corridor in search of the doctor. "Shannon," she answered back over her shoulder.

Part Two

Shannon!

The name struck Randy like a thunderbolt. With Shannon sick, the skipper would have to take over. Well, she could just put the spaceship on automatic and coast on in, as Shannon had said.

Suddenly Randy sat bolt upright on his bunk. Something that Shannon had told him rang through his head: "A big meteor coming our way last time I looked."

With an effort, Randy relaxed. Just because a meteor was coming toward them didn't mean that it was going to smash the *Lotus.* It didn't even mean that the *Lotus* was going to be in danger at all. Still . . .

Randy leaped to his feet. "Captain Williams!" he shouted as he raced down the corridor. "Captain!"

Shannon had the fever, there was no doubt about it. The doctor had given him medicine, and Shannon had gone to sleep.

Captain Williams, however, seemed to doubt Randy's story about the meteor.

"Are you sure about it?"

"No, I'm not sure. All I know is what Shannon told me. But it wouldn't hurt to take a look."

"You're right," the skipper said. "It certainly wouldn't hurt to take a look." Randy followed her into the navigator's quarters.

"Check the instruments," the skipper ordered. "I'll see if I can find Shannon's charts."

"He keeps them locked up, captain," Randy said.

"I know," Captain Williams replied. "I have a key here. What does the radar show?"

Randy could feel the blood draining from his face. "It's coming all right—no doubt about it. Unless we change our course, it will hit the *Lotus* dead center in about thirty minutes."

"Are you sure?" asked the skipper. "Let me see."

Randy saw the skipper turn pale. "Listen, Randy, get Dr. Curry here. Let's see if she can bring Shannon around for just a few minutes."

"I'm on my way to sick bay right now, captain."

Randy was back in a few minutes with the doctor. She looked grim.

"I can't do it," Dr. Curry said. "I could revive him a little, yes, but he wouldn't be in complete control. Then we might be in worse shape than we are now."

"I see." The captain's face was still pale. "Randy, do you think you could swing the *Lotus* off course enough to miss that meteor?"

"I could try, ma'am, with the help of Shannon's charts."

Captain Williams paused, her eyes steely. "Take the controls," she ordered. "I'll get out the charts."

For the first time in his life, Randy sat in the navigator's chair. It wasn't the way he imagined it would be. He had thought of smooth sailing, not something like this. Failure meant the loss of the serum needed so badly on Earth. Failure could mean the death of all on board the spacecraft.

"My key doesn't fit," Captain Williams said. "The lock's jammed."

"I'll get Shannon's key," Dr. Curry said. "We emptied his pockets when we took him into sick bay."

"I said the lock's jammed," the skipper repeated, an edge to her voice. "Neither his key nor my key nor anyone else's will do any good now."

"The *Lotus* mechanic can have that lock off inside of thirty minutes," the doctor said.

"Thirty minutes! Do you realize . . ."

"Captain," Randy said. He took a deep breath. "At our rate of speed, I won't be able to move the spacecraft off course in time."

The captain thought for a minute. "Suppose we dump the cargo of serum?" she asked quietly. "That would lighten our load and we'd pick up speed."

"That might work," Randy said. "But is it worth it?"

"That's a difficult question to answer," the skipper said. "By dumping the serum, we may save the *Lotus,* but the whole trip will have been in vain. On the other hand, if we keep the serum aboard, it may mean that we lose both it and ourselves."

She leaned over Randy's shoulder, studying the instruments closely. "Suppose we don't dump the cargo," she suggested. "Is there something else we could try?"

"We could try slowing down the spacecraft," Randy answered promptly. "If I can slow it down enough, the meteor will pass in front of us."

"It's a big meteor," said Captain Williams.

"Big enough to tear us in two," Randy added. "A small hole could be repaired, but . . ."

"Slowing down means wasting a lot of fuel," the skipper said. "More than if we change course. Now—if we slow down, will we have enough fuel to reach Earth?"

"I don't know, captain," Randy replied. "Whatever we do, our position will be changed and will have to be recharted. I'll need the last charts on our position to know how much fuel we'll need."

The skipper frowned. "I told you there isn't time to get to Shannon's charts!"

Randy was silent, his eyes glued to the instruments.

The problem was growing more serious. Now the meteor was only minutes away.

"You said you have your own set of charts." The captain's voice was calmer now. "Shannon helped you with them, you said. Remember?"

"Yes, captain, I did have some charts, but . . ."

His own charts, the ones he thought were useless, had suddenly become very important.

CRASH ALERT

CRASH ALERT

"Get those charts!" said the skipper. "I'll keep my eye on the instruments."

Randy hurried down the corridor to his bunk, almost blinded with tears. Everything was lost because he had done something very foolish. How could he tell Captain Williams that he'd dumped the charts into the chute?

When he arrived at his bunk, the loudspeaker was blasting.

"Crash alert! Crash alert! Stand by to crash! Meteor approaching! Crash alert! All crew members in vacuum suits! All who are able help the men and women in sick bay into their vacuum suits. Crash alert! Crash alert!"

The vacuum suits would preserve a life for a time. Equipped with radios, the women and men could keep in touch with each other unless they drifted too far apart. Drift—that was all they could do. There was no way to put the vacuum suits to flight. They might drift within range of a planet or another craft and hope to be rescued, or they might drift without limit until—the end.

251

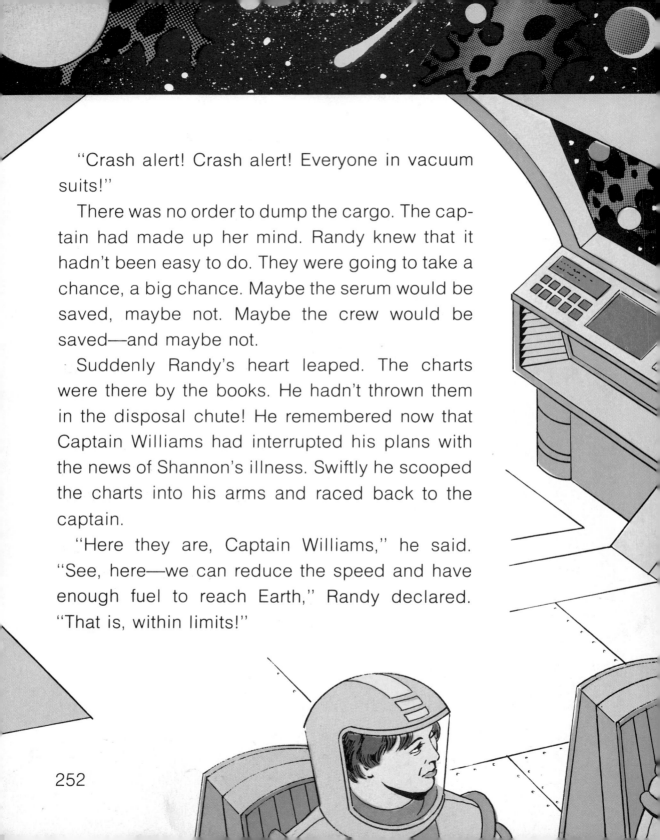

"Crash alert! Crash alert! Everyone in vacuum suits!"

There was no order to dump the cargo. The captain had made up her mind. Randy knew that it hadn't been easy to do. They were going to take a chance, a big chance. Maybe the serum would be saved, maybe not. Maybe the crew would be saved—and maybe not.

Suddenly Randy's heart leaped. The charts were there by the books. He hadn't thrown them in the disposal chute! He remembered now that Captain Williams had interrupted his plans with the news of Shannon's illness. Swiftly he scooped the charts into his arms and raced back to the captain.

"Here they are, Captain Williams," he said. "See, here—we can reduce the speed and have enough fuel to reach Earth," Randy declared. "That is, within limits!"

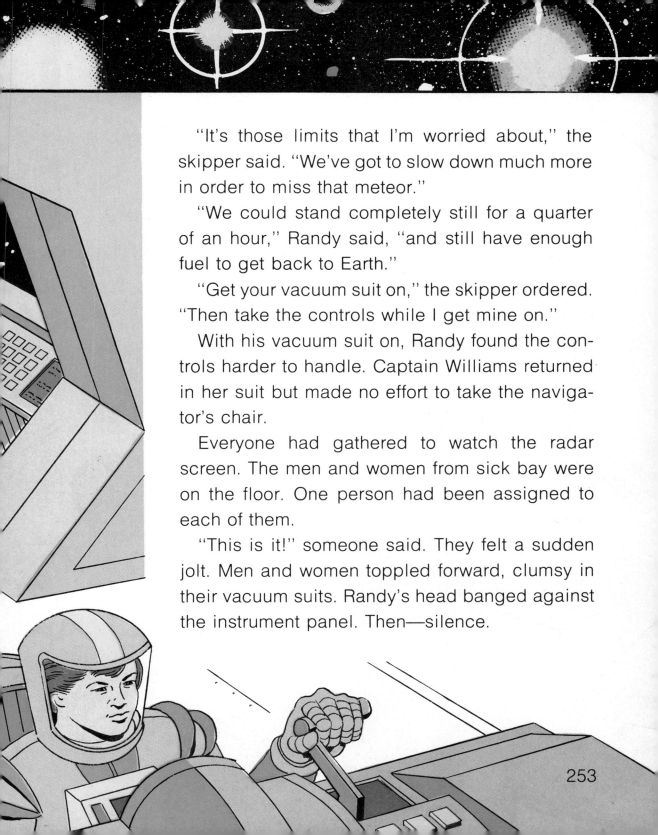

"It's those limits that I'm worried about," the skipper said. "We've got to slow down much more in order to miss that meteor."

"We could stand completely still for a quarter of an hour," Randy said, "and still have enough fuel to get back to Earth."

"Get your vacuum suit on," the skipper ordered. "Then take the controls while I get mine on."

With his vacuum suit on, Randy found the controls harder to handle. Captain Williams returned in her suit but made no effort to take the navigator's chair.

Everyone had gathered to watch the radar screen. The men and women from sick bay were on the floor. One person had been assigned to each of them.

"This is it!" someone said. They felt a sudden jolt. Men and women toppled forward, clumsy in their vacuum suits. Randy's head banged against the instrument panel. Then—silence.

Randy was the first to speak. "I—I guess I slowed down the craft a little too much," he confessed. But the radar showed that the meteor was gone now, hurtling away from them into the vastness of space.

"A little too much?" One of the men from sick bay propped himself up on an elbow. "If it had been a little less, the meteor would have crashed into us."

Someone gave a laugh of relief, and the crew began to climb out of their suits.

"Take us on in, Randy," Captain Williams said. "I mean right on to Earth. If the union or the government makes any charges, I'll be glad to answer for your ability. More than glad."

Randy smiled happily. "All's well that ends well," he thought.

1. Why wouldn't Captain Williams let Randy Blanchard pilot the spacecraft?

2. Do you think Shannon believed Randy could pilot the spacecraft? Why or why not?

3. What danger did the spacecraft face?

4. Why were so many crew members of the *Lotus* in sick bay? Why wasn't Randy sick?

5. Why did Randy suggest that they slow down the spaceship? Why did the skipper at first object to slowing down the spaceship?

6. Why was Randy so upset when the skipper first asked him to get his charts? How did Randy's charts come in handy?

7. How did Randy feel when he first sat down in the navigator's chair?

8. What profession do you think Randy might choose later in life? Why?

9. Have you ever been in a situation where your thinking helped other people avoid danger? Tell what happened.

METEORITES: STONES FROM THE SKY

What Are Meteorites?

Have you ever walked through an open field or down a dirt road? Or have you ever climbed in the mountains? If you have, there's a good chance you stepped over a *meteorite*. But it's not likely that you noticed. Most meteorites, on first glance, look like any ordinary earth rock.

What exactly is a meteorite? A meteorite is a body of material that has fallen to the earth from space. It is most often in the shape of a stone or large rock. The size of a meteorite can be anywhere from that of a small stone to that of a huge boulder.

Since the time the earth was formed, many millions of meteorites have landed on its surface. And since the time that people have lived on Earth, hundreds of meteorites have been seen falling to the ground.

As far back as the year 476 B.C., ancient Greeks recorded that "a stone the size of a chariot" fell from the sky. Other ancient peoples also recorded meteorite events. Among these peoples were the Romans, the Egyptians, and the Chinese.

Some groups of early people used meteorites as weapons. Others used them as tools. There were also superstitions about meteorites. It has been said that the Chinese buried meteorites shortly after they were found. This was done so that their crops would not be ruined. Some early peoples even believed that meteorites were messengers from the gods!

Meteorite on scale, American Museum of Natural History

What Are Meteorites Made Of?

It is not easy to tell the difference between a meteorite and an earth rock. It sometimes requires special equipment, such as powerful microscopes. However, there is one big difference between a meteorite and an earth rock.

Nearly all meteorites contain *metal*. Metal is rarely present in earth rocks.

The metal in meteorites is gray or silver in color. It looks much like the metal in forks and spoons, only it is much heavier. The metal is made up mostly of iron and a small amount of nickel.

Cross section of meteorite showing metal content

Falls and Finds

There are two ways to find a meteorite. You may see a meteorite falling to the earth and may then be able to find it. This kind of meteorite is called a *fall*. The other way to find a meteorite is to come upon one by chance. Then the meteorite is called a *find*. A find may have been on the earth for a thousand years.

Scientists are interested in whether a meteorite is a fall or a find. A find may have been exposed to rain, snow, heat, and cold for hundreds of years. Then its chemical make-up is changed. For example, the metal in a find could be rusted.

On the other hand, a freshly fallen meteorite will have nearly all of its original characteristics. A fresh

Meteorite from Canyon Diablo, Arizona

Moving a meteorite, early 1900's

sample is more likely to be useful to a scientist than one that is "weathered."

Sizes and Shapes of Meteorites

The sizes and shapes of meteorites vary greatly. The largest known meteorite was found in South-West Africa. It is about the size of a small truck. It weighs as much as twelve full-grown elephants, or 60 tons (54 metric tonnes).

The second largest meteorite was found in West Greenland. It was brought to New York City by Admiral Peary in 1897. It can now be seen in the Hayden Planetarium at The American Museum of Natural History. This meteorite measures about the size of a small car. It weighs as much as six full-grown elephants, or 31 tons (28 metric tonnes).

The Fall of a Meteorite

Before a meteorite lands on Earth, it is called a *meteor*. As a meteor falls through space toward Earth, it is slowed down by the atmosphere. This causes friction and produces heat and light.

If the meteor falling through space is very small, it will melt and burn up before it reaches Earth. But during the heating-up process, the meteor will glow for one or two seconds. People call such streaks of light "shooting stars." Meteors are visible in the sky almost every cloudless evening.

What happens if a meteor is so large that it does not burn up immediately? Then, a very large and bright meteor will result. This is known as a *fireball*. Light from a fireball may last a minute or two as the meteor glides several hundred kilometers across the sky.

Fireballs are bright enough to be visible in the daytime. Some people have claimed that they have seen fireballs about as bright as the sun!

Fireballs may be of different colors. They may appear to be white, red, green, or yellow. They also may change colors as they fall through the atmosphere and get closer to Earth.

Many people think that meteorites are quite hot when they land on Earth. But this is not true. There are no reports of a meteorite ever starting a fire. However, upon landing, a meteorite may be a little warm to the touch.

What Happens When It Hits?

A meteorite will usually leave a hole, or crater, in the ground. The size of the hole depends on the size, weight, and speed of the meteorite when it hits. The depth of the hole depends on the softness of the ground.

One of the largest craters carved out by a meteorite is Meteorite Crater in Arizona. The crater is nearly one mile (about 1,300 meters) across. It is about 600 feet (180 meters) deep. It is not known when the crater was made, but it must have been several thousand years ago.

(Photograph, page 262)
Meteorite Crater, northern Arizona. The meteorite that made this crater weighed a million tons or more.

Where Do Meteorites Come From?

Scientists think that meteorites come from within our solar system. They probably come from small planet-like bodies that are between Mars and Jupiter.

What to Do If You See a Fall

Someday, you may be lucky enough to see a meteor falling through the sky. If you do, you should make note of the following facts:

1. What time did you first see the meteor or fireball? Include the date, hour, and minute.
2. How long did the fireball last in the sky?
3. What color was the fireball? How bright was it, compared to the sun, moon, or stars?

4. Did the meteor make any sounds? What were the sounds like?
5. Was there a smoke trail? What color was it?
6. In which direction did the fireball travel across the sky?

If you should discover a meteorite, either after seeing one fall or just by chance, you should note these things:

1. What was the size of the hole or crater (if any) made by the meteorite?
2. What was the ground like where the meteorite fell? Was it soil, gravel, or rock?
3. Was the meteorite warm or cold when you touched it?

You should report a new meteorite discovery to any natural history museum. Here are some museums with experts on meteorites:

The American Museum of Natural History
New York, New York
Center for Meteorite Studies
Tempe, Arizona
Field Museum of Natural History
Chicago, Illinois
Institute of Meteoritics
Albuquerque, New Mexico
Smithsonian Institution
Washington, D.C.

1. What is a meteorite?

2. How are meteorites different from ordinary earth rocks?

3. What is the difference between a *find* and a *fall?* Why is it important that scientists know whether a meteorite is a find or a fall?

4. How is a shooting star different from a fireball?

5. If you should discover a meteorite, what three things should you make note of?

6. Why do you think scientists are so interested in studying meteorites?

7. Have you ever seen a shooting star or a fireball? What did it look like?

8. Have you ever seen a meteorite, either on the ground or in a museum? What did it look like?

five

Pioneer Family

MEET THE AUTHOR *Laura Ingalls Wilder*

Laura Ingalls Wilder was sixty-three years old in 1930 when she first began to write stories about her childhood on the prairie. Since then, her *Little House* books have helped children and adults alike understand the life of the American pioneer family.

Charles and Caroline Ingalls and their daughters were a nineteenth century pioneer family. Laura, their second daughter, was born in Pepin, Wisconsin, on February 7, 1867. Soon after Laura was born, the Ingalls family set out in a covered wagon. Their route took them across Wisconsin, Kansas, and Minnesota. Their last home was in DeSmet in the Dakota territory.

In each place the Ingalls family settled, they ate and slept near the wagon till they could build a house. Sometimes the houses were log cabins. On the prairie, where trees and wood were scarce, they built a house of sod. The side of a hill formed one wall. The other walls were built from chunks of earth or sod "bricks." The roof was made of woven

In this photo are from left to right: Ma, Carrie, Laura, Pa, Grace, and Mary. It was 1891 and Laura was 24 years old.

willow branches. The branches were covered with hay and then more sod was placed on top.

The Ingallses were hardworking and fun-loving. They had to use their wits and courage to fight prairie fires, blizzards, and disease. Sometimes the family crops were ruined by heavy rains or droughts.

Laura remembered all these things and wrote about them. But she wrote about the good times as well. She told of love and laughter, of hay rides and pony races. From Ma and Pa, Laura learned the simple beauty of a prairie sunrise. She loved to help Pa with everything. She delighted in going after the cows. She broke her own ponies.

Laura in her sixties

The Hard Winter
Chapter One
Making Hay.
    The whirr of the mowing machine sounded
cheerfully from the old buffalo wallow
south of the claim shanty. Blue stem grass
stood thick and tall there and Pa was
cutting it for hay.
    Laura brought a pailful of water from
the well at the edge of the Big Slough. She
rinsed the stone water jug to cool it, then

An original page from *The Long Winter*
(Notice that the title has been changed.)

When Laura grew up, she married Almanzo Wilder. In fact, Laura wrote one of her books just about Almanzo's pioneer boyhood. She named it *Farmer Boy*.

Together, Laura and Almanzo built their own home in Mansfield, Missouri. They felled trees. They cut and planed the boards. When they were finished, they named their home Rocky Ridge. It reminded them of their hard work.

Rocky Ridge is now the Laura Ingalls Wilder Museum. It is bursting with treasures of Laura's childhood. There is Pa's fiddle—which Laura featured in many of her stories. There is the organ that Pa and Ma and Laura bought for Laura's sister, Mary. Here you will also find Laura's original *Little House* stories. She handwrote them on school tablet paper.

Pa's fiddle

Ox on the Roof

Now Laura and Mary had chores to do.

Every morning before the sun was up they had to drive Spot to the big grey rock to meet the herd, so that Johnny could take her with the other cattle to eat grass all day. And every afternoon they had to remember to meet the herd and put Spot in the stable.

In the mornings, they ran through the dewy chill grass that wet their feet and dabbled the hems of their dresses. They liked to splash their bare feet through the grass all strung with dewdrops. They liked to watch the sun rise over the edge of the world.

First everything was grey and still. The sky was grey, the grass was grey with dew, the light was grey, and the wind held its breath.

Then sharp streaks of green came into the eastern sky. If there was a little cloud, it turned pink. Laura and Mary sat on the damp, cold rock, hugging their chilly legs. They rested their chins on their knees and watched, and in the grass below them Jack sat, watching, too. But they never could see when the sky first began to be pink.

The sky was very faintly pink, then it was pinker. The colour went higher up the sky. It grew brighter and deeper. It blazed like fire, and suddenly the little cloud was glittering gold. In the centre of the blazing colour, on the flat edge of the earth, a tiny sliver of sun appeared. It was a short streak of white fire. Suddenly the whole sun bounded up, round and huge, far bigger than the ordinary sun and throbbing with so much light that its roundness almost burst.

Laura couldn't help blinking. While she blinked just once, the sky turned blue, the golden cloud vanished. The everyday sun shone over the prairie grasses where thousands of birds were flying and twittering.

In the evenings when the cattle came home, Laura and Mary always ran fast to get up on the big rock before all those heads and horns and trampling legs reached them.

Pa was working for Mr. Nelson now, and Pete and Bright, the oxen, had no work to do. They went with Spot and the other cattle to eat grass. Laura was never afraid of gentle, white Spot, but Pete and Bright were so big that they would scare anybody.

One evening all the cattle were angry. They came bellowing and pawing, and when they reached the big rock they did not go by. They ran around it, bawling and fighting. Their eyes rolled, their horns tossed and slashed at each other. Their hoofs raised a smudge of dust and their clashing horns were frightful.

Mary was so scared that she could not move. Laura was so scared that she jumped right off the rock. She knew she had to drive Spot and Pete and Bright into the stable.

The cattle towered up in the dust. Their feet trampled and their horns slashed and they bawled. But Johnny helped to head Pete and Bright and Spot toward the stable. Jack helped, too. Jack growled at their heels and Laura ran yelling behind them. And with his big stick Johnny drove the herd away.

Spot went into the stable. Then Bright went in. Pete was going in, and Laura was not scared now, when suddenly big Pete wheeled around. His horns hooked and his tail stood up, and he galloped after the herd.

Laura ran with all her might, to get in front of him again. But her legs were short and Pete's were long. Jack came running as fast as he could, but he only made Pete jump longer jumps.

Pete jumped right on top of the dugout. Laura saw his hind leg go down, down through the roof. She saw him sit on it. That big ox was going to fall on Ma and Carrie, and it was Laura's fault because she had not stopped him.

He heaved and pulled his leg up. Laura had not stopped running. She was in front of Pete now and Jack was in front of him, too.

They chased Pete into the stable and Laura put up the bars. She was shaking all over and her legs were weak. Her knees kept hitting together.

Ma had come running up the path, carrying Carrie. But no harm had been done. There was only a hole through the roof where Pete's leg had come down and gone up again. Ma said it had given her a turn to see it coming down through the ceiling.

"But there's no great damage done," she said.

She stuffed the hole full of grass, and swept out the earth that had fallen into the dugout. Then she and Laura laughed because it was funny to live in a house where a steer could step through the roof. It was like being rabbits.

Next morning while Laura was doing the dishes, she saw some little dark things rolling down the whitewashed wall. They were crumbs of earth. She looked up to see where they came from, and she jumped away from there quicker than a rabbit. A big rock smashed down, and the whole ceiling poured down over it.

The sun shone down into the house and the air was full of dust. Ma and Mary and Laura choked and sneezed, looking up at the sky where a ceiling should have been. Carrie sat sneezing in Ma's arms. Jack rushed in, and when he saw the sky overhead he growled at it. Then he sneezed.

"Well, that settles it," said Ma.

"What does, Ma?" Laura asked. She thought
Ma meant that something was settling the dust.

"This does," Ma said. "Pa will have to mend
that roof tomorrow."

Then they carried out the rock and the earth
and the bunches of hay that had fallen. Ma
swept and swept again with the willow-twig
broom.

That night they slept in their house, under
the starry sky. Such a thing had never happened before.

Next day Pa had to stay at home to build a
new roof. Laura helped him carry fresh willow
boughs and she handed them to him while he
wedged them into place. They put clean fresh
grass thick over the willows. They piled earth
on the grass. Then over the top Pa laid strips of
sod cut from the prairie.

He fitted them together and Laura helped
him stamp them down.

"That grass will never know it's been
moved," Pa said. "In a few days you won't be
able to tell this new roof from the prairie."

He did not scold Laura for letting Pete get
away. He only said, "It's no place for a big ox
to be running, right over our roof!"

The Black Ponies

When Laura was a child, pioneers with European backgrounds were finding new homes in North America. It was hard to learn to live in the new land. Often, the pioneers did not understand the ways of the American Indians they found living there. For example, in this story you will see that Ma calls Laura a "wild Indian." To Ma, her American Indian neighbors seemed to live a "wilder" life than the settlers.

In this story, Laura and the family are moving to Silver Lake in the Dakota Territory. On the way, they stop to visit Aunt Docia, Ma's sister, and Laura's two cousins, Lena and Jean.

"May I drive now?" Laura asked. She wanted to forget about growing up.

Lena gave her the lines. "All you have to do is hold the lines," Lena said. "The ponies know the way back." At that instant, the ponies touched noses and squealed.

"Hold onto them, Laura! Hold onto them!" Lena screeched.

Laura braced her feet and hung onto the lines with all her might. She could feel that the ponies didn't mean any harm. They were running because they wanted to run in the windy weather; they were going to do what they wanted to do. Laura hung onto them and yelled, "Yi, yi, yi, yip-ee!"

She had forgotten the basket of clothes, and so had Lena. All the way back to camp across the prairie they went whooping and singing, the ponies went running, trotting, and running again. When they stopped by the shanties to unhitch and picket the ponies, they found all the top layers of the clean washing on the buggy floor under the seats.

Guiltily they piled and smoothed them and lugged the heavy basket into the shanty where Aunt Docia and Ma were dishing up the dinner.

"You girls look as if butter wouldn't melt in your mouths," said Aunt Docia. "What have you been up to?"

"Why, we just drove out and brought back the washing," said Lena.

That afternoon was even more exciting than the morning. As soon as the dishes were washed, Lena and Laura ran out again to the ponies. Jean had gone on one of them. He was riding away at a run across the prairie.

"No fair!" Lena yelled. The other pony was galloping in a circle, held by its picket rope. Lena grabbed its mane, unsnapped the rope, and sailed right up from the ground onto the back of the running pony.

Laura stood watching Lena and Jean race in circles, yelling like Indians. They rode crouching, their hair streaming back, their hands clutched in the flying black manes and their brown legs clasping the ponies' sides. The ponies curved and swerved, chasing each other on the prairie like birds in the sky. Laura would never have tired of watching them.

The ponies came galloping and stopped near her, and Lena and Jean slid off.

"Come on, Laura," Lena said generously. "You can ride Jean's pony."

"Who says she can?" Jean demanded. "You let her ride your own pony."

"You better behave or I'll tell how you tried to scare us last night," said Lena.

Laura took hold of the pony's mane. But the pony was much larger than she was, its back was high, and the pony was strong. Laura said, "I don't know if I can. I never did ride horse-back."

"I'll put you on," said Lena. She held her pony by the forelock with one hand, and bending down she held her other hand for Laura to step onto.

Jean's pony seemed larger every minute. It was big and strong enough to kill Laura if it wanted to, and so high that to fall off it would break her bones. She was so scared to ride it that she had to try.

She stepped onto Lena's hand, she scrambled up the warm, slippery, moving mass of pony, while Lena boosted. Then she got one leg over the pony's back and everything began moving rapidly. Dimly she heard Lena saying, "Hang onto his mane."

She was holding onto the pony's mane. She was hanging onto deep handfuls of it with all her might, and her elbows and her knees were holding onto the pony, but she was jolting so that she couldn't think. The ground was so far beneath that she didn't dare look. Every instant she was falling, but before she really fell she was falling the other way, and the jolting rattled her teeth. Far off she heard Lena yell, "Hang on, Laura!"

Then everything smoothed into the smoothest rippling motion. This motion went through the pony and through Laura and kept them sailing over waves in rushing air. Laura's screwed-up eyes opened, and below her she saw the grasses flowing back. She saw the pony's black mane blowing, and her hands clenched tight in it. She and the pony were going too fast but they were going like music and nothing could happen to her until the music stopped.

Lena's pony came pounding along beside her. Laura wanted to ask how to stop safely but she could not speak. She saw the shanties far ahead, and knew that somehow the ponies had turned back toward the camp. Then the jolting began again. Then it stopped, and there she sat on the pony's back.

"Didn't I tell you it's fun?" Lena asked.

"What makes it jolt so?" Laura asked.

"That's trotting. You don't want to trot, you want to make your pony gallop. Just yell at it, like I did. Come on, let's go a long ways this time, you want to?"

"Yes," said Laura.

"All right, hang on. Now, yell!"

That was a wonderful afternoon. Twice Laura fell off; once the pony's head hit her nose and made it bleed, but she never let go of the mane. Her hair came unbraided and her throat grew hoarse from laughing and screeching, and her legs were scratched from running through the sharp grass and trying to leap onto her pony while it was running. She almost could, but not quite, and this made the pony mad. Lena and Jean always started the ponies to running and then swung up. They raced each other from the ground, trying which could sooner mount and reach a certain mark.

They did not hear Aunt Docia calling them to supper. Pa came out and shouted, "Supper!" When they went in, Ma looked at Laura in shocked amazement and said mildly, "Really, Docia, I don't know when Laura's looked so like a wild Indian."

"She and Lena are a pair," said Aunt Docia. "Well, Lena hasn't had an afternoon to do as she liked since we came out here, and she won't have another till the summer's over."

THINK ABOUT IT

1. Why did pioneer families build sod houses? How were sod houses built?

2. In "Ox on the Roof," what happened when Laura was unable to stop Pete after he raced out of the stable? How did Laura's father repair the roof?

3. In "The Black Ponies," how did Laura hold on to the pony she was riding? Why did the pony jolt her? How did Lena and Jean mount the pony?

4. Did Laura Ingalls Wilder use mostly simple words or difficult words to describe pioneer life? Why do you think she wrote in this way?

5. What would you have done in Laura's place when she saw the big ox running toward her family's sod house?

Encounter

We both stood
heart-stopping
still,

I
in the doorway
the deer
near
the old apple tree,

he
muscle wary
straining
to hear

I
holding breath
to say
do not fear.

In the silence
between us
my thought said
Stay!

Did it snap
like
a twig?
He rose on a curve
and fled.

Lilian Moore

Arthur Mitchell's Dream

© Jack Vartoogian

Arthur Mitchell was born in 1934. He grew up in Harlem, a large black community in New York City. In junior high school, one of Arthur's teachers saw how well he danced at parties. She urged him to become a dancer.

At fourteen, Arthur went to a special school called the High School of Performing Arts. Most people who want to become dancers begin their studies when they are between eight and eleven years old. At this time it is easy to train one's muscles. But it was hard for Arthur to retrain his stiff, tight

288

© Martha Swope

Arthur Mitchell became one of the world's most famous ballet dancers with the New York City Ballet.

muscles at his age. After a year, his teachers told him he would never be a dancer.

That challenged Arthur. He really began to work. Arthur said later, "I'm the kind of person who should never be told that I *can't* do something. The minute you tell me I *can't*, that's the moment that I'm *going* to do it."

Arthur worked so hard that he hurt his muscles. But he was determined. His hard work began to pay off. He earned a scholarship to the School of American Ballet.

The School of American Ballet is the official school of the New York City Ballet Company. Its director is George

Balanchine, one of the best choreographers in the world. It can take a dancer ten to fifteen years to move up from the school to the company and then become a leading dancer. Arthur did it in five years. He was also the first black American ever to dance with a leading American ballet company. He became famous all over the world.

Arthur had always admired Dr. Martin Luther King, Jr. When Dr. King died, Arthur wanted to find a way to honor his memory. Arthur felt that he could do this best through his art. He said, "When you pay homage, you do the thing you do best. If you make music, you beat your drum. If you are a singer, you sing your song. If you are a dancer, you dance."

Martin Luther King, Jr. had said, "I have a dream." Arthur Mitchell had a dream, too. He would form a ballet company right in Harlem and train the children of Harlem to be ballet dancers. No one had done this before. People asked Arthur why he wanted a *ballet* company. Why not form a modern dance company? Arthur felt that ballet would give his students the best training. To perform well in ballet, a dancer must be able to control *every* part and *every* movement of his or her body. With ballet training, Arthur's students could compete with any dancer in the world.

Arthur asked his former teacher Karel Shook to work with him. Other teachers came to help. In the summer of 1969, Arthur began his ballet school with thirty pupils. They found an empty garage to work in temporarily. Arthur left the door

Co-Director Karel Shook teaches a class at the Dance Theatre of Harlem.

open during class. Children wandered in and watched as if something magical were happening before their eyes. By the end of the summer, Arthur Mitchell and Karel Shook had four hundred pupils.

Arthur's pupils "caught" his dream. They learned that they could do anything they wanted to. They did more than dance. They learned to make music, build stage sets, and sew their own costumes.

Soon the Dance Theatre of Harlem needed money. Costs were going up. The company also needed a permanent home.

Arthur began having "Open House" every week. At Open House, Arthur gave lecture-demonstrations. That is, he talked and explained ballet while his best pupils danced.

Some of the people who came to Open House gave the company money. People from the neighborhood helped, too.

The Dance Theatre of Harlem performs Louis Johnson's "Forces of Rhythm."

Soon Arthur found a permanent home for the Dance Theatre of Harlem. It was an old warehouse, two blocks from the house in which he was born.

Not long after, Arthur took some of the dancers on the road. They gave lecture-demonstrations all over America. The group made this tour for three reasons. They needed more money to fix up the ware-

292

Judy Tyrus and Mel Tomlinson dance while Arthur Mitchell talks during a lecture-demonstration.

The Dance Theatre of Harlem performs "Holberg Suite."

house. The young dancers needed more chances to perform in public. And Arthur wanted to take ballet to people who had never seen it before.

The tour was a big success everywhere it went. The company got better and better. In a few short years, the Dance Theatre of Harlem created its own style. The company combined ballet with dances that grew out of the heritage of black people. They learned Balanchine's ballets and created their own.

The dancers went to Europe, Mexico, and South America. In London, England, the newspapers called them "a knockout." Karel Shook remembers what happened when they returned from that trip. "The response in London was beyond our wildest dreams—yet, the day we started back to work in Harlem, Arthur told the company: 'Now, this was wrong, and that was wrong…' It could have been a very tense moment, but the dancers

Arthur Mitchell brought ballet to new audiences across America. Here, on stage at the Apollo Theatre in Harlem, Arthur "learns" from children in the audience.

realized that triumph is as frightening as failure...one success challenges you to another, and a greater success."

More than ten years have now passed since Arthur started the company. Not long ago a New York newspaper said the dancers were "stronger than ever." That is because they have never stopped working. For Arthur Mitchell, the dream is never finished. He will always keep working with young dancers to make his dream come true.

1. When was Arthur Mitchell born? Where did he grow up?

2. What was Arthur's dream? How did he begin to make his dream come true?

3. How did people in the neighborhood react when they saw young people dancing in an empty garage in Harlem?

4. Why did Arthur want his pupils to learn ballet?

5. Why did Arthur take some of his best dancers on a tour of the country?

6. Why do you think the Dance Theater of Harlem has been so successful?

7. What do you think makes Arthur Mitchell such a fine teacher?

8. Have you ever seen a ballet performed? Did you enjoy it? Tell about the performance.

THE SEEING STICK

Once, in the ancient walled citadel of Peking, there lived an emperor who had only one daughter. Her name was Hwei Ming.

Now this daughter had carved ivory combs to smooth back her long black hair. Her tiny feet were encased in embroidered slippers, and her robes were woven of the finest silks.

But rather than making her happy, such possessions made her sad. For Hwei Ming was blind, and all the beautiful handcrafts in the kingdom brought her no pleasure at all.

Her father was also sad that his only daughter was blind, but he could not cry for her. He was the emperor, after all, and had given up weeping over such things when he ascended the throne.

Yet still he had hope that one day Hwei Ming might be able to see. So he resolved that if someone could help her, such a person would be rewarded with a fortune in jewels.

The emperor sent word of his offer to the inner and outer cities of Peking and to all the towns and villages for hundreds of miles around.

Monks came, of course, with their prayers and prayer wheels, for they thought in this way to help Hwei Ming see.

Magicians came, of course, with their incantations and spells, for they thought in this way to help Hwei Ming see.

Physicians came, of course, with their potions and pins, for they thought in this way to help Hwei Ming see.

But nothing could help. Hwei Ming had been blind from the day of her birth, and no one could effect a cure.

Now one day an old man, who lived far away in the south country, heard tales of the blind princess. He heard of the emperor's offer.

And so he took his few possessions—a long walking stick, made from a single piece of golden wood, and his whittling knife—and started up the road.

The sun rose hot on his right side and the sun set cool on his left as he made his way north to Peking to help the princess see.

At last the old man, his clothes tattered by his travels, stopped by the gate of the Outer City.

The guards at the gate did not want to let such a ragged old man in. "Grandfather, go home. There is nothing here for such as you," they said.

The old man touched their faces in turn with his rough fingers. "So young," he said, "and already so old."

He turned as if to go. Then he propped his walking stick against his side and reached into his shirt for his whittling knife.

"What are you doing, grandfather?" called out one of the guards when he saw the old man bring out the knife.

"I am going to show you my stick," said the old man. "For it is a stick that sees."

"Grandfather, that is nonsense," said the second guard. "That stick can see no farther than can the emperor's daughter."

"Just so, just so," said the old man. "But stranger things have happened."

And so saying, he picked up the stick and stropped the knife blade back and forth three times to sharpen its edge.

As the guards watched from the gate in the wall, the old man told them how he had walked the many miles through villages and towns till he came with his seeing stick to the walls of Peking.

And as he told them his tale, he pointed to the pictures in the stick:
an old man,
his home,
the long walk,
the walls of Peking.
And as they watched further, he began to cut their portraits into the wood.

The two guards looked at each other in amazement and delight. They were flattered at their likenesses on the old man's stick. Indeed, they had never witnessed such carving skill.

"Surely this is something the guards at the wall of the Inner City should see," they said.

So, taking the old man by the arm, they guided him through the streets of the Outer City,
past flower peddlers and rice sellers,
past silk weavers and jewel merchants,
up to the great stone walls.

When the guards of the Inner City saw the seeing stick, they were surprised and delighted. "Carve our faces, too," they begged like children.

And laughing, and touching their faces as any fond grandfather would, the old man did as they bid.

In no time at all, the guards of the Inner City took the old man by his arm and led him to the wall of the Innermost City and in through the gate to the great wooden doors of the Imperial Palace.

At last, leading the old man by the arm, the guards arrived in the throne room of the Imperial Palace.

It just so happened that the emperor's blind daughter, Hwei Ming, was sitting by her father's side, her hands clasped before her, silent, sightless, and still.

As the guards finished telling of the wonderful pictures carved on the golden stick, the princess clapped her hands. "Oh, I wish I could see that wondrous stick," she said.

"Just so, just so," said the old man. "And I will show it to you. For it is no ordinary piece of wood, but a stick that sees."

"What nonsense," said her father in a voice so low it was almost a growl.

But the princess did not hear him. She had already bent toward the sound of the old man's voice. "A seeing stick?" she asked.

The old man did not say anything for a moment. Then he leaned forward and petted Hwei Ming's head and caressed her cheek. For though she was a princess, she was still a child.

Then the old man began to tell again the story of his long journey to Peking. He introduced each character and object—
the old man,
the guards,
the great walls,
the Innermost City.
And then he carved the wooden doors,
the Imperial Palace,
the princess, into the golden wood.

When he finished, the old man reached out for the princess's small hands. He took her tiny fingers in his and placed them on the stick.

Finger on finger, he helped her trace the likenesses.

"Feel the long flowing hair of the princess," the old man said. "Grown as she herself has grown, straight and true."

And Hwei Ming touched the carved stick.

"Now feel your own long hair," he said. And she did.

"Feel the lines in the old man's face," he said. "From years of worry and years of joy."

He thrust the stick into her hands again. And the princess's slim fingers felt the carved stick.

Then he put her fingers onto his face and traced the same lines there. It was the first time the princess had touched another person's face since she was a very small girl.

The princess jumped up from her throne and thrust her hands before her. "Guards, O guards," she cried out. "Come here to me."

And the guards lifted up their faces to the Princess Hwei Ming's hands. Her fingers, like little breezes, brushed their eyes and noses and mouths, and then found each one on the carved stick.

Hwei Ming turned to her father, the emperor, who sat straight and tall and unmoving on his great throne. She reached out and her fingers ran eagerly through his hair and down his nose and cheek. They rested curiously on a tear they found there.

And that was strange, indeed, for had not the emperor given up crying over such things when he ascended the throne?

They brought her through the streets of the city, then, the emperor in the lead. And Princess Hwei Ming touched men and women and children as they passed.

At last Hwei Ming stood before the great walls of Peking and felt the stones themselves. She turned to the old man. Her voice was bright and full of laughter. "Tell me another tale," she said.

"Tomorrow, if you wish," he replied.

For each tomorrow as long as he lived, the old man dwelt in the Innermost City, where only the royal family stays. The emperor rewarded him with a fortune in jewels, but the old man gave them all away.

Every day, he told the princess a story. Some were tales as ancient as the city itself. Some were as new as the events of the day.

And each time he carved wonderful images in the stick of golden wood.

As the princess listened, she grew eyes on the tips of her fingers. At least this is what she told the other blind children whom she taught to see as she saw.

Certainly, it was as true as saying she had a seeing stick.

But the blind Princess Hwei Ming believed that both things were true. And so did all the blind children in her city of Peking.

And so did the blind old man.

THINK ABOUT IT

1. Who was Hwei Ming? Even though she had many beautiful things, why was she still sad?

2. What did the emperor offer to the person who could help Hwei Ming?

3. What were the only possessions that the old man brought with him when he visited Peking?

4. What did the old man carve on his stick?

5. After he had carved her picture on the walking stick, what did the old man help the princess do? Why was touching people's faces so exciting for the princess?

6. Why did the princess say she "grew eyes on the tips of her fingers"?

7. Close your eyes and then touch your face or the face of a friend. How does this help you "see" the face you are touching?

As long as people have been trading messages, there has been the need to speak in secret form or code. There are many ways of coding a secret message.

A code can be a set of *signals*. Signals are messages without words. American Indians left each other wordless messages. They laid sticks in certain patterns. Each pattern had a meaning. Telegraph messages are also signals. They are made up of sound patterns.

A code can also be a set of *symbols*. Symbols stand for something else. They can be letters, numbers, or whole words. Your zip code is made up of symbols which tell the mail carrier where you live.

There are many uses for codes. They inform people briefly and secretly.

Ancient Written Messages

Secret message writing goes back to the time of the ancient Greeks. The Spartans of ancient Greece used a special belt to hide messages. They wrapped the belt in a spiral around a stick. Then they wrote a message along the wrapped belt. When the belt was unwrapped, people could not understand the message. People who had the same size stick could rewrap the belt. Only then could they read and understand the message.

Later, in Roman times, Julius Caesar made up his own code. He replaced letters with other letters. He used the third letter to the right of the letter he wanted in the alphabet. For example, he used the letter *d* for the letter *a*. He might write the word *road* as *urdg*. In his code the word *fun* becomes *ixq*. *Child* is *fklog,* and so on. Imagine you are reading a message from Julius Caesar. Try to decode this: *frghv duh ixq.*

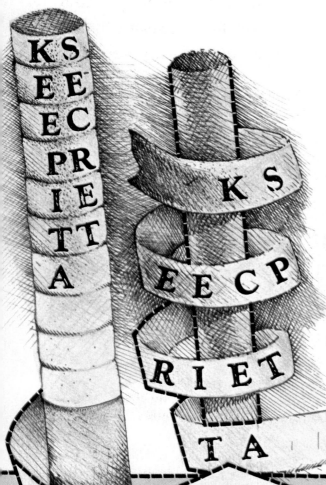

In the 1600's, a "grille" was invented. The grille was a card with holes in it. The grille fit over paper. The secret message was written on the paper in the grille holes. The grille was then removed and the rest of the paper was filled in with other letters. A person had to have the same kind of grille in order to be able to read the secret message.

You can make a grille with a piece of paper and a hole punch. Make two grilles alike. Give one to a friend so that you can exchange messages.

Ciphers

Cipher is a word used to describe a message whose meaning is hidden in a code of some kind. Caesar's code is an example of a simple cipher.

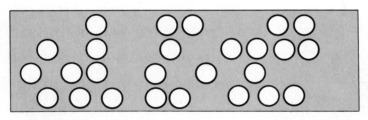

Grille

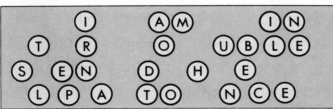

Grille over paper with message

B I T L I K E A P A M E L A B L I N K S
O T H E R S A S H O W A B U B B L E S A
S E V E N A K I D S O H I D E A B O U T
A L F P L A Y S T O B E I N A C E N T S

Paper without grille, real message is hidden

Another famous cipher uses scrambled letters. For example, the letters that spell the words ENEMY SECRET are scrambled to read:

YMNEE ETCRES.

Some ciphers may use signs instead of letters. Special "alphabets" are used in which symbols stand for letters. Look at the set below. How would you write the word *cab* using these symbols?

A = ** B = # C = ! D = +

Breaking a Cipher

A message sent in cipher can be read, or *deciphered,* only by someone who knows the *key.* That person need not guess at the message. He or she already knows how the message has been coded.

Some people become experts at breaking ciphers without a key. To do this they learn the history of ciphers. They study and work hard.

Colorless Ink

Sometimes secret messages are written with a colorless ink. The whole idea of invisible writing seems baffling. But a little work will prove that there is no mystery here.

Many liquids around the house can be used as colorless ink. Lemon juice and orange juice will both do. So will vinegar. Dip a smooth-pointed pen into one of these liquids. Then write your message between the lines of a fake message. Better still, write the fake message in cipher.

Writing done in colorless ink must be exposed to heat before the writing can be seen. An unshaded lamp bulb that has been lit for a while will do the trick. As you move the paper back and forth over the heat, the message will appear.

Modern Uses of Codes

Today, new international codes are being developed for our busy world. We need codes for record keeping. Being brief saves both time and money. Factories, schools, and businesses of all kinds use codes. We use a code when we dial a telephone.

Secret codes are often needed in government work. Some companies use codes to keep their work private.

Looking for Codes

Reading codes and ciphers can be a lot of fun. You may be surprised to find how important codes are to our lives today.

The next time you receive a greeting card, look on the back for a code of numbers and letters. Do you know what the code means?

Watch for code numbers in the printed ads you see. Most of the bills your parents receive have codes in them. Sometimes things you buy at a grocery store have codes on them, too.

It shouldn't take you long to collect a list of codes. You may even try breaking some of them!

ODOG UCKL!

Some fun with TIC TAC TOE

Did you know that you can turn your tic tac toe game into a code? Here's how...

1. Write the alphabet into the tic tac toe diagram this way. →

2. Encode the word DOT. Make your key by drawing lines to show which "box" in the diagram contains each letter of your word.

Example: ⅂=D,E,F / ☐=M,N,O / L=S,T,U

CODE A

A B C	J K L	S T U
D E F	M N O	V W X
G H I	P Q R	Y Z

3. Then make a dot inside the lines to show which letter you want.

Example: ⅂=D / ☐=O / L=T

The word CODE looks like this: ⌐⌐.☐⅂.⅂

Try to decode this message: ⅂☐LL ⅂☐⅂ L.⅂☐⅂L ☐⅂.L⅂ L⌐ L⅂⅂L ⅂☐⅂⅂.

You can change the code by changing the place of the letters in the diagram.

Rewrite the alphabet like this:

CODE B

A B C	D E F	G H I
J K L	M N O	P Q R
S T U	V W X	Y Z

Scramble the alphabet like this:

CODE C

A V G	R H	X S B
U N M	I C T	O Y F
D Z K	L E W	J Q P

In Code A, DOT=⅂.☐L. / In Code B, DOT=L⌐.☐ ⅂ / In Code C, DOT=⌐⅂☐.

Now you try a message!

1. What are two methods of putting a message in code?

2. How did the ancient Spartans hide their secret messages?

3. What secret code did Julius Caesar invent?

4. What is a cipher? How would someone read or decipher a message sent in cipher?

5. Name two ways in which codes are being used today.

6. Why do you think it is important to understand what codes are and how they are written?

7. Why do you think people have always had the need to communicate in code?

8. Have you ever made up a code that you used to communicate with a special friend? What was the key to this code?

9. What codes have you seen recently at home or at school?

WATCH IT!

In "Keep It a Secret" you learned that *symbols* stand for something else. Symbols can be letters, numbers, or whole words. They can also be signs—as in picture writing.

You can see signs and symbols everywhere in your daily life. For example, what do these mean?

Suppose you took a trip to Tokyo, Japan. You might not know what people said to you, but you could "read" signs.

These signs were designed for the Tokyo Olympics in 1964 so that people from around the world would understand them. Which sign means "dining room"? Which means "first aid"? Which one shows that there is a shower?

The signs are now part of a set of international symbols that countries all over the world want to use. They show people where to go, what to do, and how to stay out of danger.

When you see a diagonal line (\) through a sign or symbol, the line means "NO." Now look at these signs.

1. Which sign means "no right turn"?
2. Which means "no crosswalk"?
3. Which says "no telephone"?

Often the *shape* of signs has a meaning, too. In these, the **circle** gives orders or directions. The **square** gives information. The **triangle** means "danger." How many signs can you find and read?

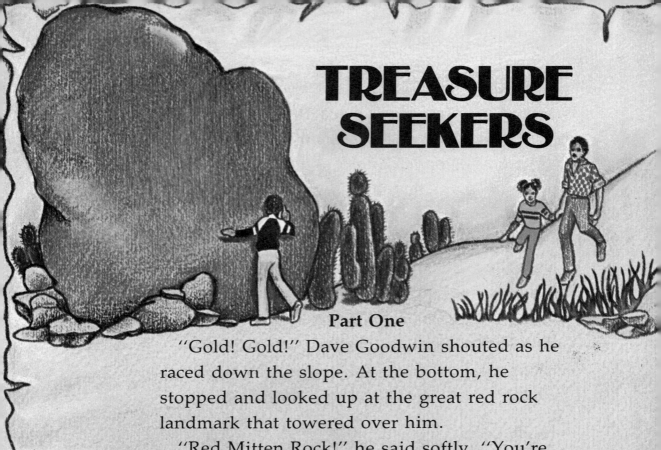

TREASURE SEEKERS

Part One

"Gold! Gold!" Dave Goodwin shouted as he raced down the slope. At the bottom, he stopped and looked up at the great red rock landmark that towered over him.

"Red Mitten Rock!" he said softly. "You're the end of a long search for the Old Spaniard's Gold Mine."

By the time his father and his sister, Pard, had reached the bottom of the slope, Dave had a map spread out on the ground. "Now I'll find that gold mine," he shouted, looking up from the map.

"*We'll* find it!" Pard corrected him. "We're in this together, you know. But it doesn't really matter. I don't think we're going to find the gold, anyway."

318

"I'm afraid she's right, Dave," said their father. "You know this whole Thunder Mountain area will be declared a national park area tomorrow. After that, it will be closed to gold miners forever. Besides, people have been looking for that mine for a hundred years, ever since the big earthquake covered it up."

"I know, but I've worked out a system," Dave answered. "I've got the map that I bought at the Old Treasure Chest. The woman in the store said that it was made over a hundred years ago, way back before the big earthquake."

"You lost *that* map," Pard said. "That map you have now is the one I made for you. I drew it from memory. Remember?"

"You might also remember that you've got the smartest girl in the state helping you," said their father with a smile.

Dave knew his father was right. His sister had a fine mind and a fantastic memory. "A photographic memory with total recall" was what people called it.

Dave squirmed as he thought of the way he'd used Pard's fantastic memory. He'd treated his sister like a computer, storing up information. "We're going to read every book we can find about the Old Spaniard's Gold Mine. You'll have it all in your head!" he'd told her.

Once, Pard had thrown up her hands and cried, "I'm tired of thinking about it!"

"I need your help!" Dave had shouted. "You'll be glad if you help, because when we find that gold you'll get your fair share of it!"

Now, they were at Red Mitten Rock—or they *thought* they were. It was difficult to tell one red rock formation from another. Dave was trying to match what he saw in the area to the symbols on the map. "Pard!" he barked. "There's supposed to be a spring here."

"Clearwater Spring," Pard said, tapping her head and frowning.

Dave kicked at the ground. "Dry as a bone," he said. "There's no spring here now."

"There could have been a spring here," Pard said. "It may have dried up."

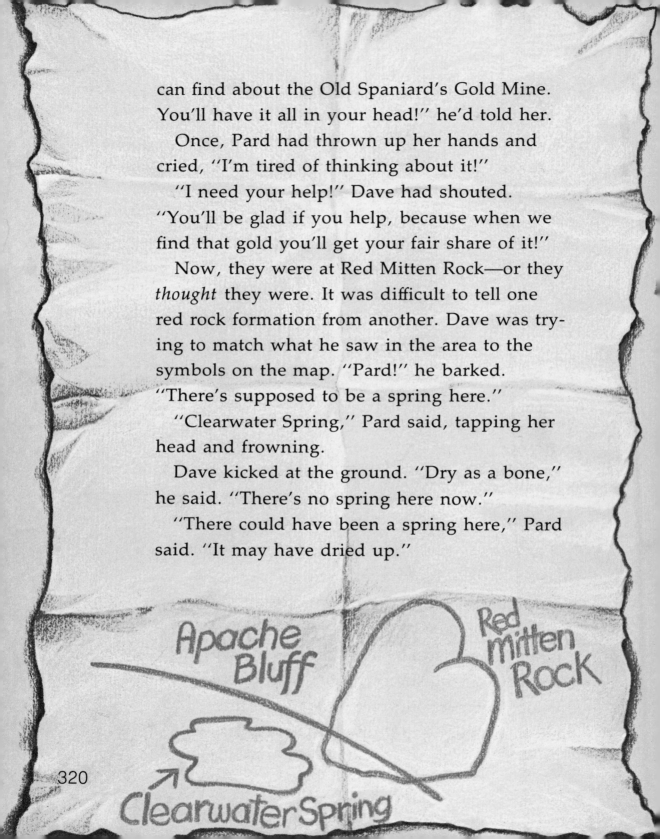

"But something else is wrong. Where is Apache Bluff? On the map it's right next to the spring." He crumpled the paper. "The map is all wrong, Pard. The Mitten doesn't look right, and Apache Bluff is in the wrong place. You drew it all wrong, Pard!"

Pard tossed her head. "I drew it exactly like the old map," she said.

"Don't waste time fighting about it," said their father. "If you're going to find that mine today, you'd better hurry. We have to head back to camp soon."

"Oh, no," groaned Dave. "That's not fair! I need more than a few minutes!"

Frantically, he looked back at the map. It was wrong, all wrong! He was filled with anger. "You drew it wrong on purpose, Pard!" he shouted. "You don't want us to find the gold!"

"You don't really believe that, do you, Dave?" Father said firmly.

"Well . . . no," said Dave, calming down. "I'm sorry. Forget about the map, Pard. Just tell me everything you remember about the location of the mine. What did the old books say about the mine? You've *got* to put it all together, Pard. You've just *got* to!"

Dave groaned. He strode to the base of the great red rock and whammed his hand against it.

Mr. Goodwin laughed. "Not even the earth-quake could have knocked that rock over," he said.

"The earthquake!" Pard shouted. "That's it! That explains our confusion."

"What are you talking about?" asked Dave.

"Red Mitten Rock is back at camp—only we've been calling it the Devil's Firelog," Pard said. "Don't you see? The earthquake must have knocked over Red Mitten Rock. If you stood the Devil's Firelog up, it would look just like Red Mitten Rock. And that rock formation next to it would be Apache Bluff—just as on the map."

Pard grabbed a stick and began to scratch out on the ground the shapes of the Devil's Firelog and the Mitten.

"You're right," said Pard's father. "The map isn't wrong. We're looking in the wrong place. You remember how bumpy the ground is around our campsite? I bet Clearwater Spring is buried there."

"That gold mine *is* back at the camp!" said Dave.

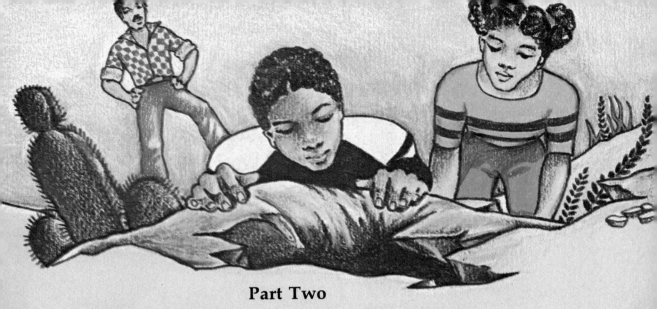

Part Two

The shadows grew longer and longer as the
treasure seekers made their way back to camp.
When they got there, Dave dashed to the end
of the Devil's Firelog and started digging
wildly. "Look!" he shouted as the soft earth
gave way. "It's damp under here."

"This must be the right place!" shouted Pard,
jumping up and down. "The spring *was* buried
in the earthquake! Dig faster, Dave! See if . . ."

Dave gave a whoop. "It's got to be the
entrance to the mine! Look! Here's an opening!" He lay flat and peered into the opening.
"Dad! Pard! It's the underground entrance!"

"Hold it, Dave," said his father. "Let me
have a look first." He slid through the opening.
"Come on, both of you!" he cried.

Pard slid through the opening next.

"Is there gold?" Dave shouted. "Is there lots of it?" Dave sat down and slid his legs through the opening. He was just about to slide all the way through when a whirring sound stopped him. He looked up. A helicopter hung over Apache Bluff. Then it started down toward him. Soon it was hanging right above his head. It was so close that he could see the face of the pilot.

"Why is it up there?" Dave wondered as he let go of the ledge and slid through the opening. But he forgot about the helicopter as soon as he was inside. He couldn't believe his eyes. He was standing in a large cave that was bathed in a misty green light. Giant ferns grew all along the dark green walls. And small green lizards crawled in and out among the ferns.

"Wow!" Dave whispered. "It looks like a million years ago!"

Slowly, they started through the cave. From time to time, Mr. Goodwin tested the ground by stamping on it. "There's a turn up ahead," he said at last. "It looks brighter and not quite so green."

"Gold!" Dave whispered, grabbing Pard's hand as they rounded the turn.

They hurried forward, their footsteps echoing on the stone. A shimmering light grew brighter and brighter as they went. They turned another bend, and Pard gasped as they stared down at the thing that lay in the golden light.

"A skull!" she whispered.

"And some bones!" Dave gulped.

The skull seemed to be grinning.

"I see a metal object, too," said their father, walking toward it.

Mr. Goodwin picked up the object. "A belt buckle," he said. "It's solid gold!" Squinting, he added, "It has initials on it—R . . . H . . . A."

"R . . . H . . . A," Pard repeated. "Ramón Hernández Alvarado! The Old Spaniard! It's the Old Spaniard's belt buckle!"

The skeleton grinned up at them.

Part Three

Moving on, they came to a crude archway cut into the stone. Beyond it, the golden light glowed brighter.

Stepping through the archway, they were blinded by a shining, dancing light. It rippled on the walls around them and bounced off the ground at their feet. It flashed in the late afternoon sunlight that streamed through an opening at the end of the inner cave.

Dave put up a hand to shield his eyes. "Wow!" he whispered softly. "It's just as the Old Spaniard said. It's more than all the gold in the world!"

Suddenly, there was a scratching sound behind them. Whirling, Dave saw someone standing in the narrow archway to the inner cave.

Sunlight flashed on the man's face. "The helicopter!" thought Dave. For once again, he was staring at the face of the man he had seen in the helicopter.

Mr. Goodwin stepped in front of Dave and Pard. He stood waiting with his arms folded.

"Welcome to the Old Spaniard's Gold Mine," he said.

"Thanks," said the man, stepping through the archway. He was tall and lean with striking features.

"Who is he?" Pard whispered.

The man held out a small folded card. "This will identify me," he said. "I'm a special agent for the National Park Service—John Silko."

Dave and Pard stepped from behind their father. "Isn't that a Laguna Indian name?" Pard asked.

"Right," said the man, smiling at her. "I got this particular assignment because I used to spend a lot of time in these mountains when I was your age. My agency has been keeping an eye on this area for a long time. We've been trying to find this mine by using one of our best government computers. But when we finally zeroed in on the Devil's Firelog, we found you going in ahead of us."

"Wow, Pard!" said Dave. "You beat the computers to the gold!"

Pard grinned. "Oh, I beat them by only five minutes," she said.

"We knew the opening had to be in this area," said Special Agent Silko. "But it's taken a long time to find it. The entrance slants in, under a ledge. And there's plenty of heavy brush growing above it."

The agent chipped at the wall with a small pick. "You can't file a claim on this gold," he said. "It's too late. This whole Thunder Mountain area will be closed to prospecting and mining."

"Yes, we know," Mr. Goodwin said. "Wilderness Day is tomorrow."

"A good thing, too," the agent said. "We've got to save America's wilderness—what's left of it. That's why the government wanted to find this mine."

"Wow!" Dave said. "All this gold going to waste!"

The agent chuckled. "All this *glitter* is more like it. It's mostly quartz, with tiny gold flakes in it. But in the setting sun it makes a dazzling sight."

Dave and Pard stared at each other. "But—but—" Dave started. "The books all told how the Old Spaniard said . . ."

"I know," John Silko answered slowly. "The Old Spaniard said his mine had all the gold in the world. But I think he must have gotten out whatever gold there was here, or someone else did."

Mr. Goodwin took the Old Spaniard's belt buckle from his pocket and handed it to Special Agent Silko. "We found this beyond that archway back there. Go have a look."

The agent left. When he came back a few minutes later, he held out the buckle to Pard. "Why don't you keep this as a souvenir?" he said, smiling. "It proves you did what nobody else could do. You found the Old Spaniard's mine."

"I'll let you wear it sometimes, Dave," Pard said, taking the buckle.

"Thanks!" said Dave, beaming at Pard. "I'll bet nobody we know ever saw such a sight!"

he added, looking around at the glittering walls. "Thanks again, Pard."

"That's OK, Dave," said Pard, beaming back at him while she polished the gold buckle on her sleeve. "Any time you need a photographic memory with total recall, just call on me!"

THINK ABOUT IT

1. What were Dave and Pard looking for?

2. How did Pard make the map they were using?

3. Where was Red Mitten Rock located after all? Why had Pard and Dave been confused about Red Mitten Rock and the Devil's Firelog?

4. What did the inside of the cave look like? Whose skeleton did Dave and Pard find?

5. Who was John Silko? Why couldn't Pard and Dave file a claim on the gold?

6. What was the "gold" really composed of?

7. What do you think happened to the old Spaniard?

8. Have you ever gone on a treasure hunt? What were you looking for? What happened?

six

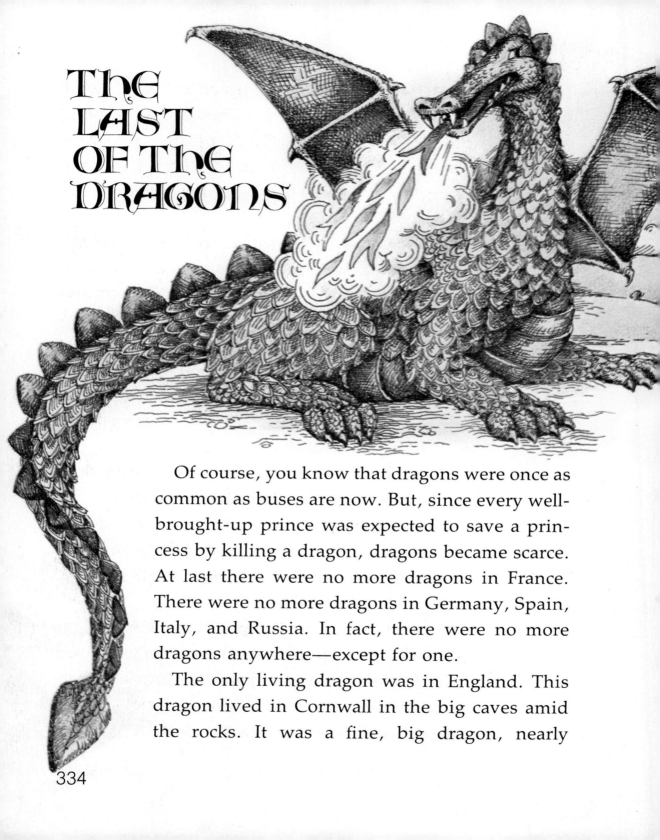

THE LAST OF THE DRAGONS

Of course, you know that dragons were once as common as buses are now. But, since every well-brought-up prince was expected to save a princess by killing a dragon, dragons became scarce. At last there were no more dragons in France. There were no more dragons in Germany, Spain, Italy, and Russia. In fact, there were no more dragons anywhere—except for one.

The only living dragon was in England. This dragon lived in Cornwall in the big caves amid the rocks. It was a fine, big dragon, nearly

334

seventy feet long from the tip of its fearful snout to the end of its tail. It breathed fire and smoke and rattled when it walked, because its scales were made of iron. Its wings were like half-umbrellas, or like bat's wings, only several thousand times bigger.

Now, the King of Cornwall had one daughter, Princess Kim. When she was sixteen, Princess Kim would have to face the dragon. The princess knew what to expect. The dragon would not eat her, of course, because a prince would save her in time. Besides, no dragon ever ate a person in a fairy tale. But the princess could not help thinking that it would be better to have nothing to do with the dragon at all.

"Why do I have to face the dragon? Why can't someone else do it?" she asked her father.

"It's always been done this way, my dear," said the king, taking his crown off. "And when you've finished with the dragon, we'll celebrate with a birthday party."

"Father dear," said Princess Kim, "couldn't we tie up one of the princes for the dragon to look at? Then I kill the dragon and save the prince. I fence better than any prince we know, especially Prince Albert, who must save me."

"What an idea!" said the king. He put his crown on again, for he saw someone coming with a basket of fresh bills for him to sign. "Forget the idea, dear. A princess must always face the dragon. And she must always be saved by a prince. It's a tradition in royal families. You wouldn't want to break the tradition."

"But this is the *last* dragon," said Princess Kim.

And so Princess Kim went off to her fencing lesson. She took great pains with all her lessons. She took such pains that she became the strongest, boldest, and most skillful princess in Europe.

The day before Princess Kim was to face the dragon, Prince Albert came to a feast at the palace. The prince was thin and had large, sad eyes. He had studied art and science and was quite smart. But unfortunately, Prince Albert had neglected his fencing lessons.

After the feast, Princess Kim sent her pet parrot to Prince Albert with a note. It said: "Please, Prince Albert, come onto the terrace. I want to talk to you without anybody else hearing.— Princess Kim."

So, of course, the prince went. When he came quite close to Princess Kim, he said, "Princess, I am at your service."

"Do you think that you will be able to kill the dragon?" the princess asked with a worried look.

"I will kill the dragon," said the prince firmly. "Or, I will die trying," he added less firmly.

"There's no reason to die!" said the princess.

"I cannot escape the dragon," he said, "unless I kill him first. But I've never killed anything before. I'm afraid I might not be able to kill a dragon. Actually, there is a very good chance that I will be the first fairy-tale prince to die in such a way."

Prince Albert looked so sad that the princess felt sorry for him. She thought very hard about how she could help the prince.

"Look here," said Princess Kim. "You know that I'll be tied to a rock and left there. Then everybody will run home and put up the shutters and keep them shut till you ride through the town. Then you will shout that you've killed the dragon, and I will ride on the horse behind you, weeping for joy."

"I've heard that that is how it is done," said Prince Albert.

"Well, I have another idea. Why don't you set me free before the dragon comes. Then we'll fight the dragon together!"

337

"It wouldn't be safe for you."

"Much safer for both of us if I am free with a sword in my hand than if I am tied up and help-less. Do you agree?"

Prince Albert needed her help, so he agreed. The next day everything happened as Princess Kim had described.

When he had cut the cords that tied her to the rocks, the prince and the princess stood on the lonely mountainside looking at each other.

"It seems such a pity to kill the dragon—the last in the world," said the prince.

"Well, then, let's not do it!" said the princess. "Let's tame it so that it eats out of our hands. They say everything can be tamed by kindness."

"I like that idea. We will tame the dragon by giving it things to eat," said the prince. "Have you any food?"

She hadn't, but the prince said that he had bananas. They ran along the path toward the cave.

"Look, that's where the dragon has dragged its huge tail and planted its steel claws," said Prince Albert, pointing to a cave.

"Let's not talk about the dragon's tail and claws," said Princess Kim. "It's too frightening to even think about. And I know we can't tame anything, even by kindness, if we're frightened of it. Come on. It's now or never."

As they stood outside the cave, the prince shouted, "What ho! Dragon there! What ho within!"

From the cave they heard a great clattering and creaking. The prince and the princess were afraid, but they stood firm.

"Dragon—I say, Dragon!" said the princess boldly. "Come out and talk to us."

"We've brought you a present," said the prince.

"Oh, yes—I know your presents," growled the dragon in a loud, deep voice. "One of those precious princesses! And I'm supposed to come out and fight for her. Well, I'm not going to do it. I wouldn't say *no* to a fair fight. But one of these fairy-tale fights, where I'm going to lose? Never! No, I won't even try."

The princess's voice grew firmer. "Do you like bananas?" she asked.

"No," growled the dragon.

"Not even nice ripe ones?"

"*No,*" growled the dragon.

"Then what *do* you like?" asked Prince Albert.

"I'd like you to go away and stop bothering me," growled the dragon. They could hear it turn over, the clang and clatter echoing in the cave.

The prince and the princess looked at each other. This dragon was not like any other. They did not want to go into the cave and kill the dragon. Indeed, unless he attacked the princess, it did not seem fair to kill him at all.

"He must like something," whispered Princess Kim. She called out to it in a clear voice. "Dragon! Would you like to come to my birthday party?"

340

"WHAT?" shouted the dragon. "Say that again!" They could hear the dragon coming toward them through the darkness. The princess and the prince looked at one another, and they both shivered.

"Please come to my birthday party," said the princess shyly.

And then the dragon came out. The prince drew his sword and the princess drew hers, but they did not attack. They moved slowly back as the dragon came out, all the vast scaly length of him.

The dragon drew nearer and nearer. Now they saw that it was not breathing fire and smoke as they had expected. The dragon came crawling slowly toward them. It was wriggling a little as a puppy does when it wants to play and isn't quite sure whether or not you're cross with it.

341

Then they saw that great tears were streaming down the dragon's cheeks.

"Whatever's the matter?" asked Prince Albert.

"Will there be balloons and streamers?" sobbed the dragon.

"Don't cry, dragon," said the prince. "There'll be lots of balloons and streamers in all colors—red, green, yellow. Every party has balloons and streamers."

"I've never been to a party," said the dragon. "People were always afraid of me. And the truth is I'm so tame that I'd eat out of your hands."

"*Really?*" said the princess.

"No one has ever asked me what I like to eat. Never once! They offer me princesses but then they rescue them," the dragon wept.

"Well, what *would* you like to eat at the party?" asked the prince.

"I do enjoy hamburgers," said the dragon. "I even barbecue them myself. Would you like to see how I do it? I'd be glad to show you."

The prince and the princess nodded eagerly.

"All I need is just a tiny, tiny drop of gasoline," said the dragon. "Fuel for my flames, you know. Then I'll be able to breathe the best fire you've ever seen."

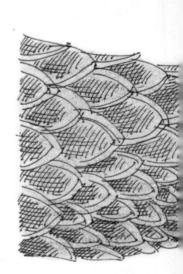

"I've lots in my room," said the prince, and he was off down the mountain. Prince Albert was a good judge of character, and he knew that with this dragon, the princess and he would be safe.

"While we're waiting," said the dragon to the princess, "I'd like us to become friends. Perhaps, just to pass the time, you'd be so kind as to talk with me awhile. And if you'd shake claws with a poor old dragon that's never been anybody's enemy but his own . . . Well, the last of the dragons will be the proudest dragon there's ever been!"

He held out a huge paw, and the great steel hooks that were his claws gently closed over Princess Kim's hand.

343

Later, the prince and the princess went back to the palace, the dragon following them. They were all eager to roast hamburgers. All through the birthday party no one played games more happily or sang "Happy Birthday" more loudly than the joyful dragon.

After the last party balloon had popped, the dragon asked the prince and the princess to be allowed to stay at the palace and make himself useful.

The prince had a special saddle made for him, on which one hundred and fifty seats were fitted. The dragon, whose greatest joy now was to give pleasure to others, delighted in carrying children to and from parties. He would speed his hundred and fifty young passengers to the party and would patiently wait till they were ready to return home.

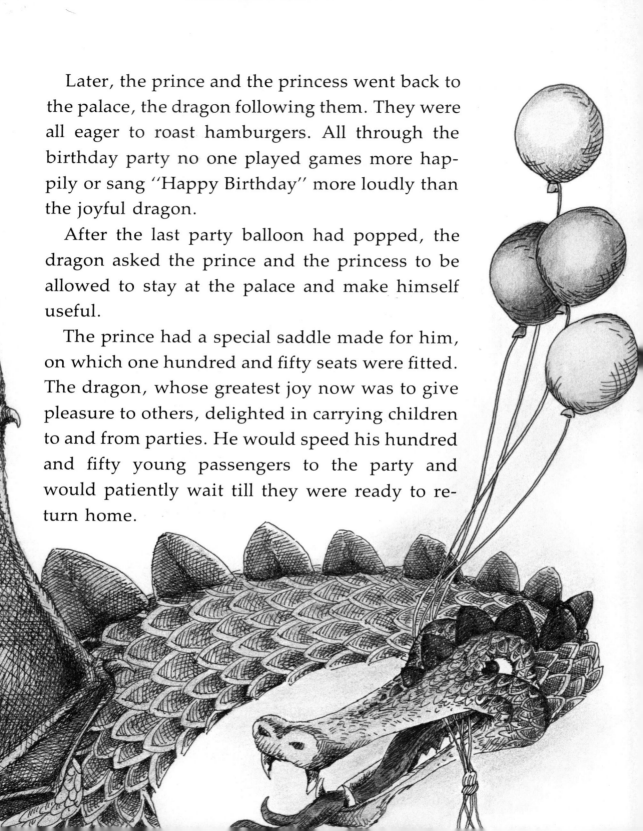

The children and, of course, the prince and the princess were very fond of him. Even the king delighted in seeing the dragon with the children. So, as in all good fairy tales, this one ended happily, too!

THINK ABOUT IT

1. Where did the dragon live? What did it look like?

2. According to tradition, what would happen to Princess Kim on her sixteenth birthday? How did the Princess suggest that her father change this tradition?

3. What did Princess Kim suggest that Prince Albert do instead of leaving her tied to a rock?

4. How did the prince and the princess finally befriend the dragon?

5. After the dragon came to the palace, how did he make himself useful?

6. How is this story different from fairy tales you have read? How is it like them?

7. Do you like fairy tales? Why or why not?

Belinda lived in a little white house,
With a little black kitten and a little gray mouse,
And a little yellow dog and a little red wagon,
And a realio, trulio, little pet dragon.

Now the name of the little black kitten was Ink,
And the little gray mouse, she called her Blink,
And the little yellow dog was sharp as Mustard,
But the dragon was a coward, and she called him
　　Custard.

346

Custard the dragon had big sharp teeth,
And spikes on top of him and scales underneath,
Mouth like a fireplace, chimney for a nose,
And realio, trulio daggers on his toes.

Belinda was as brave as a barrel full of bears,
And Ink and Blink chased lions down the stairs,
Mustard was as brave as a tiger in a rage,
But Custard cried for a nice safe cage.

Belinda tickled him, she tickled him unmerciful,
Ink, Blink, and Mustard, they rudely called him Percival,
They all sat laughing in the little red wagon
At the realio, trulio, cowardly dragon.

Belinda giggled till she shook the house,
And Blink said Weeck! which is giggling for a mouse,
Ink and Mustard rudely asked his age,
When Custard cried for a nice safe cage.

Suddenly, suddenly they heard a nasty sound,
And Mustard growled, and they all looked around.
Meowch! cried Ink, and Ooh! cried Belinda,
For there was a pirate, climbing in the winda.

Pistol in his left hand, pistol in his right,
And he held in his teeth a cutlass bright,
His beard was black, one leg was wood;
It was clear that the pirate meant no good.

Belinda paled, and she cried Help! Help!
But Mustard fled with a terrified yelp,
Ink trickled down to the bottom of the household,
And little mouse Blink strategically mouseholed.

But up jumped Custard, snorting like an engine,
Clashed his tail like irons in a dungeon,
With a clatter and a clank and a jangling squirm
He went at the pirate like a robin at a worm.

The pirate gaped at Belinda's dragon,
And gulped some grog from his pocket flagon,
He fired two bullets, but they didn't hit,
And Custard gobbled him, every bit.

Belinda embraced him, Mustard licked him;
No one mourned for his pirate victim.
Ink and Blink in glee did gyrate
Around the dragon that ate the pyrate.

Belinda still lives in her little white house,
With her little black kitten and her little
    gray mouse,
And her little yellow dog and her little red wagon,
And her realio, trulio, little pet dragon.

Belinda is as brave as a barrel full of bears,
And Ink and Blink chase lions down the stairs,
Mustard is as brave as a tiger in a rage,
But Custard keeps crying for a nice safe cage.

Ogden Nash

The Street of the Flower Boxes

Part One

"Look!" cried Little Luis, pointing.

Carlos looked. Something was happening *again* at the New House. This time a truck had parked in front of it: a truck filled with flowers!

The two brothers ran up the street and stood watching as a man in overalls lifted out dozens of flower pots. Suddenly the brick paved areaway of the New House was turned into a small field of flowers.

"*Caramba!*" [1] Little Luis exclaimed. "What's goin' on at the New House now?"

The New House was, in fact, as old as any of the other old houses on the block. For a time it had looked even sadder than the rest. That was after the fire. All the people had moved out. The broken windows stared like blind eyes. And when the boys on the block climbed inside, hoping to find a place for a clubhouse, they saw that the floors had been burned through. And the sharp smell of smoke still hung about the empty rooms.

Then in April, workers had arrived. It took a year. But finally the place was finished.

And a month ago the Lady and the Man had moved in.

[1] *Caramba!* (kä räm′bə) Oh no!

"They must be crazy," Carlos had said. "Why spend all that money fixing up a house on *this* crummy block?"

The thing the block kids had wondered about most was the large brick box-like things a worker had built in the areaway.

"Maybe they're to keep goldfish in," Clarence had said.

"I think they're some fancy new kinda garbage cans," said Carlos.

Now, however, the mystery was solved. The man from the flower truck filled the brick boxes with dirt. Then he started planting. First, long strands of ivy. And finally the flowers—red, white, pink.

"What kind of flowers are they?" asked Little Luis.

"Petunias," said the man in overalls.

"*Petoonias?*" Carlos laughed. "What kinda nutty name is that? Petoonia."

The other kids, who had come to watch, laughed loudly.

"I think they're pretty!" Little Luis said. But he was only five years old and no one ever took any notice of what he said. He was allowed to tag along only because he was Carlos's brother.

Carlos was nine. Carlos was tough. And what's more he was good at making up games. Now—after the man in overalls had driven off in his flower truck—Carlos invented another game. "Let's play cat-o'-nine-tails!" he shouted.

He pulled out one of the long strands of ivy and slung it around his head like a cowhand with a lasso. And he caught Eddie around the waist with the ivy roots. Eddie had his mouth wide open, laughing.

"Whatchu doin'?" Clarence shouted. He was Eddie's older brother. He pulled a long strand of ivy from the brick box, and wrapped the roots into Little Luis's waist.

Then the Battle of the Ivy began. It was followed by the Rain of the Petunia Petals. And when there was nothing left to fight with, they ran off down the street, screaming with laughter.

The men and women sitting out on the front steps watched the boys and laughed with them. The Lady and Man would sure have a fit when they got home!

As five-thirty came close, the people on the block crowded onto the front steps of the rundown houses which lined the street. The Lady always came home from work at five-thirty. And everyone wanted to see what she would say.

And at five-thirty she came down the street, carrying a bag of food from the supermarket. The people of the block kept talking as usual, pretending not to notice her. But all voices fell to a hush as she started up the front steps of the New House. Then she looked into the areaway.

"Goodness!" she said.

She stood for a long moment staring at the broken ivy and crushed flower petals on the brick floor of the areaway.

Then she looked at the people sitting on the steps of the house next door. "Do you know who—did all this?" she asked.

The people stared back at her. No one spoke. A few of them shrugged. The Lady stretched her mouth in a polite smile. Then she went into the house. And shut the door behind her.

Immediately, the street broke into its usual hubbub of sound. The bongo drums began. Mothers leaned out of upstairs windows to call their children in the street. And the conversation from the people on the stoop rose like a wall. It was even louder than usual, as people told each other what the Lady had said when she saw her broken flowers.

It was also reported that Carlos and his friends had done it. No one seemed to blame Carlos. It was just part of the news.

Then an old lady stuck her head out of the window to learn what was going on. This was Carlos's grandmother. She was very strict.

When Carlos came in for supper she told him that he must go at once to the Lady and Man and say he was sorry for what he had done.

"Listen, Grandmother," Carlos said. "Those
flowers were bound to be pulled up by *someone*!
Who plants flowers on this crummy street?"

The grandmother, who knew little English, did
not understand what Carlos had said. Nor did she
care. *"Anda!"*[2] she said, pointing at the door. "Go!"

Carlos went.

As he rang the bell of the New House he hoped
very hard that it would be the Lady who came to
the door. Not the Man.

[2] *Anda!* (än′də) Go!

It was the Man.

"Hi," Carlos said, looking up. The Man seemed much taller than usual. "Hello," he said.

"I—I come to tell," Carlos said, "I'm sorry about the flowers."

"So am I," the Man said. "I wonder who did it." Carlos shrugged.

"Do you think," the Man said, "if we order some more flowers they will be ripped up, too?"

"The people on this crummy block," said Carlos, "they're just not *used* to flowers."

"I guess we could put up a fence," the Man said, "to keep the kids out of our areaway."

The Lady had come to the door. "I don't like fences," she said. Then she smiled at Carlos. "If we get some more flowers, would you be their—guardian?"

Carlos frowned. "What's—guardian?"

"Well," she said, "sort of a mixture between gardener and guard. Part of the job would be to water the flowers three times a week. But the main thing would be protecting the plants. *This* time we'd get little seedlings. They're not as expensive as full-grown flowers. You'd have to see that nothing or nobody harmed them. So they can grow big. Like the ones we had."

"Your pay," the Man added, "would be two dollars a week. How about it?"

"Well—" Carlos said. "Sure. Why not?"

"What's your name?" the Man asked.

"Carlos Gomez."

"We're the Mitchells," the Man said. "I'll go order the flowers now. I'll ask them to make the delivery on Saturday. Would you like to help us plant the flowers?"

"Sure," said Carlos again. "Why not?" Then he turned, ran down the steps and up the block. Two dollars a week for spilling water on little flowers!

Then another thought hit him. What would the other kids say about it? Especially Angel. Angel was tough. Maybe he'd lose his friends if he took on this crazy job. Protecting *flowers!* He could just hear his friends laughing. He decided not to take the job. After all, his friends were more important than two dollars a week!

Part Two

The following Saturday morning Carlos watched
the City Gardener truck pull up in front of the New
House. When the truck had left, Carlos went up
the steps and rang the bell. He would tell the
Mitchells they had better find someone else to
mind their flowers.

The Lady opened the door and gave him a
wide smile. "Hi!" she said. "Just on time. Your
flowers have just come. And this, too—for you."
And she handed him a big plastic watering can.

Carlos took it.

"If you're free now," the Lady said, "let's start
planting the seedlings. Okay?"

Carlos said nothing.

"*Are* you free now?" the Lady asked. "Otherwise we could do it later in the day."

There was a long pause.

"Is—anything wrong, Carlos?"

He suddenly remembered the look on her face when she had first seen her torn-up flowers on the brick floor of the areaway. Somehow he didn't want to *ever* see her look like that again.

"Sure, lady," he told her. "*Bueno vamos!*[3] That's Spanish—for let's get going!"

Some of the kids on the block came around to watch him and the Lady do the planting. Certain remarks were made in Spanish. But the Lady didn't understand. And Carlos didn't translate. He did, however, warn the kids that no one better hurt these flowers.

[3] ***Bueno vamos!*** (bwā'nō vä'mōs)

After awhile, the kids went away, the Lady went inside. Carlos was alone, watering down the tiny seedlings. It was then that Angel Andino came along.

He stood for a moment, watching Carlos. Then he said, "Man, you kill me! Your little green watering can and all!"

"Listen," Carlos told him, "if someone gave you two bucks a week to slop some water on some ol' weeds, would you turn it down?"

"I got a lot better ways to get me two bucks a week," Angel said.

Carlos watched him walk off down the street. There was no way to protect the flowers if Angel and his friends decided to ruin them.

Each morning when he woke Carlos ran to the window. He could see the brick flower boxes from there. And each morning he sighed with relief. No one had bothered the flowers.

It was the same thing at school. At the end of the day he got jumpy, wondering whether the Kings had ripped up his plants. When the bell rang, he'd be out of the seat and through the door while the sound of the school bell was still clanging in the air. And each afternoon he found that the boxes were fine.

Furthermore, the flowers grew!

It was like a miracle. In this street littered with overflow from the garbage pails, torn newspapers, empty tin cans, these tiny seedlings slowly stretched up green and tall, and sprouted flowers! Just like they were in the fresh air country someplace. They sprouted and budded like crazy and made new blossoms all through the summer.

It was like a miracle.

But then the real miracle happened. The miracle made by Carlos Gomez. The miracle which turned "this crummy block" into the Street of the Flower Boxes.

How did it happen?

How did Carlos deal with Angel Andino, who wanted to destroy the flowers?

Why did Carlos have to visit the 24th Precinct Police Station?

Why was Carlos Gomez written up in the Sunday newspaper?

If you want to know the answers to these questions, you'll find them in the book called *The Street of the Flower Boxes*.

It's a true story. It happened in New York City on West 94th Street.

It could happen on your street, too. When you read the book, you'll find out how!

1. What was so unusual about the New House on West 94th Street?

2. What did Carlos and the other children do to the flowers that had been planted at the New House?

3. What did Carlos's grandmother insist that he do? What happened as a result?

4. Why did the people in the neighborhood not tell the Mitchells what had happened to their first batch of flowers?

5. How did Carlos feel at first about being asked to guard the Mitchells' flowers? How did his feelings change?

6. Why do you think West 94th Street eventually became known as "The Street of the Flower Boxes"?

7. Have you ever tried to fix up something that you thought looked "crummy"? What did you fix up? How did you do it?

8. Do you think that changing the appearance of a neighborhood might change the lives of the people who live there? How?

Wind

Wind is to show
  How a thing can blow,
And especially through trees.
  When it is fast
  It is called a blast,
And it's otherwise known as a breeze.

It begins somewhere in the sky,
  Like a sigh,
Then it turns to a roar,
And returns to a sigh once more.

366

Wind is the air
In your hair.
When you stand
On the sand
By the shore.

Wind will shake the lattices late at night;
It will make the clouds go by.
Anything easy that's hard to do,
It is pretty sure to try:

Blow down a pine,
Clothes from a line.
Tumble a chimney top.
Wind is the general sound
You hear around,
That suddenly likes to stop.

Leonard Feeney

MINERVA and ARACHNE

Long, long ago people believed in gods and goddesses and told wonderful tales about these beings who could not die. The gods and goddesses were thought to rule the lives of all men and women. It was believed they often walked the earth using their magical powers.

One of the greatest of these superbeings was Minerva.[1] She was the goddess of wisdom and war. She was also skilled in the arts of spinning and weaving. Minerva was looked up to by all who practiced those arts—all, that is, except Arachne.[2]

Arachne was a young girl highly skilled in weaving. So skilled was Arachne that many said Minerva herself must have taught her. Arachne was too proud to admit this. Although she was not a goddess herself, Arachne believed herself to be as talented as Minerva—maybe even more talented.

"Let Minerva try her skill against mine!" Arachne boasted.

[1] **Minerva** (mə nėr'və)   [2] **Arachne** (ə rak'nē)

368

When Minerva heard of this boast, she was most displeased at Arachne's lack of respect for a goddess. Minerva decided to pay her a visit. As she often did when calling upon human beings, Minerva disguised herself. She made herself up as an old woman.

"I have had much experience," Minerva, as the old woman, said to Arachne, "so I hope you will take my advice. Challenge your friends if you will, but do not compete with a goddess. In fact, I advise you to ask Minerva's forgiveness."

Oh, but Arachne was a proud one! She stopped her weaving. She looked at the old woman with anger in her face. "Keep your advice to yourself," said she. "You will not change my mind. Why does not the goddess herself come? Why does she refuse to compete with me?"

"She is here!" said Minerva. She dropped her old woman's disguise and stood before Arachne as a goddess.

Sudden color rushed to Arachne's cheeks. Then she grew pale. But she was firm. "I stand by what I say," Arachne said.

Minerva gave no more advice. The contest began. Each took her place at a loom and attached the threads for the weaving to begin. Then the slender shuttles of the loom were passed in and out, in and out among the threads. Both the girl and the goddess worked with speed. Their skillful hands moved swiftly, and the excitement of the contest grew.

The cloths took shape. The designs took on color and form and beauty. Indeed, such beauty and imagination in weaving had never before been seen.

Minerva wove into her cloth scenes showing the anger of the gods when humans dared to compete with them. This Minerva wove as a warning to Arachne. But proud Arachne only smiled, as she filled *her* work with scenes showing the failings and errors of the gods.

Arachne's work was wonderfully well done, and, as a weaver, Minerva could not help admiring it. But as a goddess, Minerva was greatly insulted. She grew more and more angry with Arachne. At last she struck Arachne's work with her shuttle, tearing it to pieces. Then she decided to punish the girl, as was the custom when the gods and goddesses were threatened or rivaled by humans.

Today, Arachne's name lives on, in the name that scientists give to spiders and certain other creatures: *arachnid*. What do you think Minerva did to Arachne? Yes! Minerva changed Arachne into a *spider*, so that she would have to spend the rest of her life spinning.

THINK ABOUT IT

1. Who was Minerva? What arts was she especially skilled in?

2. Who was Arachne? How did she compare her skills with Minerva's talents?

3. How did Minerva disguise herself? What did she advise Arachne to do?

4. What did Minerva's woven cloth look like? What did Arachne's woven cloth look like?

5. How did Minerva feel when she saw Arachne's cloth? How did Minerva punish Arachne?

6. Did you like Minerva? Why or why not?

7. If you had been Arachne, what would you have done after you heard the old woman's advice?

8. Have you ever challenged someone who was an expert in a particular field or subject? What happened?

THE FIRST BALLOONISTS

What is the creature in the picture above? Is it a monster from an unknown planet? Not at all! It is quite an earthly creature, a very lowly creature, to some people's minds. Yet it is a great builder, a hard-working trapper, a designer of beautiful things, and also a skilled balloonist.

The picture above is a close-up of one of the great space travelers of all time—the spider. Here the spider is shown many times its actual size. People have always marveled at what a spider can do. It has one skill quite suited to our times: it can move through the air without wings.

374

Silk Spinning

Long before humans could fly, members of the spider family were already traveling through space. Spiders are able to float in the air. This feat is due to the spider's skill in making silk.

Spiders are well-known for their silk "spinning." The silk is made inside the spider's own body in what are called the silk glands. Some silk glands produce a liquid silk that hardens outside the body. Other glands produce a sticky silk. Hundreds of tiny tubes connect the silk glands to the spinnerets, which spin the silk. Spinnerets work something like the fingers of a hand.

Ballooning Through Space

In order to move through the air, a spider climbs to the

Garden spider hanging by its silken thread

top of a leaf or a tall blade of grass. Since the spinnerets are on the underside of its body, the spider turns over on its back with the spinnerets facing upward. The moving air brushes across them and the liquid silk is pulled out. It hardens at once. The silken threads are carried upward with the rising air.

One thread is not enough to lift the spider from its blade of grass. But all the threads, moving steadily upward, act like a balloon and lift the spider. Then the spider travels wherever the wind blows it.

Though the spider cannot guide its own flight, it can come down when it chooses. It just pulls in its threads. As they become shorter, the spider sinks slowly down. The threads act like a parachute. When it lands, the spider rolls up the threads and goes exploring on the ground.

It is almost always a young spider that travels in this way. Often the journeys are made very soon after the baby spiders hatch from their eggs. Baby spiders have been known to travel hundreds of miles by balloonlike action. They have even been seen drifting far out over the ocean. Most of the journeys take place in the fall and the spring, when the young usually hatch.

In Search of Food

Why should spiders go on long journeys at all? Scientists disagree over the reason. Some say we simply cannot explain why. Others say it is because great numbers of spiders hatch at the same time. Instinct tells them that there will be more food if they do not all stay in the same place.

Because spiders are able to travel and live in many places, they are found almost everywhere on earth. Spiders live anywhere they can find food—in houses,

Spider moving along its web

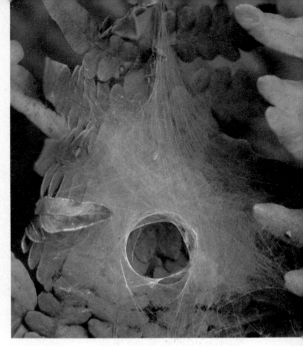

Tunnel web

woods, swamps, deserts, even under water. They have been adapting and using their skills for millions of years.

The Many Uses of Silk

It is likely that the spiders of a million years ago spun their silk only to cover their eggs. Today, however, a spider uses its silk in many ways. The thread makes a handy swing. The spider can move from a tree to the ground, or from limb to limb, like a monkey on a vine. Also, when a spider is in danger, the silken line often proves a perfect means of escape.

The silk can also be used as a tunnel in which to hide or as a warm covering for eggs. And, of course, it makes the spider's web, which is a net for catching the spider's food.

Garden spider with a trapped grasshopper

Trapping Food

Spiders are able to make different kinds of silk for all these uses. Those spiders that make webs spin two special kinds of silk for the web. One is dry and tough to make the web strong. The other is sticky and will stick to the feet of a bug, helping to hold it fast in the trap. The spider does not even need to stay at home to make sure of a catch.

If it wishes to leave the trap it has laid, a spider fixes a line to the center of the web. Then holding the line, it moves away. It draws out more silk as it goes, making the line longer. In this way the spider can wander some distance and still keep in touch with the web.

The instant something hits the net, the spider feels the line jerk and shake. The spider draws the line tight and "listens" with the leg that holds the line. Quickly it decides what is in the net,

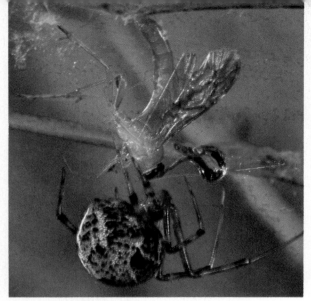

House spider binding a fly

and it is not often wrong. The spider can generally tell whether it has caught a useless leaf or a live creature. It can even tell if the live creature is a safe meal or an enemy, such as a wasp. If it feels safe, the spider hurries home to make certain of its catch.

The trapper will often shake the web hard, to tangle it around a large insect. Then the spider may tie up its prisoner with the silken threads. A very small spider can quickly rope and bind a creature many times its own size.

When it is ready at last for its meal, the spider sucks the food dry of liquids. It eats this way because it cannot chew its food. A spider has no jaws to chew with. It can go a long time on one good meal. A big catch, like a grasshopper, will generally give a spider enough food for a day or longer.

People are likely to think of spiders and their webs together, believing that all spiders weave webs. Yet, many spiders are not web spinners; they get their food in other ways. Some hide in flowers to catch the insects that come to feed there. Some roam about, ready to jump on smaller creatures.

Web Spinners

Three kinds of spiders are web spinners: the house spider, the grass spider, and the garden spider. Both males and females weave webs, but the female is usually the spinner; her web is larger and far more beautiful than the male's.

A spider web shining in the morning sun is such a beautiful sight. It seems hard to believe that such a lovely thing was made—as someone once said—"just to catch bugs!"

The best-known spider web is the orb web of the garden spider. This spider takes an hour to weave its beautiful, wheel-shaped design. It works carefully, weaving back and forth and round and round.

The work is not easy. Gusts of wind may break the web more than once before it is finished. The little weaver is not discouraged. It would not give up if the web were broken a hundred times. It simply repairs the broken threads and goes on with its work.

A Place in Nature

Often people sweep spiders and their webs out of the house when they see them. Yet, in some parts of the world, spiders are brought indoors to help rid the house of swarms of flies. Indoors and out, spiders destroy millions of insect pests each

Spider jumping with anchor line

Orb web of garden spider

Black widow spider

year. For that, gardeners and many other people are grateful.

Many people dislike spiders. Some people even believe them to be harmful. Actually, only six kinds of spiders in North America have bites that can harm humans. Maybe you have heard of the best known of the harmful spiders, the black widow.

Certainly, a close-up view of a spider makes this animal seem threatening. It takes little imagination to see the spider as some dreadful beast, what with its eyes in odd places and its long, crooked legs!

Like all earth's creatures, the spider has an important place in the world of nature. To people with enough imagination to find it interesting, the spider is a constant wonder. Its skills and strange instincts make it one of the great marvels of all time. Then, too, the spider was a skillful balloonist many centuries before the space age began.

1. How do spiders move through the air without wings?

2. Where in the spider is the silk made? What are the spider's spinnerets used for?

3. How does a spider come down when its flight is over?

4. Where are spiders found? Why?

5. How do spiders use their silk?

6. How can the spider leave its web and still make sure of what it has trapped?

7. Which types of spiders are web spinners?

8. Why do you think this article is titled "The First Balloonists"?

9. Do you agree with the author that the spider is a "constant wonder"? Why or why not?

WHAT'S SO SPECIAL
ABOUT A SPIDER?

Many people believe spiders are just like insects. But spiders are really quite different.

All insects, like bees, ants, flies, and grass-hoppers, have six legs, while all spiders have eight. All insects have three main body parts, while spiders have only two. Also, most insects have wings and antennae or feelers. Spiders don't.

An easy way to see the differences between an insect and a spider is to study a diagram of each. A diagram is a simple drawing with labels point-ing out different parts. Study the two diagrams below. The one on the left is of a spider. The one on the right is of a grasshopper.

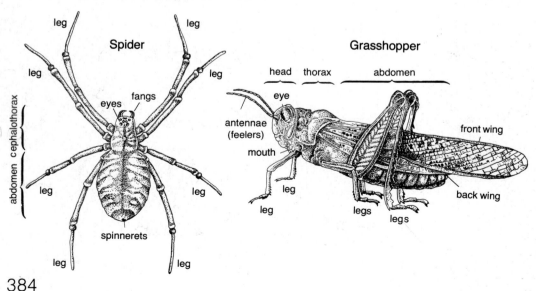

384

Now use the diagrams to answer these questions:

1. Which animal has wings?
2. Where are the spinnerets on the spider?
3. How many eyes are shown on the spider?
4. Which animal has fangs?
5. Where are the feelers on the grasshopper?

As you can see, diagrams are a clear way to show a whole object and label its important parts. Try to make a diagram of something on your own. Pick a simple household machine, like a television, radio, or telephone. Pretend that you have a friend who has never seen the machine before. Make a diagram with labels that will help your friend understand how the machine works.

The following selections are from *Charlotte's Web*, a book about the friendship between a pig named Wilbur and a spider named Charlotte.

Wilbur is born the runt of a litter on the Arable family farm. Mr. Arable usually kills the runt and is about to shoot Wilbur when his daughter Fern stops him. Wilbur is saved, and, with Fern caring for him, he soon grows strong and happy.

One day, however, Mr. Arable decides to sell Wilbur. The young pig is taken down the road to a farm owned by Edith and Homer Zuckerman, Fern's aunt and uncle.

Fern visits Wilbur often in his new home, but Wilbur still feels lonely without the constant company and love of Fern. Finally Wilbur's life is brightened when he meets Charlotte, a beautiful grey spider. Wilbur and Charlotte quickly grow to like one another, and Wilbur becomes a happy young pig once again. But his happiness doesn't last. This first selection tells how some bad news upsets Wilbur's carefree life.

CHAPTER VII

Bad News

Wilbur liked Charlotte better and better each day. Her campaign against insects seemed sensible and useful. Hardly anybody around the farm had a good word to say for a fly. Flies spent their time pestering others. The cows hated them. The horses detested them. The sheep loathed them. Mr. and Mrs. Zuckerman were always complaining about them, and putting up screens.

Wilbur admired the way Charlotte managed. He was particularly glad that she always put her victim to sleep before eating it.

"It's real thoughtful of you to do that, Charlotte," he said.

"Yes," she replied in her sweet, musical voice, "I always give them an anaesthetic so they won't feel pain. It's a little service I throw in."

As the days went by, Wilbur grew and grew. He ate three big meals a day. He spent long hours lying on his side, half asleep, dreaming pleasant dreams. He

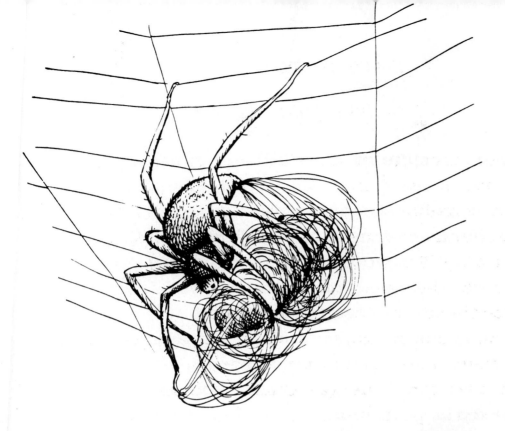

enjoyed good health and he gained a lot of
weight. One afternoon, when Fern was sitting on her stool, the oldest sheep walked
into the barn, and stopped to pay a call on
Wilbur.

"Hello!" she said. "Seems to me you're
putting on weight."

"Yes, I guess I am," replied Wilbur. "At
my age it's a good idea to keep gaining."

"Just the same, I don't envy you," said
the old sheep. "You know why they're
fattening you up, don't you?"

"No," said Wilbur.

"Well, I don't like to spread bad news," said the sheep, "but they're fattening you up because they're going to kill you, that's why."

"They're going to *what?*" screamed Wilbur. Fern grew rigid on her stool.

"Kill you. Turn you into smoked bacon and ham," continued the old sheep. "Almost all young pigs get murdered by the farmer as soon as the real cold weather sets in. There's a regular conspiracy around here to kill you at Christmastime. Everybody is in the plot—Lurvy, Zuckerman, even John Arable."

"Mr. Arable?" sobbed Wilbur. "Fern's father?"

"Certainly. When a pig is to be butchered, everybody helps. I'm an old sheep and I see the same thing, same old business, year after year. Arable arrives with his .22, shoots the . . ."

"Stop!" screamed Wilbur. "I don't want to die! Save me, somebody! Save me!" Fern was just about to jump up when a voice was heard.

"Be quiet, Wilbur!" said Charlotte, who had been listening to this awful conversation.

"I can't be quiet," screamed Wilbur, racing up and down. "I don't want to be killed. I don't want to die. Is it true what the old sheep says, Charlotte? Is it true they are going to kill me when the cold weather comes?"

"Well," said the spider, plucking thoughtfully at her web, "the old sheep has been around this barn a long time. She has seen many a spring pig come and go. If she says they plan to kill you, I'm sure it's true. It's also the dirtiest trick I ever heard of. What people don't think of!"

Wilbur burst into tears. "I don't *want* to die," he moaned. "I want to stay alive, right here in my comfortable manure pile with all my friends. I want to breathe the beautiful air and lie in the beautiful sun."

"You're certainly making a beautiful noise," snapped the old sheep.

"I don't want to die!" screamed Wilbur, throwing himself to the ground.

"You shall not die," said Charlotte, briskly.

"What? Really?" cried Wilbur. "Who's going to save me?"

"I am," said Charlotte.

"How?" asked Wilbur.

"That remains to be seen. But I am going to save you, and I want you to quiet down immediately. You're carrying on in a childish way. Stop your crying! I can't stand hysterics."

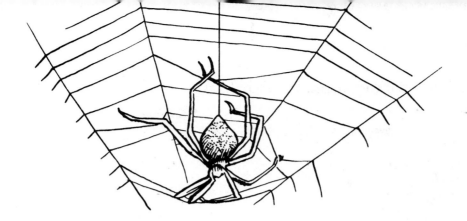

Wilbur is calmed by Charlotte's promise to save him. He patiently waits for her idea. Charlotte hangs for days with her head down so the blood is in her head and she can think clearly. Then finally she decides on an answer. She knows she must convince the Zuckermans that Wilbur is both an unusual and a very special pig. Charlotte's solution is to weave words into her web—words that describe what a great pig Wilbur really is.

The first words Charlotte weaves are SOME PIG! When the Zuckermans and their hired hand, Lurvy, discover Wilbur standing under these words, everyone thinks it is a miracle. They also begin to think that Wilbur is, in fact, SOME PIG!

The following selection tells about Charlotte's next word. Templeton, the barnyard rat, is a big help in finding just the right word to describe Wilbur.

CHAPTER XIII

Good Progress

Far into the night, while the other creatures slept, Charlotte worked on her web. First she ripped out a few of the orb lines near the center. She left the radial lines alone, as they were needed for support. As she worked, her eight legs were a great help to her. So were her teeth. She loved to weave and she was an expert at it. When she was finished ripping things out, her web looked something like this:

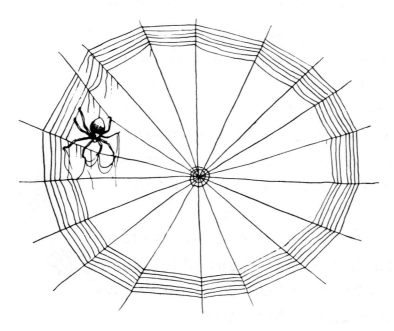

A spider can produce several kinds of thread. She uses a dry, tough thread for foundation lines, and she uses a sticky thread for snare lines—the ones that catch and hold insects. Charlotte decided to use her dry thread for writing the new message.

"If I write the word 'Terrific' with sticky thread," she thought, "every bug that comes along will get stuck in it and spoil the effect.

"Now, let's see, the first letter is T."

Charlotte climbed to a point at the top of the left hand side of the web. Swinging her spinnerets into position, she attached her thread and then dropped down. As she dropped, her spinning tubes went into action and she let out thread. At the bottom, she attached the thread. This formed the upright part of the letter T. Charlotte was not satisfied, however. She climbed up and made another attachment, right next to the first. Then carried the line down, so that she had a double line instead of a single line. "It will show up better if I make the whole thing with double lines."

She climbed back up, moved over about an inch to the left, touched her spinnerets to the web, and then carried a line across to the right, forming the top of the T. She repeated this, making it double. Her eight legs were very busy helping.

"Now for the E!"

Charlotte got so interested in her work, she began to talk to herself, as though to cheer herself on. If you had been sitting quietly in the barn cellar that evening, you would have heard something like this:

"Now for the R! Up we go! Attach! Descend! Pay out line! Whoa! Attach! Good! Up you go! Repeat! Attach! Climb! Attach! Over to the right! Pay out line! Attach! Now right and down and swing that loop and around and around! Now in to the left! Attach! Climb! Repeat! O.K.! Easy, keep those lines together! Now, then, out and down for the leg of the R! Pay out line! Whoa! Attach! Ascend! Repeat! Good girl!"

And so, talking to herself, the spider worked at her difficult task. When it was completed, she felt hungry. She ate a small bug that she had been saving. Then she slept.

Next morning, Wilbur arose and stood beneath the web. He breathed the morning air into his lungs. Drops of dew, catching the sun, made the web stand out clearly. When Lurvy arrived with breakfast, there was the handsome pig, and over him, woven neatly in block letters, was the word TERRIFIC. Another miracle.

Lurvy rushed and called Mr. Zuckerman. Mr. Zuckerman rushed and called Mrs. Zuckerman. Mrs. Zuckerman ran to the phone and called the Arables. The Arables climbed into their truck and hurried over. Everybody stood at the pigpen and stared at the web and read the word, over and over, while Wilbur, who really *felt* terrific, stood quietly swelling out his chest and swinging his snout from side to side.

"Terrific!" breathed Zuckerman, in joyful admiration. "Edith, you better phone the reporter on the *Weekly Chronicle* and tell him what has happened. He will want to know about this. He may want to bring a photographer. There isn't a pig in the whole state that is as terrific as our pig."

The news spread. People who had journeyed to see Wilbur when he was "some pig" came back again to see him now that he was "terrific."

That afternoon, when Mr. Zuckerman went to milk the cows and clean out the tie-ups, he was still thinking about what a wondrous pig he owned.

"Lurvy!" he called. "There is to be no more cow manure thrown down into that pigpen. I have a terrific pig. I want that pig to have clean, bright straw every day for his bedding. Understand?"

"Yes, sir," said Lurvy.

"Furthermore," said Mr. Zuckerman, "I want you to start building a crate for Wilbur. I have decided to take the pig to the County Fair on September sixth. Make the crate large and paint it green with gold letters!"

"What will the letters say?" asked Lurvy.

"They should say *Zuckerman's Famous Pig.*"

Lurvy picked up a pitchfork and walked away to get some clean straw. Having such an important pig was going to mean plenty of extra work, he could see that.

Below the apple orchard, at the end of a path, was the dump where Mr. Zuckerman threw all sorts of trash and stuff that nobody wanted any more. Here, in a small clearing hidden by young alders and wild raspberry bushes, was an astonishing pile of old bottles and empty tin cans and dirty

rags and bits of metal and broken bottles
and broken hinges and broken springs
and dead batteries and last month's magazines and old discarded dishmops and
tattered overalls and rusty spikes and
leaky pails and forgotten stoppers and
useless junk of all kinds, including a
wrong-size crank for a broken ice-cream
freezer.

Templeton knew the dump and liked it.
There were good hiding places there—
excellent cover for a rat. And there was
usually a tin can with food still clinging
to the inside.

Templeton was down there now, rum-
maging around. When he returned to the
barn, he carried in his mouth an advertisement he had torn from a crumpled
magazine.

"How's this?" he asked, showing the ad
to Charlotte. "It says 'Crunchy.' 'Crunchy'
would be a good word to write in your
web."

"Just the wrong idea," replied Charlotte.
"Couldn't be worse. We don't want Zuckerman to think Wilbur is crunchy. He might

start thinking about crisp, crunchy bacon and tasty ham. That would put ideas into his head. We must advertise Wilbur's noble qualities, not his tastiness. Go get another word, please, Templeton!"

The rat looked disgusted. But he sneaked away to the dump and was back in a while with a strip of cotton cloth. "How's this?" he asked. "It's a label off an old shirt."

Charlotte examined the label. It said PRE-SHRUNK.

"I'm sorry, Templeton," she said, "but 'Pre-shrunk' is out of the question. We want Zuckerman to think Wilbur is nicely filled out, not all shrunk up. I'll have to ask you to try again."

"What do you think I am, a messenger boy?" grumbled the rat. "I'm not going to spend all my time chasing down to the dump after advertising material."

"Just once more—please!" said Charlotte.

"I'll tell you what I'll do," said Templeton. "I know where there's a package of soap flakes in the woodshed. It has writing on it. I'll bring you a piece of the package."

He climbed the rope that hung on the wall and disappeared through a hole in the ceiling. When he came back he had a strip of blue-and-white cardboard in his teeth.

"There!" he said triumphantly. "How's that?"

Charlotte read the words: "With New Radiant Action."

"What does it mean?" asked Charlotte, who had never used any soap flakes in her life.

"How should I know?" said Templeton. "You asked for words and I brought them. I suppose the next thing you'll want me to fetch is a dictionary."

Together they studied the soap ad. " 'With new radiant action,' " repeated Charlotte, slowly. "Wilbur!" she called.

Wilbur, who was asleep in the straw, jumped up.

"Run around!" commanded Charlotte. "I want to see you in action, to see if you are radiant."

Wilbur raced to the end of his yard.

"Now back again, faster!" said Charlotte.

Wilbur galloped back. His skin shone. His tail had a fine, tight curl in it.

"Jump into the air!" cried Charlotte.

Wilbur jumped as high as he could.

"Keep your knees straight and touch the ground with your ears!" called Charlotte.

Wilbur obeyed.

"Do a back flip with a half twist in it!" cried Charlotte.

Wilbur went over backwards, writhing and twisting as he went.

"O.K., Wilbur," said Charlotte. "You can go back to sleep. O.K., Templeton, the soap ad will do, I guess. I'm not sure Wilbur's action is exactly radiant, but it's interesting."

"Actually," said Wilbur, "I *feel* radiant."

"Do you?" said Charlotte, looking at him with affection. "Well, you're a good little pig, and radiant you shall be. I'm in this thing pretty deep now—I might as well go the limit."

Tired from his romp, Wilbur lay down in the clean straw. He closed his eyes. The straw seemed scratchy—not as comfortable as the cow manure, which was always delightfully soft to lie in. So he pushed the straw to one side and stretched out in the manure. Wilbur sighed. It had been a busy day—his first day of being terrific. Dozens of people had visited his yard during the afternoon, and he had had to stand and pose, looking as terrific as he could. Now he was tired. Fern had arrived and seated herself quietly on her stool in the corner.

"Tell me a story, Charlotte!" said Wilbur, as he lay waiting for sleep to come. "Tell me a story!"

So Charlotte, although she, too, was tired, did what Wilbur wanted.

"Once upon a time," she began, "I had a beautiful cousin who managed to build her web across a small stream. One day a tiny fish leaped into the air and got tangled in the web. My cousin was very much surprised, of course. The fish was thrashing

wildly. My cousin hardly dared tackle it.
But she did. She swooped down and threw
great masses of wrapping material around
the fish and fought bravely to capture it."

"Did she succeed?" asked Wilbur.

"It was a never-to-be-forgotten battle,"
said Charlotte. "There was the fish, caught
only by one fin, and its tail wildly thrashing and shining in the sun. There was the
web, sagging dangerously under the
weight of the fish."

"How much did the fish weigh?" asked
Wilbur eagerly.

"I don't know," said Charlotte. "There
was my cousin, slipping in, dodging out,
beaten mercilessly over the head by the
wildly thrashing fish, dancing in, dancing out, throwing her threads and fighting
hard. First she threw a left around the
tail. The fish lashed back. Then a left to
the tail and a right to the mid-section.
The fish lashed back. Then she dodged to
one side and threw a right, and another
right to the fin. Then a hard left to the
head, while the web swayed and stretched."

"Then what happened?" asked Wilbur.

"Nothing," said Charlotte. "My cousin kept the fish for a while, and then, when she got good and ready, she ate it."

"Tell me another story!" begged Wilbur.

So Charlotte told him about another cousin of hers who was an aeronaut.

"What is an aeronaut?" asked Wilbur.

"A balloonist," said Charlotte. "My cousin used to stand on her head and let out enough thread to form a balloon. Then she'd let go and be lifted into the air and carried upward on the warm wind."

"Is that true?" asked Wilbur. "Or are you just making it up?"

"It's true," replied Charlotte. "I have some very remarkable cousins. And now, Wilbur, it's time you went to sleep."

"Sing something!" begged Wilbur, closing his eyes.

So Charlotte sang a lullaby, while crickets chirped in the grass and the barn grew dark. This was the song she sang:

"Sleep, sleep, my love, my only,
Deep, deep, in the dung and the dark;
Be not afraid and be not lonely!
This is the hour when frogs and thrushes
Praise the world from the woods and the rushes.
Rest from care, my one and only,
Deep in the dung and the dark!"

But Wilbur was already asleep. When the song ended, Fern got up and went home.

THINK ABOUT IT

1. Who was Wilbur? Where did he live? Who was Charlotte?

2. What frightening news did the old sheep tell Wilbur? How did Wilbur react to this news?

3. What was Charlotte's plan to help Wilbur?

4. After Mr. Zuckerman saw the words in Charlotte's web, where did he decide to take Wilbur? How did other people react to Wilbur?

5. Who was Templeton? How did Templeton help Charlotte decide what to write next?

6. What stories did Charlotte tell Wilbur?

7. In what ways were Charlotte and Wilbur alike? In what ways were they different?

8. What do you think will happen to Wilbur and Charlotte? Do you think they will continue to be close friends? Why or why not?

9. Did the animals in this story seem like people to you? Why or why not?

10. Do you think animals are capable of a friendship such as that shared by Charlotte and Wilbur? Explain your answer.

seven

MEET THE AUTHOR
Jane Langton

Jane Langton feels lucky to live in the town next to Concord, Massachusetts. In Concord, Mrs. Langton says, the air "seems thick with meaning." So much American history, both during the Revolution and later on, took place there.

Henry David Thoreau*, the great nature writer, lived in Concord. Thoreau's famous cabin at Walden Pond was nearby. At Concord, Mrs. Langton

*Thoreau (thə rō′ *or* thôr′ō)

412

feels that the present time is "littered about with the past."

Jane Langton often draws upon the past in her fantasies about present-day children living in Concord. She likes to put real children into this real setting and then pull some kind of fantasy out of the past that lies all around them. So far, Mrs. Langton has written several fantasy books about Concord. Some of these are *The Diamond in the Window, The Swing in the Summerhouse,* and *The Astonishing Stereoscope.*

Mrs. Langton was born in Boston. Before she began writing books, she worked for a Boston TV station. She did art work for a science program called "Discovery." Married to a scientist, Jane Langton has three children. Besides writing, she likes gardening and playing in a string group. Her house is on the shore of Flint's Pond. Henry Thoreau first wanted to build his house there, but the owner wouldn't let him.

Like Jane Langton's earlier fantasies, *The Fledgling* is set in Concord. Walden Pond plays a part in the story, which was a Newbery Honor Book in 1981. In the following chapters from *The Fledgling,* you will meet Georgie, a girl who has an odd wish. She wants to learn how to fly like a bird.

THE FLEDGLING

Georgie

Georgie was reading a book on the landing of the front-hall stairs. The window on the landing was open. She looked up to see the wind tossing the branches of the big tree outside.

Whenever one leaf touches another leaf, thought Georgie, it doesn't make any noise at all. But when all the leaves touch each other, the tree whispers all over.

414

Then she saw the big birds in the sky. They were flying over the tree, making a loud noise, *a-WARK, a-WARK!*

Oh, swans! thought Georgie.

She jumped up and watched the swans fly in a ragged line over the house. They were not white like swans in a book. They were white and gray and black. They were flying so low over the tree Georgie could hear the sound of the air flowing through their feathers. It made a soft noise, *sssh, sssh, sssh.*

415

If only I could fly like that, thought Georgie. If only I could do it again.

Because she had done it. She had. She knew she had. She had waked up in the middle of the night. She had jumped down the stairs in two great floating bounds.

Unless it was only a dream.

Georgie turned around on the landing and looked at the twelve stairs falling steeply to the downstairs hall. Below her the bronze woman stood on the newel-post, gazing as usual out the front door, holding her light fixture in one upraised hand. Her light was turned off. The hall was dark.

Only the white marble head of Henry Thoreau glimmered in the watery gloom. Henry was a statue in the curve of the stairs, a carved bust on a tall stand. Everything else in the front hall was nearly invisible in the murky shade of the downstairs, but through the oval glass of the door Georgie could see a piece of the front yard.

The sun was shining brilliantly on the green grass beyond the porch, and on scraps of long legs and big feet and shorts and skirts and blue jeans. Georgie's mother and Uncle Freddy were teaching a Saturday morning class in the front yard. Teachers and students were sitting in a circle on the grass. It was Uncle Freddy's school. Georgie's mother and Uncle Freddy had a school, right here in the house, and in the front yard and the backyard, and sometimes they even held classes way up in the branches of the apple tree.

417

This year they were studying a book by Henry Thoreau, who had lived in Concord, Massachusetts, down the road at Walden Pond, a very long time ago.

Uncle Freddy liked to pretend Mr. Thoreau wasn't dead. He called him Henry, as if he were an old friend.

"Nice morning, Henry," he would say to the white marble bust in the hall, or "Henry, old man, listen to this." And then Henry would gaze wisely at the wall with his unblinking marble eyes as if he were listening with his stony ears and wondering and thinking it all over in his mind.

Georgie stood on the landing and listened. From the kitchen she could hear a murmur of voices and a clatter of dishes. Eddy and Eleanor were bumping around in the kitchen, having a snack.

She put her feet side by side on the top step. Then she took something out of her pocket and looked at it. It was a milkweed pod from the meadow across the street. Downy seedlings were puffing out of the pod. Georgie pulled one free, tossed it over her head, and blew it high. The milkweed seedling twirled, then wafted sideways like a fluffy parasol. Georgie took a deep breath and blew it down the stairs. Lightly it drifted halfway down, and then it was caught by a little draft from the crack around the front door. Up it went again. At last it floated against Henry Thoreau's marble ear and clung there.

I can do that, too. Georgie put the milkweed pod back in the pocket of her red overalls. I know I can. Two big jumps. Just floating. I did it before. I think I did. I can do it again.

Georgie clenched her fists. I've got to. I've just got to.

In the kitchen Eddy and Eleanor heard the *thumpity-bump* and the thin squeal.

"Oh, no," said Eddy, jumping up, "it's Georgie! There she goes again!"

"Oh, poor Georgie!" Eleanor ran out into the hall after Eddy. "Georgie, not again!"

Georgie lay in a heap at the bottom of the stairs, a jumble of red overalls and skinny arms and legs. Whimpering, she looked up at the two big faces bending over her with the light from the front door fuzzing around their hair. "Honestly, Georgie," said Eleanor. Gently she picked up Georgie and sat down with her on the bottom step. Georgie pressed her face against Eleanor's sweater. "Now, promise me, Georgie dear," said Eleanor, "you won't ever do it again."

"You nutty little kid," said Eddy. "You know you can't fly downstairs. I told you that the last time. Next time you'll break your neck. Nobody can fly downstairs. Jump, maybe—sure, you can jump. But you can't fly."

Eddy and Eleanor were much older than Georgie. They were like a king and queen, towering and majestic and kind. It was true that they shouted at each other sometimes, but they were always nice to Georgie. "Look," said Eddy, "I'll show you how to jump, Georgie. Just move over. Come on, get out of my way."

"Don't push," said Eleanor testily. But she hitched over on the bottom step and squeezed up against the newel-post, while Eddy demonstrated exactly how far it was possible to jump down the flight of stairs.

Eddy's final mighty leap was a tremendous plunge from halfway to the second floor. Eddy thundered down with an enormous crash that shook the bust of Henry Thoreau. Then he staggered to his feet, breathing heavily. "Just try it a few at a time, you see, Georgie. Work your way up. But don't try it from the top. You couldn't

ever jump from the top of the stairs. Well, maybe after years of practice, sure. But not now."

Eleanor was scornful. "Oh, Eddy, Georgie doesn't want to jump down the stairs. Look, Georgie, I'll show you something better than jumping. Something that feels like flying, it really does. Are you all right now?"

Carefully Eleanor set Georgie on her feet, and then she stood up, too. "Watch this, Georgie." For a moment Eleanor stood erect, scowling at the thick dark air. Then she ran forward and made a mighty spring. In midair she whirled around, her orange pigtail flying. She came down hard at the other side of the dim, hollow hall, facing the other way. Breathing heavily, she grinned at Georgie, feeling pleased with herself. "There, you see, Georgie? Didn't that look like flying? It feels like flying, it really does." I should have gone on with those ballet lessons, thought Eleanor. I could be dancing before the whole world right now, instead of just Eddy and Georgie. "When you flew downstairs, that wasn't real at all, Georgie. It was just a dream. I mean, come on now, Georgie, really."

Georgie stared at Eleanor and waited a minute. (Georgie often waited a minute before she said anything.) "Well, I guess so," she said. "Well,

maybe." But she didn't really think it had been a dream. It had been so bright! It had felt so lovely! She had flown! Like the swans!

The jumping and dancing lessons were over. Georgie went out on the front porch. "I'm all right now," she said, shutting the door behind her. Then she opened it again and put her head back inside. "Thank you," said Georgie.

Eddy shook his head and grinned at Eleanor. "What a nutty little kid." Then he looked up quickly. There was a noise in the sky. "Listen, you hear that? It's geese, Canada geese!"

A-WARK, a-WARK! High over the town of Concord the great flock of sixty geese was banking and turning, flying back from Walden Pond to feed on the marsh grasses of the Great Meadows. Their wings pumped strongly. They made a waving pattern like an arrow in the balmy September sky. From wing to laboring wing they passed the creamy air, gabbling to each other in their hoarse strident talk. *Go DOWN! go DOWN! go WHERE? go THERE? where, WHERE? here, HERE? no, THERE! there, THERE! come DOWN! down, DOWN! right HERE? yes, HERE! down, DOWN! come DOWN! right DOWN!* Far below them lay the town of Concord, its rooftops barely visible under the puffy green and yellow trees, the streets running straight and black, the rivers looping in round curves, flashing back the image of the racing sun.

425

The largest bird of all flapped heavily at the end of the line. No longer was the old goose flying with his mate, guiding another young family of excited half-grown fledglings from the blue northern lake where the goslings had been born. His mate had died long ago. He was a lone bird, old but mighty in wingspread, an outsider, traveling with a busy, clamorous flock of younger geese— mothers and fathers and children, sisters and brothers, cousins and uncles and aunts.

Now the old goose slowed the rhythmical beat of his wings. He lowered his long black neck to stare down at the roofs of the houses running away below him. One house was different from the rest, odd and tall, with a tower at one side. Straining his bulging eyes, he saw a circle of men and women sitting in the front yard. Their heads were lowered. They were looking down.

A small red person was standing on the front porch, looking up.

For an instant the old goose wavered in his flight, staring down at the small red spot. But then the circle of people in the front yard looked up, too. They became a ring of eager faces, gazing back at him, jumping to their feet, pointing upward. The old goose summoned the powerful muscles that flexed and stretched his wings. He caught up with the rest of the flock as it began its long gliding descent—down, down to the sheet of blue water and the sedgy marsh grass of the Great Meadows.

And all along Walden Street and Main Street and Monument Square, all the way down Monument Street to the North Bridge, people ran to the windows and looked up and smiled, pleased by the racket and the sight of the strong pumping wings against the sky.

"It sounds like fall," they said to each other. "When the geese come back, you know it must be fall."

Flyyyyyyyyyyy!

Georgie makes friends with the big, lonely old goose. She calls him the Goose Prince. Sitting on the Goose Prince's strong back, Georgie soars into the air on long flights. But Georgie still wants to fly by herself. Early one morning, when Georgie first wakes, the Goose Prince decides that Georgie is ready. He will teach her how to fly.

428

They took off from the pond. The ascent was not like their clumsy upward struggles from the roof of the porch at home. This time the Goose Prince made a rush forward through the water, his wings flapping, his beak open in a loud triumphant shout. *"A-WARK, a-WARK!"*

At once he was aloft, with a rain of crystal drops falling from his webbed feet and streaming backward from Georgie's soaked pajama legs as they rose higher and higher over the pond. Georgie hung on tight, feeling the cold rush of air on her wet legs. Now the Goose Prince was flapping strongly over the southern shore, turning in a wide arc. Then Georgie gasped. They were not alone. There was a flock of geese below them in the water, a whole flock. They were clustered along the shore with their drowsing heads tucked into their backs, fast asleep.

"*A-WARK, a-WARK!*" As the Goose Prince
shouted above them, Georgie could see heads
popping up in a flurry of beating wings. She could
hear a chorus of shocked croakings. *What's that?
What's that? Who's there?* But then they recognized
one of their own, and the wings stopped fanning.
The heads sank once more into the downy backs.
They all went back to sleep.

High above the slumbering flock the Goose
Prince swam smoothly once again through the
thick river of air. His wings were moving easily,
sending pulses of the cool fragrant morning over
Georgie's smiling face, lifting the lank wisps of
her fine hair, blowing it backward. Below them
the pine trees flung up their dark arms, as if they
were pointing at Georgie—*Oh, look! Look at Georgie!*
And then the Goose Prince turned his head on
his long neck and gazed back at her, the dawn
light shining through his bulging eyes. "Now,"
he said, "try it now."

At the top of the sky, clinging to him with her fingers knotted together around his throat, Georgie looked back at him, trying to understand, whispering, "Try what?"

"*Flyyyyyyyyyyy,*" said the Goose Prince. On the moving air the word flowed on and on, not dying away. Georgie was filled with longing. But she was afraid. She held on, wrapping her fingers together more tightly, shutting her eyes and pressing her cheek against the soft feathers of his neck. Not now. She couldn't do it now. Not yet.

"Just slip off and glide," said the Goose Prince. "You'll see. The wind is just right. It will hold you, if you try it now." And then he warbled it again in his soft fluting voice, "*Flyyyyyyyyyyy.*"

431

For a moment longer Georgie kept her shoulders stiff and her arms pressed close against him. But then she opened her eyes and commanded all her muscles to go limp. Letting go, she slid down the feathery slope of his back until she felt something nudge at her from below. It was a pillow of air, lifting her, holding her steadily and firmly like the palm of a supporting hand.

Then at last all the stringy little muscles in Georgie's body loosened. Spreading her arms, she floated on the column of air. Beside her, the Goose Prince floated, too, watching her, his hovering wingtips brushing her fingers. Together they drifted, wheeling down and down in slowly descending circles, around and around the pond. Georgie wanted to say, "Oh, look, look at me!" But whenever she opened her mouth, the wind filled it.

They were floating, soaring, skimming like sea gulls, like hawks, like swallows. Above them there was nothing but crystal air. And below them— and then for the first time Georgie looked down, and at once she was frightened. The emptiness below her was an immense gulf of nothingness. There was only the steely surface of the gray pond, far down, and the dark bristle of the trees poking up around it. Georgie gave a strangled cry, and dropped one arm.

Instantly she was falling, spinning over and over, plummeting straight down. But only for an instant. With a tremendous jerk and a terrible pinching pain in her left arm, she was snatched out of her plunging fall. The Goose Prince was dragging her through the air, his wings thundering, struggling to hold her aloft. And soon he was lowering her ever so gently to the ground on the nearest shore.

Georgie lay on the stony path for a moment. Then she stood up, trembling, rubbing her arm. "I'm sorry," she said.

But the Goose Prince was gallant. "Oh, it's *quite* all right," he said. "I hope I didn't hurt you?"

"No, no," said Georgie. "Could we try again?"

"Try again? Are you sure?" The Goose Prince cocked his head at her, and she couldn't help laughing. In his tender concern he looked for a minute more like her mother than like the splendid prince he really was.

"Oh, yes!"

They tried again. Once more the Goose Prince paddled out into the water. Once more they took off in a rush of beating wings. Once more he lifted Georgie high over the pond. And once again Georgie let go.

This time when she clenched her teeth and slid off the back of the Goose Prince, she was careful not to look down. This time she lay perfectly still on the cushion of air. Keeping her arms spread wide, she circled like the Goose Prince as he rested beside her on the same sturdy ridge of warm vapor rising from the pond. She was safe now, perfectly safe. Watching her companion out of the corner of her eye, Georgie obediently copied his slightest motion. Whenever he adjusted the curve of his pinions to change the direction of his flight, Georgie bent her elbows, too, and followed his lead. When the wind rocked him, and he spread the tips of his wings to let it flow through the gaps between his feathers, it rocked Georgie, too, and she opened her fingers.

Glide, glide, float and glide, lift and soar! Oh, how far she could see! All the way to Boston! There it was, the city of Boston, a cluster of dark towers against the sunrise. And there were the shadowy mountains, still blue with night, far away on the other side!

Proudly the Goose Prince flew beside Georgie, wingtip to fingertip, his head bent on his long neck to watch her. The sunlight was shining redly on his belly with the same streaking ray that warmed her own face. And then, at last, Georgie dared to cock her head and look down. She saw Route 2, there at the place where it turned the corner. And, look! There was the train! It was rattling along the shore of the pond on its toy track, shaking from side to side.

Now the sun had risen far enough to shine on the trees around the pond. The tops of the trees were pink. For an instant the sun flashed back into Georgie's eyes from the window of a car in the parking lot, making her blink. But she banked and turned, following the lead of the Goose Prince, lifting her head to gaze once again over

the whole broad landscape from horizon to horizon, feeling the sleeves of her jacket fill with air, listening to the legs of her pajamas flap like the laundry at home on a breezy day.

She was free. Georgie exulted. At last she was free as air. With the Goose Prince she could fly everywhere, all over the world. There were no fences to keep them out. So this was the way birds felt! They could fly to China and France and Africa! To Africa, where there were lions and elephants! She could fly to the elephants' jungle! She could see monkeys, leaping in the trees!

Georgie has more adventures with the Goose Prince before her story is over. If you would like to find out what else happens, read the book The Fledgling *by Jane Langton.*

1. What did Georgie want to learn how to do? Why did Eleanor and Eddy try to stop her?

2. Where did Georgie and her family live? Tell something about their house.

3. What were the birds that Georgie called "swans"?

4. Who was the Goose Prince?

5. Why did Georgie fall when she first flew with the Goose Prince?

6. How did the Goose Prince feel about Georgie? How do you know?

7. What was it like to fly? How did Georgie feel when she flew?

8. What kind of person was Georgie? Explain your answer.

9. Could a human really fly like Georgie? Why or why not?

10. Suppose you could fly like a bird. Where would you fly? Why?

Stories, Dreams, and Flying Machines

People have probably always dreamed of flying. Picture people living many, many years ago. They are walking across a vast plain. It is cold. Their feet hurt. Their legs are spattered with mud. It is a hard, long trip, the only kind they know how to make, on land. Suddenly they look up. A flock of birds soars gracefully overhead. The birds don't look cold or tired or unhappy. They look free.

"If only we could be free like the birds," the people think. "If only we could get from one place to another so quickly, so easily. If only we could fly!"

If only . . .

Early Stories

People began making up stories. They told tales of humans who did what others only dreamed of doing—who lifted off the ground and flew.

The earliest such story we know about comes from China. About four thousand years ago, the story goes, the Emperor Shun flew. One time he escaped from an enemy by putting on the "clothes" of a bird. Another time Shun turned into a huge flying dragon.

Still another time, Shun was on top of a burning grain storehouse. To get away, he grabbed two hats with very wide brims. He used these hats like a parachute. Holding them, he floated safely to the ground.

[1] **Daedalus** (ded'l əs)
[2] **Icarus** (ik'ər əs)

Later, the Greeks told the story of Daedalus[1] and Icarus.[2] Daedalus and his son Icarus had been captured by the evil ruler of Crete. Crete was an island. To escape, Daedalus built two pairs of wings. These wings were made of feathers held together by wax. Wearing these wings, father and son took off from their island prison. They flew high over the sea. But Icarus flew too high. He got too close to the sun. The sun's heat melted the wax in Icarus's wings. The wings fell apart. Icarus plunged into the sea and was drowned.

Perhaps this is only a story. But some scientists wonder. They say that Crete has very high cliffs by the sea. Strong drafts come up from the water there. An inventor could have built a glider of wood and cloth and taken off from these cliffs. The drafts would have held the glider up—for a while. There may never have been a Daedalus and an Icarus. But there may have been a brave, foolish inventor who died in a glider flight many hundreds of years ago in Crete.

As the ages passed, there were many other stories about flying. Some stories told of flying carpets. Rulers were said to have flying thrones drawn by eagles. There were winged horses, griffins, and, of course, dragons.

Scientific Ideas

The first really scientific ideas about flying appeared in the Middle Ages. One thinker in the 1200's wrote about a flying "instrument." In such a machine, the thinker said, an engine might move artificial wings. The wings could "beat the air" like a flying bird.

The idea of a flying machine was picked up around 1500 by one of the world's greatest minds. Leonardo da Vinci had many talents. He was a great artist. He was also known for his studies in mathematics and science. Da Vinci made many notes and drawings about flying—nearly 5,000 pages worth.

Da Vinci spent much time studying birds. He studied their flight from a scientist's point of view. He thought long and hard about the way a bird's wings worked. He came up with a design for an ornithopter. An ornithopter is a kind of airplane with birdlike wings. A human pilot flaps the wings to fly short distances.

Ornithopters do not work well. The chest muscles of birds are very different from those of humans. People do not have the right muscles to make wings fly. But da Vinci came close to the idea of a glider. A glider has wings that do not flap. A glider is lifted by air power.

Da Vinci also worked on a design for a helicopter driven by a spring. His design was good. The helicopter really did fly. Da Vinci knew, however, that in his time there was no way to power a full-size helicopter. His helicopter was only a small-scale model.

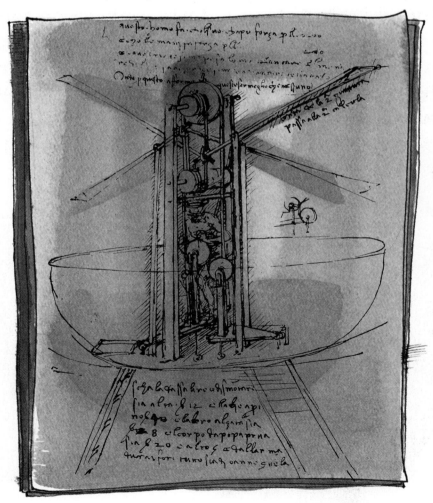

A better idea of da Vinci's was the parachute. He called his design "a tent made of linen." His parachute was shaped like a pyramid. With it, he said, a person could be thrown down from a great height and not be hurt.

In 1618 someone used da Vinci's pattern to build a better parachute. This inventor jumped off several high buildings and floated down safely.

Perhaps more of da Vinci's designs could have been turned into real flying machines. If they had, people would have been flying several hundred years sooner. But when da Vinci died, he left his notes to a friend. This friend did not make the notes known. Da Vinci's work was forgotten for more than three hundred years.

In 1670 someone thought of a different way to fly. An

Hot-Air Balloons

Still, the idea of a hot-air balloon was not far away. On August 8, 1709, a small hot-air balloon was flown in Portugal. The balloon was sent up inside a building. This was not wise. The balloon did go up. But when it came down, something went wrong with the hot air. The balloon caught fire and set the building on fire, too.

airship could be built that would have four copper globes. All the air would be taken out of the globes to make them lighter than air. Then the globes would lift the airship.

This idea was fine as far as it went. But the airship could never have worked. The globes would have been lighter than air, all right. But air pressure would have crushed them.

The first successful balloon flight was made in France. Two brothers, Joseph and Jacques Montgolfier, had been reading books about air. One day in 1782, they were sitting by a fireplace. Joseph threw a paper bag into the fire. The bag filled with smoke and floated up through the chimney. The brothers were excited. They figured that

the bag rose because smoke is lighter than air. They decided to make more paper-bag balloons.

In the months that followed, the Montgolfiers made larger and larger balloons. By spring, they were working on a balloon that was 110 feet around. This balloon was made of linen and lined with paper. The neck was open at the bottom. Smoke from a fire below the opening would go into the balloon. Then the balloon would rise.

The Montgolfiers tried out their big balloon on June 5, 1783. When the ropes were cut, the balloon began to go up, up, up. The people watching were amazed. The balloon flew as high as 6,000 feet. It traveled almost two miles before it came down.

News of this wonderful flight spread. People in Paris gave the brothers money to go there and try the balloon again. On September 19, the Montgolfier brothers sent their balloon up from the palace at Versailles.

Many famous people watched the balloon lift off. Two of the watchers were Queen Marie Antoinette and an American, Benjamin Franklin. This was a special flight. This time the balloon carried passengers in a basket. The passengers were animals: a sheep, a duck, and a rooster.

The balloon did not stay up very long. The flight lasted only eight minutes.

One of the basket ropes broke. Down came the balloon, landing on a treetop. But the animals were found alive and mostly unhurt. (The rooster had a slightly damaged wing.)

Not long after, the balloon went up again. This time a human rode in the basket. However, the balloon was tied to the ground by ropes. It could travel only a very short distance.

Six weeks after the September 19 flight, in November 1783, two people made the world's first free balloon flight. In twenty-five minutes, they flew more than five miles.

At last, the many, many years of making up stories about flying were over. Now the stories had come true. People could really fly.

THINK ABOUT IT

1. How old is the earliest story we know about a person flying? Who was that person?

2. Who was Icarus? What happened to him?

3. Name three of Leonardo da Vinci's ideas for flying.

4. In what ways was da Vinci "ahead of his time"? Why did some of his ideas not work?

5. What mistake was made in the hot-air balloon flight in Portugal?

6. What gave the Montgolfier brothers the idea to build a large balloon?

7. Why do you think people in Paris gave the Montgolfiers money to try out their balloon again?

8. What stories about flying—real or make-believe—have you read? Which is your favorite? Why?

The First Free-Fall
PARACHUTE JUMP

Do you know who was the first person to make a free-fall parachute jump from an airplane? Do you know where and when that jump occurred?

There's an easy way to find out. Look it up in the encyclopedia. An encyclopedia is a set of books with information on many subjects.

Each book in the set is called a volume. In most encyclopedias, each volume has a number and one or more letters on it. Entries in an encyclopedia appear in alphabetical order. The letter *A* on an encyclopedia volume tells you that all the entries in that book start with *a*.

You want to find out about the first free-fall parachute jump. What entry word will you look up? Probably *parachute*. Look at the encyclopedia pictured below. Which volume should you try? Yes, try volume 16. Why? All of the entries in that volume begin with *p*.

Once you find the right volume, the next step is to locate the entry you are looking for. Remember that entries are in alphabetical order. Guide words can help you find the right page for your entry word. Guide words usually appear at the top of each pair of pages. They show the first and the last entry words on those two pages. The other entry words on the two pages come between the two guide words in alphabetical order.

Look at the encyclopedia pages shown below. What are the guide words for those two pages? Yes, the guide words are **Pacific** and **Perkins, Frances.** (People's names are always listed last name first.) Does *parachute* come between *Pacific* and *Perkins* in alphabetical order? Then you would expect to find *parachute* on these two pages.

In the entry for *parachute*, you could find the answers to your questions. For the record, here they are. The first person to make a free-fall parachute jump from an airplane was Georgia "Tiny" Broadwick. She made that jump in San Diego, California, in 1914.

Use the pictures on pages 449 and 450 to help you answer these questions.

1. In which volume of the encyclopedia on page 449 could you find out about koalas?
2. In which volume could you read about the life of Amelia Earhart?
3. In which volume could you find out how to tell quicksand when you see it?
4. Which of the following entries would you find on the encyclopedia pages shown on page 450: peanut, Paul Robeson, panda?

What would you like to find out about? Pick a subject. Then look it up in the encyclopedia.

The Web of Winter

Bill stood by the marsh watching small flocks of birds looking for food. The birds darted among the dry reeds and barren branches, pecking at shriveled berries and pods to get at their hidden seeds. Bill wondered how the birds kept warm in the stinging cold.

At last he ran out on the ice and slid, making great long tracks. He alternately ran and slid across the marsh until he came to the turn-around—an empty barrel frozen into the ice. He sat down on the barrel to fasten his

boot. His breath came out on the cold air in thin white puffs.

The wind grew suddenly quiet. That's when Bill first heard the sound. It was so faint that he was not sure he had heard it. The sound came again, high and thin.

"Quick . . . "

Bill listened. It came again.

"Quick . . . quick."

Could it be the ice breaking under his weight? He looked carefully. No, the ice was hard and firm.

"Quick . . . quick."

What could the sound be? Bill knew the call of the winter birds—the whistle of a cardinal, the chatter of a blue jay, the *cheep* of a sparrow. It wasn't a bird he knew, and it didn't sound like the cry of an animal.

"Quick . . . quick."

The sound floated again over the marsh. Bill rose to follow it. Picking his way among the weeds and tall grasses, he came to the edge of the marsh. He pushed the reeds aside and listened. All was silent. He bent his head, waiting for the sound to come again.

"Quick . . . quick."

"I'm coming," he answered, making his way through the brush. Every few steps he stopped, waiting for the voice to guide him.

But the voice did not come again. The sun set behind the willows. It grew late and dark.

Bill waited as long as he could. Finally he had to leave. It was suppertime and his mother expected him home.

The next day, after school, Bill returned to the marsh for skating. He carried his skates and a broom on his sled and pulled them out to the center of the marsh where the ice could be cleared for skating. He sat down on the sled to put on his skates. Then he took the broom and swept the snow off the ice, leaving the surface smooth for skating.

He found an old tomato can and batted it before him as he skated around, using the broom as a hockey stick. Then he dropped the broom and raced around and around the turn-around barrel. His quick turns on the ice made a deep grating sound and threw up a cloud of white dust behind him. He practiced all sorts of turns and skated with enthusiasm—forward, backward, stopping, starting, turning, gliding.

He was skating near the turn-around barrel when he heard the sound again.

"Quick . . . quick."

It came the same as yesterday. Bill cocked his head and listened.

"Quick . . . "

The sound wasn't far away. Bill skated
quietly toward it.

"Quick . . . quick."

Now he heard quite clearly. The snow was
thicker at the edge of the marsh and was too
rough for skating. He had to walk on his
skates, leaving short thin tracks behind him.
Then suddenly, the same as the day before, the
sound stopped.

Bill stood still. He listened and watched.
After a bit, he kneeled down and called softly.
"Quick . . .quick . . ."

He waited for an answer. None came.

He called again, "Quick."

There was no reply. He listened a long time
and stood up to go. That is when he found it.
In a tangle of dry weeds, he saw a duck

huddled in the snow. It was sitting so still it looked like a decoy.

"Hello," Bill said, bending down.

The bird trembled and fluttered its wings. It was a young duck.

"It's too cold here for you, Quick-quick. Why haven't you flown away?"

The duck beat its wings frantically. The snow flew, but the bird could not. It was caught in the ice. Bill knew that birds often rested in icy water, but he had never heard of anything like this. The water had frozen firmly around the duck's feet.

Bill gently took the bird in his hands. He tried to lift, but the ice held the duck as tightly as it held the turn-around barrel.

"Don't worry," Bill said. "I'll get you out."

It was easier said than done. The duck was not only trapped, it was cold and hungry. Bill broke off some grasses and piled them in front of the bird where it could get at the seeds. But Quick-quick refused the food.

Maybe it's too weak to eat, Bill thought.

The duck cried a low pitiful sound. Bill feared the duck was nearly dead. There was no time to run two miles home for help. He himself must act—and quickly.

"Here," he said, loosening his scarf and wrapping it around the duck. "This will warm you a little."

The wind whipped the scarf out of his hands, but he grabbed it and wrapped it around the captive bird.

Now what to do?

Bill ran for his sled. He had seen people make wind shelters when they were ice fishing, so he propped the sled up to shelter the duck while he tried to free it.

Bill took off his skates and quickly put on his boots. He used the blade of one skate as a knife, trying to cut through the thick layer of ice. He cut a circle around the bird. Now, the real work began. He retraced the marks again and again, each time cutting a little deeper in the ice. This was the way Bill and his dad made fishing holes in the ice, only they used a hatchet and an ice pick.

Bill chopped at the ice. He grew warmer and warmer. He also grew more and more tired. Frequently he had to stop to rest his aching arms. He worked so hard that he didn't think about the time. The sun was low behind the willow trees at the edge of the marsh before he noticed the darkness.

Someone called. "Bill! Hey, Bill! Are you down there?" It was his sister.

"Here I am, Thelma! Over here!"

Thelma came quickly toward him through the tall weeds.

"A duck's caught here in the ice," Bill shouted. "I'm cutting him free."

"Where have you been? Mom's worried silly," Thelma said.

"I've been here," Bill said. "I can't leave or this duck will die."

Thelma saw the bird now and how Bill was trying to free it. "It's dangerous to cut holes in the ice," she said. "You should *never never* do it when you're alone."

"I know," Bill answered. "But it's shallow here and near the shore. Besides, there wasn't time to get help."

"Where's the other skate?" Thelma asked. Without waiting for an answer, she found it and started to work, using the tip of the blade like an ice pick. She chopped at the ice with the skate and gouged out good-sized chunks.

"Good work, Thelma," Bill said. "We'll have this duck free in no time." They chopped and chopped, but it was hard going, and very slow.

Soon another voice came out of the dusk. "Thelma! Bill!" Mother had come to look for them.

"We can't come," Thelma called back. "Bill found a duck frozen to the ice. We are trying to rescue it."

"Found what?" Mother called.

Mother scolded as she came across the ice.
Then she saw the bird huddled under the scarf,
and her attitude changed. "It's dangerous to
cut holes in the ice, and you should *never never*
do it without a grown-up along."

"Yes, Mom," Bill said. "Thelma said the
same thing. But there wasn't time."

"Well, I can help, too. Hand me the broom,"
Mother said. She began sweeping the ice chips

away from the crack where Bill and Thelma were chopping.

A truck came bumping along the shore road, its headlights shining through the weeds. It was Father. He pulled the truck to a stop.

His voice rang out in the dark. "Bill! Thelma!"

"Over here," Mother answered.

Father got out of the truck and came to see what was happening. When he saw them chopping, he scolded, "Why didn't you call me? It's dangerous to cut holes in the ice. You should *never* do it without a grown-up around."

"Here we go again," Bill said without looking up.

Father looked at the duck, then at the circle. "I'll get my tools," he said.

Father went back to the truck and returned with a hammer and a jack handle. Soon the ice chips were flying. The duck pulled its head back in alarm. Now it was very dark and hard to see.

"That's enough," Bill said as he tested the ice and felt it give.

Father tapped along the circle with the hammer. The tapping opened the crack. The

ice cake, still holding the bird, broke loose. Bill
and Father carefully lifted the small island of
ice and carried it, bird and all, to the truck.
Bill laid his hand on the bird's breast and felt
its heart fluttering. "He's still alive," he said.

Quick-quick, his feet still frozen in the cake
of ice, was loaded into the truck. Bill and
Thelma sat beside him on the trip home. The
duck was placed in the bathtub, and Bill drew
warm water to hurry the thawing of the ice.

"Quick . . . quick . . ." Quick-quick seemed to
know that he had been saved. His voice was
faint, but at least Bill knew he was still alive.
Bill hung over the edge of the bathtub,

encouraging the duck with kind talk and offers of food.

By morning, the duck was paddling around in the bathtub as if he enjoyed his new home. "Quick, quick, quack! Quick, quick, quack!" He fluttered his wings and splashed water over the floor.

The next week, after the duck was strong enough to go on his way, Bill and Thelma took him back to the marsh and set him free. Out he flew over the ice and, without turning back, disappeared over the woods and over the hill.

Now, in fall and spring when the birds fly overhead, Bill still watches the ducks that come to the marsh. He listens for Quick-quick, knowing that the bird may never remember him, but he will never forget the bird and his *quick . . . quick . . .* and *quick, quick, quack!*

THINK ABOUT IT

1. When did Bill first hear the "quick . . . quick" sound? What had made the sound?

2. What did Bill do with the broom he brought to the marsh?

3. How had the duck got caught in the ice?

4. Why didn't Bill go for help before he tried to free the duck? Was this wise? Explain.

5. Why did Thelma, Mother, and Father warn Bill not to cut holes in the ice when he was alone?

6. How was the duck finally set free?

7. Did Quick-quick like living in the bathtub? How can you tell?

8. Why do you think Bill would never forget Quick-quick?

9. Have you ever helped an animal in trouble? Tell what happened.

Connie's New Eyes

Connie David is blind. Ever since she was a child, Connie has dreamed of owning a guide dog. Now her dream has come true. Connie is a graduate of the Seeing Eye training program. Her "new eyes" are Blythe, a beautiful golden retriever. It is September. Connie and Blythe are about to begin a challenging new job. Connie has been accepted as a teacher at the Skyline Center in her hometown, Clinton, Iowa.

Connie and Blythe begin to get used to their new routine. Every day during the first week, Connie goes to staff meetings at Skyline. Her workday begins at six in the morning when she gets up. By seven she is dressed and downstairs. Connie feeds Blythe her daily meal. After she walks Blythe, she joins the rest of the family for her own breakfast.

By the end of the week Blythe and Connie are used to their new route. They have a ten-minute walk to the bus stop. Then there's a twenty-minute ride to the school. Blythe has already learned where they get off the bus. She stands up, ready to lead Connie to the door, when they get to their stop.

Connie is excited. This is her first full-time teaching job. Her job is a challenge in another way, too. Her students, mostly preschoolers, are all handicapped.

They will need special teaching. All the students need a great deal of attention. Class groups are small. There are two teachers for each group.

There are no teaching materials specially made for blind teachers. So Connie has made teaching tools that let her use her sense of touch. She teaches her students the names of colors with pieces of heavy felt cloth. She has cut out pieces with different shapes. Each shape has its own color. Connie can also use these felt shapes to teach her students to count. Like many teachers, Connie uses picture flash cards. These help her students learn the names of things. At the top of each card, Connie has punched a braille description of the object shown.

Connie has told her students that, since she is blind, they must answer her questions out loud. They can't just shake their heads yes or no. She has also asked them to place objects in her hand. They must not just put things down in front of her. The children do as Connie asks. But it soon becomes clear that they don't quite believe she is blind. She is just as quick to tell what's going on as any sighted teacher.

Of course the students are all curious about Blythe. None of the other teachers brings a dog to school. Connie says that Blythe is there to help her get around. Blythe acts in place of Connie's own eyes.

Connie must use her sense of hearing to know what is happening around her. She has learned to listen carefully to sounds. There is one place at the school where this skill is especially important for her. This is the Big Room. It is a large, enclosed area in the middle of the preschool section. The teachers take their children to the Big Room to play at least once a day. The Big Room is noisy! But no one tells the children to quiet down. This is their room. As long as they don't harm themselves or someone else, they can do what they like. For the teachers, it's a different matter. They must be quick to stay out of the way.

This morning some students are racing wildly up and down on tricycles. They yell like police sirens. They are having a wonderful time.

In another part of the room, a little girl is doing a live TV show. One of the teachers brought the empty cabinet of a huge TV set to school. It was a big success.

Another teacher, Mary Louise Moon, is playing a game with a group of children. Connie joins in.

"Everybody cover your eyes," Mary Louise says. "On the count of three, I'll point at one of you. Then all of you look to see who I'm pointing at. Call out the person's full name as fast as you can. No peeking until after I say 'three,' OK?"

The children giggle. They cover their eyes.

One of the children can't resist. He has to peek before Mary Louise stops counting. He is caught by surprise when she points at him.

"Kevin Cheney!" everyone shouts.

"Me!" Kevin laughs happily, thumping his chest.

The game goes on. Connie hears something wrong through all the noise and laughter. She gets up and moves toward the sound. There, on the floor, sits three-year-old Danielle Merchant. Today is Danielle's first day in any school. She isn't used to group play. She is confused and scared by the noise and the new faces.

Connie reaches out her hand to identify the child. She finds the girl's ponytail. She says, "Danielle, is that you? What's wrong, honey? Did you fall and hurt yourself?"

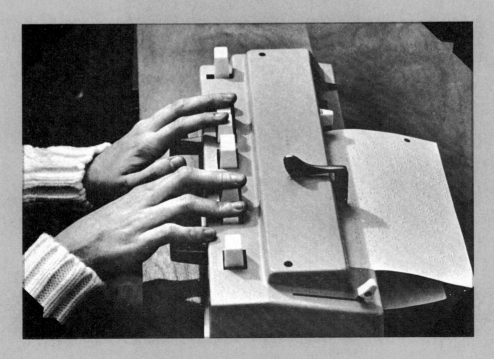

Danielle says, "Ah-ah w-w-want Mom-ee!"

Connie scoops Danielle up and rocks her gently in her arms. "It's all right, baby. It's all right," she whispers. "I understand how you feel. I know today is hard for you, but it will get better, honest it will."

Danielle begins to feel better. She snuggles tiredly into Connie's arms.

At night, after a long day of students and their problems, Connie needs to be alone. She goes to her room to relax and think. That evening Connie sits at her desk typing a braille letter to a friend. Connie writes to many people she has met over the years. She sends typewritten letters to her sighted friends. Her blind friends get braille letters or cassette tapes.

Tonight, she is punching out a letter on her braille writing machine. While this machine is far less complicated to use than a typewriter, it can do everything in braille that a typewriter can in type. By pressing a given combination of keys, Connie can make any raised-dot pattern she needs. She can make letters, numbers, or punctuation marks. Braille paper comes in stiff sheets. This paper can withstand the pounding it gets from the machine and keep a solid, raised pattern.

When the letter is done, Connie folds the sheet in half. She tapes the open ends together. She types the name and address on one side with a regular typewriter. Then she sticks on a stamp.

At last Connie gets out her guitar. She begins to sing. Connie has a lovely voice. A year ago, she taught herself to play the guitar with the help of braille books. Connie ends her day with some of her favorite songs.

If you would like to find out more about Connie and Blythe, read Connie's New Eyes *by Bernard Wolf.*

1. What are Connie's new eyes?

2. Where does Connie work? What does she do there?

3. How does Blythe help Connie?

4. Why must Connie's students answer her questions out loud?

5. Why did Connie cut out pieces of felt in different shapes? Why weren't the pieces all the same shape?

6. How is being in Connie's class the same as being in a sighted teacher's class? How is it different?

7. In what ways is the Big Room a special challenge for Connie?

8. How does Danielle feel on her first day of school? Why? How does she feel after Connie talks to her?

9. Why do you think Connie needs time alone at the end of the day?

10. Would you like to be a teacher? Why or why not?

Dogs and Weather

I'd like a different dog
  For every kind of weather—
A narrow greyhound for a fog,
  A wolfhound strange and white,
With a tail like a silver feather
  To run with in the night,
  When snow is still, and winter stars are bright.

In the fall I'd like to see
   In answer to my whistle,
A golden spaniel look at me.
   But best of all for rain
   A terrier, hairy as a thistle,
      To trot with fine disdain
      Beside me down the soaked, sweet-smelling lane.

Winifred Welles

ANIMALS
ON THE
SCENT

You know that you have five senses. You can see, hear, taste, touch, and smell. Animals, too, have senses. Not all animals have the same five senses that people have. But many animals do have the sense of smell.

Physical Senses and Chemical Senses

Scientists speak of two kinds of senses. *Physical senses* are touch, hearing, and sight. Smell and taste are called the *chemical senses*. Your chemical senses work only when the particles of a substance reach you. When you smell something, those particles come to you in the air. When you taste, your tongue touches the particles.

For some animals, taste and smell are the same thing. These animals are said to have a taste-smell sense. Jellyfish and starfish are two such animals.

The Sense of Smell

How is it that you are able to smell things? Far up inside your nose is a small membrane. When you breathe, air comes into your nose. As it goes up, the air passes your smelling membrane. A few very tiny particles of things stick to the membrane.

A nerve goes from your smelling membrane to your brain. As particles touch the membrane, there is a chemical reaction. Small electric currents go along the nerve to your brain. Your brain sorts them out. You smell something!

What do you do when you want to smell something better? You sniff. Why? Sniffing pulls more air into your nose. With more air, more particles come in, too. That makes the smell stronger.

In animals, the sense of smell works in somewhat the same way. Of course, not all animals have noses!

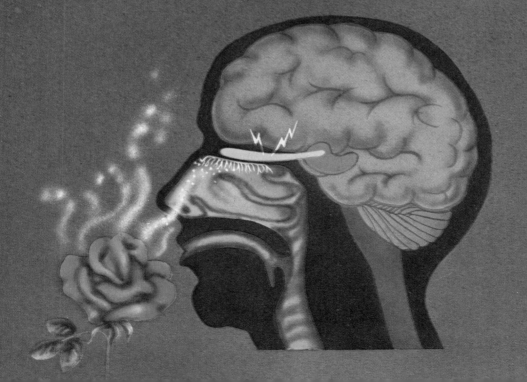

Some animals are called smell-animals. Why do you think this is? For these animals, the sense of smell is the strongest sense. They can pick out more and fainter scents than people can. And their sense of smell does not get tired as fast as people's.

The dog is a smell-animal. To get some idea of how strong a dog's sense of smell is, think about this. If a human's smelling membrane were laid out flat, it would be about the size of the stamp you put on a letter. If a dog's membrane were flattened out, it would be around forty times bigger! That's the size of a handkerchief. How can such a large membrane fit inside a dog's small nose? It is folded up many times within the nose. Think of how much better a dog can smell than a person can!

Which animal has the best sense of smell? No one can say for sure. But with its huge nose, or trunk, the elephant must be one of the champion smellers. An elephant can smell a person a mile away if the wind is right.

Which animal has the poorest sense of smell? This may surprise you. Whales, dolphins, and porpoises have no sense of smell at all!

Insects and Spiders

Insects smell and taste, or taste-smell, with their antennae. Some insects can smell much better than a human can, or even an elephant.

One sort of wasp can smell another of its kind through two inches of wood. A male moth can find the female of his kind up to seven miles away. He does this just by the scent.

Ants use the sense of smell to recognize friends as well as enemies. They can tell who belongs in their nest and who does not. If an ant is washed free of its home scent, its own relatives will kill it. Without the smell, they can no longer tell who the "stranger" is.

You may have seen ants following a smell trail back to their nest. Scientists have found out that, even blindfolded, ants can find their way back to the nest. (Can you picture a blindfolded ant?) If a person rubs a finger across an ant trail, the ants stop. They run around, all mixed up. Either the smell trail is broken or a human scent has been added to it. Whatever the case, the ants cannot go on until they find the smell again.

Spiders have an odd way of smelling. They do it partly with their "feet." In fact, spiders don't have real feet. They do, however, seem to have smell organs on the tips of their first four legs.

Fish

Fish smell things underwater. They use their nostrils only for smelling. (Fish breathe through their gills.) Fish have a sharp sense of smell.

If minnows smell another minnow that has been hurt, they swim away. They stay safely away for days. Sharks are known for being able to smell things from a long way off. That's part of what makes them so dangerous. If a shark smells the hurt minnow, the other minnows don't want to be nearby when the shark arrives to feed.

The salmon may be the best smeller of all. During their growing-up years, salmon live in the sea. But when it comes time to lay their eggs, the salmon always go back to the stream where they were hatched. This can be a swim of hundreds of miles. How do they find their way? Scientists think the salmon can tell their home stream by the smell.

Birds

Most birds do not have much of a sense of smell. They do not need it. Birds depend more on seeing than on smelling, since they spend so much time in the air.

Some water birds, however, have a fairly good smelling sense. The duck is one such bird.

The kiwi, a bird of New Zealand, has its nostrils on the tip of its bill. It cannot fly, nor can it see well. It does seem to be able to smell, though. It eats worms that it gets out of the ground. It probably finds the worms by smelling them.

Reptiles

Not much is known about most reptiles' sense of smell. Something is known, however, about how a snake smells.

Some people are afraid of the flicking tongue of a snake. They think it is some kind of weapon. It's not. The tongue of a snake is a tool that helps it smell.

The snake uses its tongue together with two special organs in the roof of its mouth. These are called *Jacobson's organs.* First the snake's tongue shoots out. It takes samples from the air. Then it goes back into the snake's mouth. One of the two branches of the forked tongue goes into each Jacobson's organ. This is how the snake smells things.

Mammals

In general, the mammals with the longest noses are the best smellers. The elephant is a good example.

Mammals use their noses in different ways for different reasons. You may have noticed that a horse likes to sniff over new things: a new stall, a new saddle, or a new person. For the horse, this sniffing means "getting to know you." It makes the horse feel better about a strange person or place.

The sense of smell serves animals in many different ways. Some herds of cattle are said to be able to smell water from thirty miles away. At sea, animals can smell land long before any human can see it.

People have trained some mammals to use their sense of smell to help humans. Dogs—such as bloodhounds and Saint Bernards—are sometimes used to follow the scents of missing people. Pigs and goats have been used to sniff out truffles. (Truffles are plants, something like mushrooms, that grow underground and are good to eat.) The list of mammals goes on and on.

One of the most interesting things about animals is that some of them can keep many different scents straight in their minds. How? It must be like a person being able to pick one color out of many others. For some animals, the world must be a colorful feast of scents.

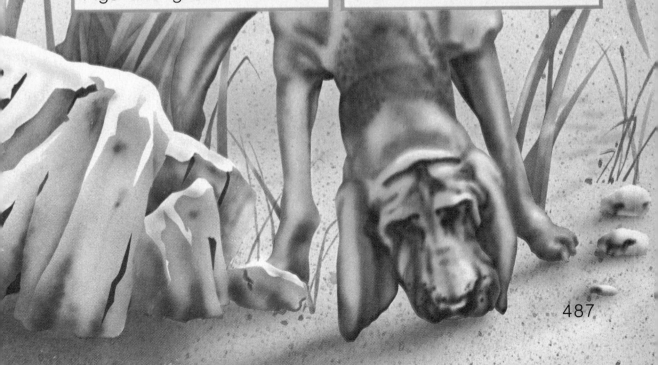

1. Do all animals have a sense of smell? Explain.

2. What are the physical senses? What are the chemical senses?

3. Tell how the sense of smell works in humans.

4. Why are some animals called smell-animals? Give an example of this kind of animal.

5. What part of the body works for an insect in the same manner that the smelling membrane works for a person?

6. Why will an ant sometimes be killed by its own relatives?

7. Why is the sense of smell not important to most birds?

8. How can an animal's sense of smell help humans? Give two examples.

9. Which facts in this article seemed to you the most interesting? the most unusual? Why?

10. What scents are part of your daily life at school? at home?

MEET THE AUTHOR
Eleanor Estes

Fans of the Moffat and Pye families know and love the town of Cranbury. The children in Eleanor Estes' books live in a pretty, small town. It's a perfect place in which to grow up. And who should know better than Eleanor Estes? She herself once lived there!

In real life, Cranbury is West Haven, Connecticut. Eleanor Estes was born and raised in West Haven in the early 1900's. Like the children in her stories, Eleanor could go to the harbor and swim, dig for clams, or go out in a rowboat.

Young Eleanor went to school in West Haven. For the first few years she went to a small wooden schoolhouse. Readers of The Moffats will recognize that building. After that, Eleanor went to a brick school with ivy-covered walls. It's the same school that Ginger Pye visits in the chapter you are about to read.

When Eleanor Estes grew up, she left West Haven. After several years as a children's librarian in Connecticut, she came to New York. There she went to school to learn more about library work. While a student, she met and married Rice Estes.

She then worked in children's rooms in the New York library system. She says, "I left because I became a writer—at last!" In 1940 her first book, The Moffats, was published.

Mrs. Estes can hardly remember a time when she did not wish to be a writer. Both her mother and her father loved books. Her parents' love of words had a strong effect on Eleanor.

After The Moffats, *Eleanor Estes wrote a number of other books. For many years children have read and loved* The Hundred Dresses, Rufus M., The Witch Family, *and others. One book,* Ginger Pye, *won the Newbery Award in 1952.*

Mrs. Estes says she doesn't really know where her ideas come from. Most of them grow out of childhood memories. She likes to feel that she is holding a mirror up to childhood. She wants "to make children laugh or cry, to be moved in some way."

When she is not writing, Eleanor Estes likes to draw and paint. She also likes to just sit by the ocean and do nothing. But with all the books she writes, Mrs. Estes says that she has "little time to develop this hobby!"

GINGER PYE

Part One

Ginger Pye was a very happy dog. The only enemy he knew he had was an enemy dog.

The enemy dog lived in the tall pier glass mirror, at least that was where Ginger first saw him—the tall pier glass mirror that stood between two windows in the horsehair parlor. This mirror had been a wedding present to the Pyes, and the three large vases that stood in its marble base were also wedding presents. One day Ginger was reaching up for his orange duster that happened to be lying on the marble base, and it was then that he made his amazing discovery.

There was another dog in this house, and he was in the shiny mirror! Yet, all along, Ginger had thought he was the only dog in this house.

Ginger Pye gave this new dog a friendly woof, for he did not realize all in a second that this was his enemy dog that was going to torment him and stay in shiny places. The dog gave Ginger a friendly woof too, only Ginger couldn't hear it. Ginger Pye then barked loudly at the new dog, and the new dog barked back at Ginger, only still he made no sound. His woofing and his barking were silent and, because of this, rather exasperating.

Ginger made a dash for the dog in the mirror, and the dog in the mirror made a dash for Ginger. They growled at each other, Ginger in his loud fashion and the new dog in his silent fashion. Their noses were plastered right close together, so close Ginger couldn't even see the other dog anymore. But the cowardly dog stayed inside where he was good and safe, and he wouldn't come out. It was infuriating and it made Ginger Pye frantic.

It was then that Ginger realized that this dog in the mirror was an enemy dog and not a friendly companion.

Moreover, it turned out that the dog did not stay inside his pier glass mirror after all. He cropped up in other places—in other mirrors, in the windowpanes, even in Ginger's own eating pan, eating up Ginger's dinner. And outside the house, he might be met up with too. For he was also a water dog, staying in puddles, the reservoir, and the harbor.

Once Jerry and Rachel took Ginger for a walk over to Gramma's. They went by way of the shore instead of the street, and it was a most interesting excursion. The tide was low. Periwinkles and horseshoe crabs lay on the beaches, and clams were spouting here and there in the wet mud of low tide. The children crawled under every little red boathouse, smelling the wonderful stale sea smells there. They walked out on every wobbly little wooden pier. And everywhere Ginger delightedly frisked ahead of them.

It went to Ginger's head to be with Jerry and Rachel on such an unusual expedition. He picked up dry chunks of wood for them to throw, and he tried to nudge the horseshoe crabs into getting a move on. He had no thought of the enemy dog. He was a carefree, happy dog, and he was always

the first one out to the end of the little piers. There he barked at the water endlessly stretching, at the sky, the singing gulls, the bobbing buoys.

At the end of one weather-beaten shaky old pier to which a little boat was tied and placidly rocking, Ginger happened, for the first time, to look straight down into the queer green water. And there, looking up at him, was his enemy, the dog!

Now Ginger was the dog of Jerry Pye. The enemy dog was not. Yet here he was, right here in the green-blue sea. Apparently he had tagged along, sneakily, all the way, hoping to become the dog of Jerry Pye. These were Ginger's thoughts as he dived into the water, with Jerry and Rachel shouting earnest instructions to him from above. Ginger had never before been in such deep water and could he swim, they wanted to know.

"Ginger, can you swim?" yelled Rachel.

"Of course he can," said Jerry. "Look at him. Swims like he's swum all his life."

It was true. Ginger could swim, and he managed to get back to dry land in a very accomplished and intense fashion. He felt refreshed from his brisk saltwater swim, and he rolled happily over and over in the warm sand.

"He's always thinking that he himself in mirrors and water is his enemy," laughed Rachel.

Ginger did not happen to have any further encounters with the enemy dog on that trip. He enjoyed a pleasant relaxed afternoon with Uncle Bennie and Jerry and Rachel, and he chased Gramma's chickens, getting a pecking or two. He tasted Gramma's homemade peach ice cream, spitting out the hard cold lumps of peach as Rachel and Jerry were doing, likewise. He really never expected to see the enemy dog again, having jumped on him in the water that way, scaring him out of his wits.

But of course, he did. When he got home, the enemy dog was right there again, in the tall pier glass mirror, tongue hanging out thirstily, ears drooping tiredly. Secretly Ginger was glad to have the other dog back so that he would have him handy for future bouts when life at home, without Jerry and Rachel, became too tame.

Soon after this wonderful expedition along the shore, however, Ginger began to suspect that the enemy dog was himself. He gave up pursuit of him in preference to the pursuit of cats. Cats certainly did not stay inside shiny things, and they really

came out to fight. They were a more satisfactory type of enemy than the enemy dog had been.

For a time Ginger had been kept in the backyard unless he was with some person. Now, however, he was allowed in either the front or the backyard. It was impossible to keep Ginger from slipping out of the house with Gracie-the-cat anyway, for Gracie had the knack of opening the front door by leaping up and undoing the latch.

So Ginger now had the run of the land. Naturally, he preferred the front to the back of the house. From the front he could survey the entire neighborhood, get into other yards besides his own, and chase all the cats.

497

There was a matter that had begun to bother Ginger, however, and it had nothing to do with cats or the enemy dog. It was this. Where did Jerry disappear every morning and afternoon with his tiresome, "Go home, Ginger!" And Rachel, too. Where did they go?

Ginger's feelings were hurt, being deserted this way, even though Jerry patted him and gave him fond scratches behind the ear and such attentions before tearing out the front door.

"Where could he go, anyway?" puzzled Ginger. Today he intended to find out. Ginger was a purposeful dog. Once he had decided to do something, he did it, provided he was not obstructed by some person. Now was the time, he felt, to investigate the constant goings away and comings back of Jerry and Rachel Pye. They had something to do with the goings past the house and the returnings past the house, twice a day, of all the boys and girls in Cranbury, practically. Wherever they all went, it might possibly be more fun than chasing cats, more fun, even, than going up to the reservoir.

At this moment Ginger happened to be lying opposite the tall pier glass mirror surveying himself with a thoughtful planning look. He arose,

stretched, and gave himself a challenging yap for
old time's sake. He made a dash for Gracie-the-cat,
leaped over her imploring crouching form, and
went into the kitchen. After a few laps of water he
looked around for something of Jerry's to smell, to
get the scent well-fixed in his scent department.

He found Jerry's sweater slung over the back of
a kitchen chair, and he pulled it to the floor and
thrust his nose in its folds. Thoughtfully and
earnestly he breathed in the essence of Jerry until it
permeated his entire being, down to his toes and
the tip of his short tail. His heart thumped with
delight and he thought excitedly, now, now, he
was going to find Jerry. "Jerry, Jerry, Jerry," his
heart sang.

Of course Ginger knew the Jerry smell perfectly without having to rely on Jerry's old sweater. But this was to be his first experience at real hard trailing. It could not be compared with the easy following of the fresh trail of a dog, a cat, a chicken, or a chipmunk. Jerry had left some time ago. This meant a real hard trailing job, and Ginger did not want to fail.

The first rule in trailing was, get the smell thoroughly inside himself. The next was, nose to ground. He had the smell. So now, nose to ground. He pushed his nose along the floor to the front door and paused, for the moment, stalled.

Fortunately, just then Gracie-the-cat decided to go outdoors herself. She leaped in the air in her own smart fashion and sprung open the latch. Then she and Ginger Pye went outside, leaving the door open behind them. And there Ginger Pye was, on his front lawn, surveying the scene.

At this moment, who should be coming home from the grocery store, her arms filled with bags

and bundles, her face stern, as stern as her gentle face could get, but Mrs. Pye.

"Ginger," said Mrs. Pye. "Where are you going? You are not to chase Mrs. Carruthers' cat anymore. And there has been a complaint that you chased a chicken. Mrs. Finney told me in the grocery store. If you keep up this outrageous behavior, you shall have to stay on the leash!"

Leash! Hated hateful word. Ginger shuddered. The leash was coiled like a snake on the stoop right now. It was an awful thing to have on the neck. Ginger had suspected it was awful, and he was wary of it the first time Jerry fastened it on. But he had not imagined, no dog could possibly imagine, how very awful, how completely horrible, a leash was, until he had one on.

When he had the leash on, Ginger would struggle and struggle to get it off, pawing at it, shaking his head wildly, and showing the whites of his eyes. And if, forgetting for a moment he had the dreadful thing on, he made a dash for the Carruthers' cat, wham! The leash would nearly break his neck and down he would fall, gasping and rolling on the sidewalk. Jerry's concern over him would be pleasant, but that was all that was pleasant about the leash.

"Aw, Ginger," Jerry would say. "You mustn't tug at the leash so."

Whenever Ginger saw the leash coming, he would cower and quiver, hoping Jerry would change his mind and put it, perhaps, on Gracie instead. But Jerry would say, "Now come on, Ginger. You've got to learn to walk nicely on the leash." Ginger merely strained the harder, and struggled and tugged and chortled and gasped and dragged Jerry along.

"Walk nicely, Ginger," pleaded Jerry. And he would point out other dogs that pranced along neatly at the end of their leashes with never a gasp or a choke. The owners of these dogs would walk along in dignity or jauntiness, in an upright position and not in this disgraceful struggling fashion.

"That way, not this way," urged Jerry.

"You must train him," suggested Mama.

"I'm tryin'," said Jerry gloomily. "But he won't walk nicely."

Jerry did try to train Ginger. Nothing did any good, not even bribery. Ginger continued to gasp and choke and drag. Sneeze, he would do for Jerry. Shake hands, he would do for Jerry. Beg, walk on his hind feet, and be dead dog. But walk nicely on the leash? Never.

At last Jerry gave up trying to train him to walk nicely on the leash. He would carry the leash along with him on their excursions, and he would put it on after Ginger had chased a cat or a chicken. *After,* not before.

Soliloquizing in this manner with his nose in the grass, Ginger looked meekly up at Mrs. Pye, who still towered over him with her bags and potatoes and things. He was winning, he thought. Mrs. Pye no longer looked so stern. Her eyes were laughing, in fact. But to assure victory, Ginger cringed. He was not cringing in his heart. But if he presented a humble front, he thought Mrs. Pye would not bother him anymore and he could finish that which he had started to do. And what was that? Chase Mrs. Carruthers' cat? Goodness no. He had almost forgotten. Interruptions were so bad for the game of scent trailing. But he remembered now. He was on the trail of Jerry Pye.

Concealing his impatience, since the leash was still handy, Ginger looked up at Mrs. Pye with what, in the past, he had found to be a winning pose, head to side, tongue dangling out. Mrs. Pye gave him a little pat, spilling out all her potatoes as she did so. Of course Ginger had to help gather these up by making a game of it, nosing them all over the lawn. When finally all the potatoes were recaptured, Mrs. Pye said, "There, there. I didn't mean to be cross, Ginger. But you must be a good dog, do you hear?"

And at last she went into the house leaving Ginger on the front lawn with his nose buried in a patch of thick short grass that was just covered with Jerry scent. Jerry must have dropped his books here, or something. Ginger decided he'd better be on the trail before Mrs. Pye again thought of putting the hated leash on him, or of giving him a bath, or a brushing. So. Now. Nose to ground.

Part Two

Leaving his own yard and going on past Dick
Badger's, it was easy enough to follow the Jerry
scent. Ginger pasted his nose to that scent. It led
past the Carruthers' house. Actually, without
sniffing so hard, Ginger knew this was the direction
Jerry had taken because he could always see him
this far. However, in trailing, a dog has to sniff and
snort furiously because that is the way it is done.
He kept his nose plastered to the ground. He was
concentrating so hard that his whole face was
pushed in and wrinkled up. It looked as though he
were pushing his nose up the street in front of him.
He kept getting sand up his nose, and he had to
wheeze it out of himself in long deep exhalings.
This was hard work, but it was wonderful work. It
was apparent he was born to be a regular trail
hound even though he was mostly fox terrier.

At a certain point, going through a small field, the scent led Ginger to a little crabapple tree. He stood on his hind legs and inhaled the scent as far up the tree as he could thrust his nose. Jerry had been up this tree, but he certainly was no longer there, for, of course, there would be a much keener scent if he were. The quest was by no means over.

Ginger remained poised there against the tree in contemplation. Jerry's going up the tree might be what was known as a decoy. Decoys were difficult, though not impossible, to outwit. For instance, the person a dog was trailing might leap from treetop to treetop. A dog had to work doubly hard and might have to explore in every direction before finding the trail again. But then, that is all part of tracking, Ginger thought.

Ginger wagged his tail in appreciation of his master's cleverness, and he keenly anticipated matching his wits against Jerry's. No doubt, Jerry had suspected that Ginger would try to trail him. So, up the tree he had gone to throw Ginger off his tracks.

Thus Ginger analyzed the difficult situation before leaping down. He then began spiritedly to go round and round the tree in ever-widening circles. By the time he was ten doglengths away from the tree, his nose picked up the scent again. And the decoy was over.

Apparently Jerry had swung out of the tree on a limber branch and had landed way over here on all fours. Here, also, was one of Jerry's pencils with Ginger's tooth marks on it as well as Jerry's own. Jerry had then proceeded in the same direction as before the tree decoy. This Ginger did likewise, with the pencil in his mouth.

The pencil made trailing considerably more difficult than hitherto, if not well-nigh impossible. In the end, Ginger had to drop the pencil, find the trail, go back for the pencil, and bring it to the farthest point of trailing. Of course he could not abandon the pencil. The going, therefore, was slower now, not only because of the complication of the pencil, but also because suddenly there seemed to be a very great many more smells to weed out before locating Jerry's.

Sniff, sniff here. Snort and blow there. A great, great many feet had passed this way, and Ginger lost the trail. He just followed the lead of all those feet, and at last he paused to take his bearings. He looked about him. He had come through the wide open gate of a tall brown wooden fence, and here he was, in an enormous yard, half pavement and half worn-down grass. He lay down on a little patch of this grass close to a big brick building. His nose stung and his neck ached from the long push and hard concentration. The pencil lay safely between his paws. He licked his tongue over his dry nose until it became moist and cool again, and he studied the building before him.

The building was big, hard, and brick. If this was where Jerry came every day and spent his time, Ginger was no longer envious. Why come here, though? Why come here when he and Jerry could tramp up Shingle Hill or tear through the woods around the reservoir picking up acorns and finding frogs? Still, inside might be pleasanter than outside, and Ginger toured the building to find a way in.

All doors were closed. All Ginger could do now was to sit and wait for Jerry to come out. Imagine Jerry's pleasure when he saw his faithful dog

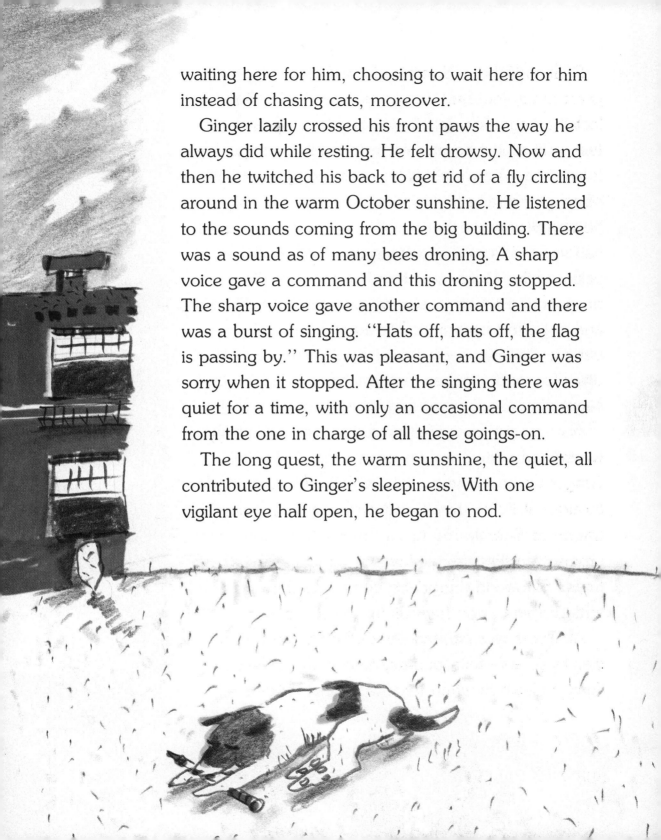

waiting here for him, choosing to wait here for him instead of chasing cats, moreover.

Ginger lazily crossed his front paws the way he always did while resting. He felt drowsy. Now and then he twitched his back to get rid of a fly circling around in the warm October sunshine. He listened to the sounds coming from the big building. There was a sound as of many bees droning. A sharp voice gave a command and this droning stopped. The sharp voice gave another command and there was a burst of singing. "Hats off, hats off, the flag is passing by." This was pleasant, and Ginger was sorry when it stopped. After the singing there was quiet for a time, with only an occasional command from the one in charge of all these goings-on.

The long quest, the warm sunshine, the quiet, all contributed to Ginger's sleepiness. With one vigilant eye half open, he began to nod.

Then—was he dreaming? He heard Jerry's voice. Jerry's voice was loud and clear and all by itself. Ginger sat up. His tail began uncertainly to wag. Then it wagged uncontrollably, for he was not dreaming. Jerry's voice was coming loud and clear from one of the high windows. Jerry was not using his regular voice that he used with Ginger or with any of the Pyes. He was using a high and loud and clear voice. But it was Jerry's voice, even so.

Ginger listened in a transport of delight. Then he gave a short bark announcing, if Jerry cared to know, that he, Ginger, was right out here. Not only was he out here, he would manage to get to Jerry somehow, so there would be no more separation.

Ginger no longer felt tired. He tore around the building barking and wagging not only his tail, wagging his whole body. He was looking again for a way in. All entrances were closed. He came back and longingly stared up at the window from which he judged Jerry's voice was coming. Jerry was still talking, though the one in command kept interrupting.

There was a perilous-looking iron stairway leading up to the open window through which

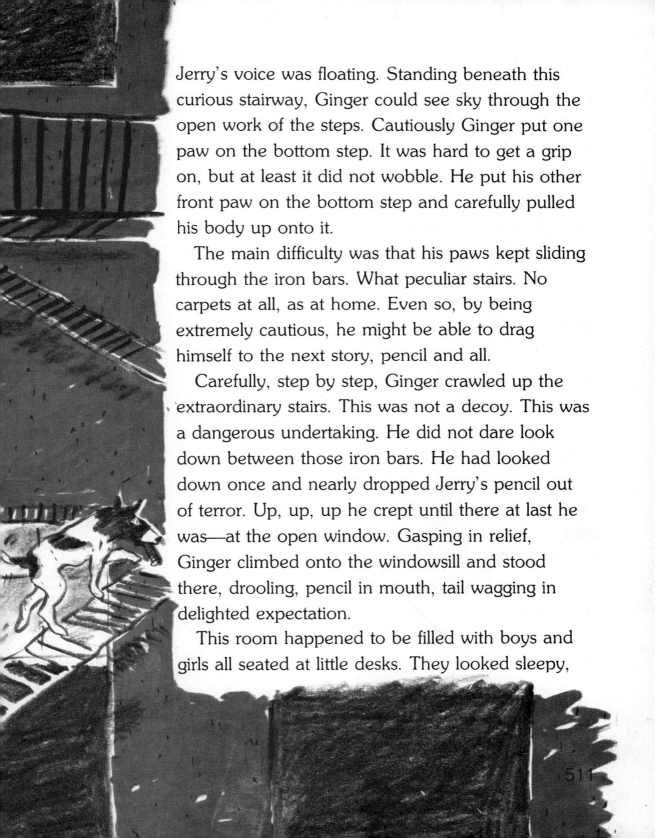

Jerry's voice was floating. Standing beneath this curious stairway, Ginger could see sky through the open work of the steps. Cautiously Ginger put one paw on the bottom step. It was hard to get a grip on, but at least it did not wobble. He put his other front paw on the bottom step and carefully pulled his body up onto it.

The main difficulty was that his paws kept sliding through the iron bars. What peculiar stairs. No carpets at all, as at home. Even so, by being extremely cautious, he might be able to drag himself to the next story, pencil and all.

Carefully, step by step, Ginger crawled up the extraordinary stairs. This was not a decoy. This was a dangerous undertaking. He did not dare look down between those iron bars. He had looked down once and nearly dropped Jerry's pencil out of terror. Up, up, up he crept until there at last he was—at the open window. Gasping in relief, Ginger climbed onto the windowsill and stood there, drooling, pencil in mouth, tail wagging in delighted expectation.

This room happened to be filled with boys and girls all seated at little desks. They looked sleepy,

511

and the place did not seem anywhere near as enticing as up at the reservoir. But anyway, there was Jerry, standing by his seat, his voice coming out clear and high and loud again.

The teacher issued a command. "Read it again, Jerry, more distinctly, and pay more attention to your final g's."

"My dog, Ginger," read Jerry Pye, and he cleared his throat.

Well. When Ginger heard Jerry say his name, he let out one short yelp of greeting. Ginger! "Yes, here I am, right here, Jerry," was what his bark

meant. Of course he dropped Jerry's pencil, but fortunately it dropped on the windowsill and not down below. Ginger quickly picked it up again and held it triumphantly in his mouth.

The minute Ginger let out that little yelp of greeting, what a hullabaloo came over the place. The person in command clapped her hands but no one paid any attention to her. Jerry dropped the paper he was holding, and for a moment he stared at Ginger, too stunned for words or action. Then he rushed to the window and patted his dog to make him feel at home.

Ginger jumped into the room, dropped Jerry's pencil at his feet, and looked up at Jerry. He was inviting him to throw it so that he could run after it and bring it back, the way they played the rock game at home, or ball, or stick.

Jerry picked up his pencil. "He even found my pencil I lost on the way to school this morning," he said in greater astonishment than ever. "What a smart dog!"

"Your dog?" asked Oliver Peacock in admiration.

"Yes," said Jerry proudly. "My dog. Trailed me all the way here."

"The dog brought a pencil with him because it's school," said one girl.

"Whew!" whistled Oliver Peacock.

Ginger wagged his tail and looked as though he were laughing, the way he always did when he understood that pleasant things were being spoken of him. He licked Jerry's hand. So. Here he was! It was not much of a place but if Jerry could put up with it, so could he. He trotted around the room, his toenails making a pitter-patter. He smelled here and sniffed there. In one corner by a cupboard he kept his nose glued for some time. There was a possibility of mice there.

He detoured around the tall person who was still clapping and giving orders.

Suddenly the tall one brought her hand down on her desk with a loud bang.

"Quiet!"

The hullabaloo stopped short then. This was a welcome relief to Ginger, who did not see how Jerry stood this sort of noisy life. His ears hurt him.

"Jared Pye!" the tall one said. "Either take your dog home or make him lie down under your desk until dismissal time. And Jared," she added, "see that this disgraceful performance is not repeated, or I shall have to report you to Mr. Pennypepper."

"Come here, Ginger," said Jerry. As though he could help it, he thought, if the dog he owned happened to be so smart he could trail him all the way to school. You would think the teacher could see that, wouldn't you? he asked himself. "Come here, pup," he urged.

Ginger recognized the pleading note in Jerry's voice and pattered over to him, for he wanted nothing to do with the tall one.

"Lie down, Ginger," begged Jerry.

Being awfully tired, Ginger was happy to lie down. He licked his nose with loud smacking noises and washed himself all over. He was right under Jerry's desk, and every now and then Jerry gave him a nice pat with his foot.

There was complete silence now except for Ginger's loud paw licking. In this quiet Ginger stopped licking himself. With a contented sigh he slipped into a thoughtful doze. He scarcely did more than twitch his ears when, from another room, he heard some more of the droning, as of bees, that he had heard outside. Now he could hear what the droning was saying, though.

C-A-T cat. Apparently the boys and girls were being instructed in the best way to manage these creatures. As for Ginger, he was too tired to listen and, besides, he knew the best way to handle them. As though one had to come to a place like this to learn such things.

1. Who was the enemy dog? Where did Ginger see him?

2. To whom did Ginger belong? Tell about the other members of the Pye family.

3. Why did Ginger wonder where Jerry and Rachel went every morning and afternoon?

4. How did Ginger feel about the leash? Why do you suppose he felt this way?

5. What were Ginger's rules for trailing? Explain how Ginger traced Jerry.

6. Why did Ginger almost lose the trail near the big, hard, brick building? What was this building?

7. How did each of the following feel about Ginger's appearance in the classroom: Jerry? the teacher? the other children?

8. What did Ginger think of the spelling lesson? Do you think he really understood what was going on? Why or why not?

9. Suppose dogs really did have to go to school every day. Who do you think should teach them? What sorts of things should the dogs learn?

WRITE AND READ ABOUT IT

ONE ———————————————————————

Encyclopedia Brown Solves a Case, 14–23

✎ Like all good detectives, Encyclopedia Brown used details to solve his case. Encyclopedia noticed that Bugs's arms and wrists were smoothly tanned. Therefore, the watch could not have been stolen from him.

Details are important to writers, too. Writers use details to describe people and things. Details help make a description clear and interesting. How good are you at using details? Describe an object such as your favorite food, a U.S. penny, or your hand. Write four sentences that tell exactly what the object looks like.

▭ *Encyclopedia Brown Tracks Them Down* by Donald J. Sobol (Elsevier/Nelson Books). In this story, you will get a chance to use details to solve a case.

The Fun They Had, 24–33

✎ "The Fun They Had" is a science fiction story. Science fiction tells how science can change the way people live. For example, Margie and Tommy had machines for books and teachers.

Pretend you live in the year 2155. Use your imagination to describe a normal day in your life. Tell what your home looks like. Describe how you get from place to place. Tell about the kinds of jobs your parents and their friends have. Name the games you play with your friends. Remember, you are writing science fiction. Be sure to describe the inventions that are around you. Also tell how new discoveries in science have changed the way you live.

📖 *The Mind Angel and Other Stories* by Michael Orgill (Lerner Publications Company). If you like starships, space monsters, and amazing machinery, this book is for you.

Play Soccer, 34–40

✎ "Play Soccer" gives directions for how to play this game. Could you follow these directions?

When writing directions, remember the following guidelines. Directions should be clear and simple. They should be easy to understand. They should be written in their correct order. That way, the directions will be easy to follow.

What games do you like to play? Choose a simple game like tag or hide-and-seek. Write directions that tell how to play this game. Be sure to write complete sentences. Pretend that a person who has never played this game will read your directions. That person will have to follow your directions to learn the game.

📖 *Games (and How to Play Them)* by Anne Rockwell (Harper and Row Publishers, Inc.). This is a book you not only can read but also can play with!

Odd Jobs, 41–48

✎ Help Wanted advertisements are found in most newspapers. Each advertisement describes a job. It tells the skills or experience a person must have to get the job. For example, a major league baseball team might put an ad like this in a newspaper:

WANTED: Ballboy or ballgirl for major league baseball team. Must be able to work evenings and on weekends. We are looking for a person who loves baseball and knows the rules of the game. The right person will also be able to field baseballs. We supply the uniform, but you'll need your own glove.

What kind of job would you like to get? Write a Help Wanted ad that describes the job of your choice. Be sure to tell the skills and experience a person needs to get this job.

☐ *Night People: Workers from Dusk to Dawn* by C. B. Colby (Coward, McCann, & Geoghegan, Inc.). Read about the thousands of people who work while everyone else is asleep.

The Girl Who Saved the Train, 52–61

✎ Stories can be told from different points of view. "The Girl Who Saved the Train" is told by someone who is *not* a character in the story. Many times, however, adventure stories are told in the first person. That means that someone who is in the story tells what happens.

Rewrite a section of "The Girl Who Saved the Train" in the first person. Pretend you are the person described in one of these paragraphs:

(1) You are a railroad worker who has fallen into Honey Creek. You are hanging from a branch of a tree, barely able to stay above water. Up above you, you see Kate Shelley. You warn her that the bridge is too dangerous to cross.
(2) You are Kate Shelley. You are in the middle of the bridge, and your lantern has just gone out. Tell how you feel as you crawl across the wet and slippery rails.

📖 *How to Run a Railroad: Everything You Need to Know About Model Trains* by Harvey Weiss (Harper & Row Publishers, Inc.). It doesn't take much to start a model railroad, which can turn into the hobby of a lifetime.

Mr. and Mrs. Juicy-O, 62–77

✎ In the story "Mr. and Mrs. Juicy-O," Peter's father worked for an advertising agency. The agency made up ads that helped the Juicy-O Company sell juice. Perhaps Mr. Hatcher made up jingles like this:

When you're hot and thirsty,
And you need a rest,
Drink Juicy-O and ice—
It's the very best!

Or Mr. Hatcher may have written a more serious advertisement:

All over America, people who know juice are drinking Juicy-O! Its natural fruit goodness and unbeatable taste are a winning combination!

Try writing a jingle and/or an advertisement for Juicy-O. Remember that advertisements should persuade. Use words that will make people want to buy Juicy-O.

📖 *Otherwise Known as Sheila the Great* by Judy Blume (Dell Publishing Company, Inc.). If you enjoyed reading about Peter Hatcher, you'll probably want to get to know ten-year-old Sheila.

—————————————————————————— **TWO**

Rococo Skates, 80–93

✏️Pretend you are a reporter for a newspaper. You have been asked to write a story about how

Mary Ann discovered that a painting had been stolen. To do this, you go to the museum. There you talk with the director, who tells you the whole story. You also talk with Mary Ann, Frances, and Ms. Ryan.

First, give your story a title, or headline. Then, write the opening, or lead, paragraph. The lead paragraph should answer the *Wh* questions—Who, What, Where, When, and Why. The next paragraphs should give more details. You can also include some quotes in the story. For this story, the quotes would be the exact words of the director, Ms. Ryan, Mary Ann, and Frances. You might want to finish the story by telling about Mary Ann's reward—the rococo skates.

Roller Skate Mania by Edward Radlauer (Children's Press). Read this book for a short colorful look at everything you could ever want to do on roller skates.

7 Silly Simons, 97–107

"7 Silly Simons" is a humorous play. One reason is that the Simons do not understand what figures of speech mean. A *figure of speech* is a colorful phrase that says one thing but means something else that is quite different. When Susie Simon says, "It's time to hit the road," she means that it is time to start walking. The Simons, however, hit the road with their hands.

Read the following figures of speech. Tell what you think the Silly Simons will do when Susie uses them. Write what happens in play form.

1. "This math problem is *over my head*," said Susie.
2. "I'm still *up in the air* about whether to go to the party," said Susie.
3. "We'll be *in hot water* if we don't get home soon," Susie added.

📖 *Soup with Quackers* by Mike Thaler (Franklin Watts, Inc.). You can read dozens of riddles in *Soup with Quackers* (the noisiest way to eat soup).

Two Months from Alice Yazzie's Year, 108–117
✎ This poem tells a story in a special way. The poet used colorful words and ideas to tell what happened to Alice during the year. She used short sentences and phrases. She started a new line whenever she wanted to.

You can write a poem like Alice Yazzie's. Think about something interesting or special that you have done this year. In what month did you do it? What else did you do that month? Tell about the month and its events in a poem. Use the same poem form that this poet used. Like this poet, you should try to describe nature and the weather in your poem. Be sure to use colorful words and ideas, too. The name of your poem should be the name of the month you write about.

⌒ *Hawk, I'm Your Brother* by Byrd Baylor (Charles Scribner's Sons). Rudy Soto is an American Indian who finds and tames a hawk as part of his dream to learn how to fly.

A Chimp Learns to "Talk," 118–125

✎ The chimp Washoe learned to talk with her friends, the Gardners. To do this she used Ameslan, the sign language that deaf people use.

The following outline gives information about sign language. Use the information to write a two-paragraph report on sign language. Each paragraph should have a *topic sentence*. The topic sentence is often the first sentence of a paragraph and tells the main idea of the paragraph. Use the information next to the Roman numerals to write topic sentences for your paragraphs. Use the details under each Roman numeral to develop the topic of each paragraph. Be sure to write complete sentences in your paragraphs.

Sign Language

I. Sign language—a substitute for spoken language
   A. Signs patterned after body and face movements that take place during speech
   B. Sign language used in past when people could not speak
      1. Monks pledged to silence
      2. American Indians "talking" to members of other tribes
II. Sign language for the deaf
   A. Developed in France—18th century
   B. Brought to U.S. by Charles Gallaude—1817
   C. Signs—hand movements with meaning
   D. Lipreading not part of sign language, but often taught along with signs
   E. Manual alphabet—holding fingers in ways to represent letters

Apes in Fact and Fiction by Gilda Berger (Franklin Watts, Inc.). Read about King Kong, Tarzan's pet ape, Washoe, and many other apes.

A Voice from Below, 126–135

What would it be like to talk with an animal? Pretend that you know. That's right, pretend that you regularly talk with a bird, a mouse, or a cricket that lives near you. You find your talking friend interesting and funny. Most of all, you like the way it answers your questions. You ask:

1. What makes you feel unhappy?
2. What's the funniest thing you ever saw?
3. If you could change something about this house, what would it be?

Tell how the animal answers some of these questions. Write a conversation with the animal. Be sure to show your exact words and the words of the animal in quotation marks. Begin a new paragraph each time the speaker changes.

Ben and Me by Robert Lawson (Dell Publishing Company, Inc.). Read about one of the most famous talking animals in literature—a mouse who lived with Ben Franklin.

THREE

Moonlight—A Horse with a Mind of His Own, 140–155

When something happens, we usually ask, "Why?" When we ask why, we are looking for a cause. A cause tells why something happens. An effect is what happens.

Each of the following sentences tells the cause of something in the story about Moonlight. Write one sentence that tells an effect of each cause.

1. A fire started in the dairy owned by Juan's parents.
2. Moonlight had once been a wild horse.
3. Dave Plummer kept his calves in a wooden pen that wasn't very strong.

Questions and Answers About Horses by Millicent E. Selsam (Scholastic, Inc.). If you have questions about horses, this book has answers.

The March of the Lemmings, 159–165

There are many different forms of writing, such as plays, stories, poems, and articles. "The March of the Lemmings" is an informational article. Use the information in this article to write a short story about one young lemming. Perhaps the lemming is upset that it has to leave its home and make a long journey. Perhaps it wants to stop and build a new home, rather than go on to the sea.

The Seventeen Gerbils of Class 4-A by William H. Hooks (Coward, McCann, and Geoghegan, Inc.). Gerbils, rodents that are a lot like lemmings, make excellent pets. In this book, you'll see just how good these pets can be.

Phoebe and the General, 168–183

"Phoebe and the General" is historical fiction. The story is based on facts from history. The important story characters—George Washington, Thomas Hickey, and Phoebe Fraunces—really lived. Many events in the story actually took place.

Other events, however, are fictional. The author made them up so that the story would come alive. All the conversations were made up. So were small details, such as Phoebe's chickens being poisoned by the peas. These fictional details make the story more interesting.

You can combine fictional details and facts to write historical fiction. Choose a topic below, or decide on your own topic to write about. First, read about the topic in an encyclopedia or a textbook. Keep a list of the facts you will use. Then make up some details that will help you tell the story. Be sure to include some conversations.

1. Sacagawea leads Lewis and Clark to the Pacific
2. Alexander Graham Bell invents the telephone
3. Harriet Tubman leads slaves to freedom on the Underground Railroad

This Time, Tempe Wick by Patricia Lee Gauch (Coward, McCann, & Geoghegan, Inc.). This book tells the exciting story of how Tempe Wick helped General Washington during the difficult war years.

Beneath the Saddle, 186–199

In "Beneath the Saddle," young Nathan Cathcart performed a brave deed. Because of Nathan's bravery, Dawson, the dispatch rider, could deliver some important papers.

Pretend you are Dawson. You think that Nathan deserves a medal for what he did. So, you write to General Washington. In the letter, you tell the general exactly what happened. Include all the necessary facts. Ask Washington if Nathan can be given a medal. Use words that will persuade the general to do this.

📖 *Hay-Foot, Straw-Foot* by Erick Berry (The Viking Press). Read all about the youngest soldier in the Continental Army.

FOUR

Mr. Business Tycoon, 202–215

✎ Pretend that you live in the same neighborhood as Tony, Mr. Business Tycoon. Tony has asked you to work for him. He says he will find you jobs walking dogs, sweeping sidewalks, and carrying groceries. In return, you are to give him half the money you earn.

Write a short letter to Tony telling him whether or not you will work for him. You can decide either way, but you must give Tony your reasons. Use information from the story "Mr. Business Tycoon" to support your decision.

📖 *Henry Reed's Baby-Sitting Service* by Keith Robertson (Viking Press). Henry Reed tries to be a business tycoon. He soon finds out that it isn't so easy to become rich, especially when the business is baby-sitting!

Spelling Bee Blues, 218–228

✎ A metaphor is an interesting way to describe something. In a metaphor, a word or phrase that means one thing is used to describe another thing. Read this metaphor: The rainbow was a colorful bridge. Two different things—a rainbow and a bridge—are said to be the same. In what ways could a rainbow be like a bridge?

Read the list of things below. What does each remind you of? Use a metaphor to describe each thing. Be sure you write a complete sentence.

    a noisy garbage truck   a delicious dessert
    a difficult math problem   an angry watchdog

📖 *Rice Cakes and Paper Dragons* by Seymour Reit (Dodd, Mead & Company). Read these true stories about Marie Chan, a Chinese-American girl who has the best of both worlds.

Talk, 230–237

✎ "Talk" is a humorous tale about everyday objects that suddenly start talking back to people. Imagine waking up one morning and finding out that the things in your home can talk. First your alarm clock tells you what is on its mind. Then the bathroom sink gets angry at you for the way you brush your teeth. The toaster, refrigerator, and kitchen table also have things to say to you.

Use your imagination to write a short story that describes this unusual morning. Tell what the objects say and how you feel knowing they can talk. Remember, your story should have a beginning, a middle, and an ending.

📖 *Behind the Back of the Mountain: Black Folktales from Southern Africa* by Verna Aardema (Dial Press). This collection of stories gives some amazing explanations for why things are the way they are.

Crash Alert, 238–255

✎ In "Crash Alert," colorful language makes the story come alive. It helps a reader see and feel the action. Look at these two sentences:

Randy was glad to take the spaceship's controls. Randy's heart leaped as he took the spaceship's controls.

The second sentence lets the reader know just how glad Randy really was.

Rewrite each of these sentences. Change the words in each sentence to make it more colorful. Use what you know about the story "Crash Alert" to do this.

1. Randy would have liked to pilot the *Lotus.*
2. The large meteor scared Randy.
3. The meteor could damage the *Lotus.*

📖*My Trip to Alpha I* by Alfred Slote (J. B. Lippincott Company). Read about Jack, a boy who likes to pilot rocket ships.

Meteorites: Stones from the Sky, 256–265

✎ The main idea of a paragraph is what the paragraph is all about. Often this main idea is given in one sentence, called a *topic sentence.* The other sentences in the paragraph contain details that tell about the main idea.

Read this topic sentence for a paragraph:
A meteorite landed in my backyard last night!

Write a paragraph to go with this topic sentence. Write at least five complete sentences that give details about this topic sentence. You can make up some of the information. But try to use the facts in the article about meteorites, too.

📖 *Meteorites: Stones from the Sky* by R. V. Fodor (Dodd, Mead & Company). If you enjoyed the story in your reader, why not read the rest of the book?

FIVE _____

Pioneer Family, 268–285

✎ The stories about the Ingalls family contain both facts and opinions. A fact can be checked or tested to see if it is true. An opinion cannot be checked. An opinion usually tells someone's feelings or thoughts.

Sometimes opinions are based on facts. Facts make an opinion more believable or convincing. Read the following sentence about the Ingalls family. It is an opinion.

The Ingallses were a hardworking, fun-loving family.

Find four facts in the story that support this opinion. Use these facts to write four sentences. Each sentence should tell how the Ingallses worked hard or had fun.

📖 *Something to Shout About* by Patricia Beatty (William Morrow & Company, Inc.). Read about twelve-year-old Hope Foster, who shows the same pioneer spirit that the Ingalls girls showed.

Arthur Mitchell's Dream, 288–295

✎ "Arthur Mitchell's Dream" is a biography. It tells the story of Arthur Mitchell's life. Usually, biographies tell about the lives of famous people. But a biography can be about anyone!

Writing a biography is fun. All you need is someone special to write about. Think of a person who means a lot to you. It could be your mother or father, a friend or neighbor, or even yourself.

After you have chosen a person, go and talk to him or her. Find out as much as you can about the person. Get answers to the *Wh* questions—Who, What, Where, When, and Why. That way you will have the correct facts to include in the biography. Present the facts in an interesting way. Make clear why the person in the biography is special to you.

Dancer by Suzanne Merry (Charles Scribner's Sons). This is the story of one young dancer and her struggle for success in professional ballet.

The Seeing Stick, 296–308

Most writers appeal to our eyes. They tell what things look like. It is also important, however, to write about how things sound, smell, taste, and feel.

Suppose you spent an entire day blindfolded. Describe your day as you wake up at home. What can you hear? What can you smell? Tell how your breakfast tastes. Remember, you are blindfolded. You can't tell what anything looks like. Next, you travel to school the way you usually do. Tell what you touch and hear along the way. End by describing what you can sense as you sit in your classroom.

📖 *The Girl Who Cried Flowers and Other Tales* by Jane Yolen (Harper & Row Publishers, Inc.). These stories are based on old fairy tales. You'll remember the stories for a long time.

Keep It a Secret, 309–315

✎ Caesar made up a code that looked something like this. Each letter stands for another letter.

A = D	F = I	K = N	O = R	S = V	W = Z
B = E	G = J	L = O	P = S	T = W	X = A
C = F	H = K	M = P	Q = T	U = X	Y = B
D = G	I = L	N = Q	R = U	V = Y	Z = C
E = H	J = M				

When writing messages in this code, use the letter *D* when you want to write *A.* Use *E* for *B, F* for *C,* and so on. In Caesar's code, the words HOW ARE YOU would look like this: KRZ DUH BRX.

Use this code to write a message to a friend. At the same time, your friend can write a message to you. Each message should be at least four complete sentences. Tell what you want to do after school or on the weekend. While your friend is decoding your message, you can try to read what he or she has written to you.

How to Write Codes and Send Secret Messages by Bernice Myers (Four Winds Press). For more practice in how to write codes and send secret messages, read the book with the same name.

Treasure Seekers, 318–331

Have you ever drawn a map or given someone directions for how to go somewhere? If so, you know that maps and directions must be clear. You know that the steps of the directions must be in the correct order.

Pretend you have a new friend at school. Write directions that tell your friend how to get to your house from the school. Make sure the directions are clear and easy to follow. If you want to, you can number each step of the directions. Next, draw a small map. The map should show the school, your house, and the streets your friend will have to travel.

Jingo Django by Sid Fleischman (Little, Brown & Company). Jingo Hawks has a treasure map. But before he can dig up any treasure, he gets involved in many adventures.

The Last of the Dragons, 334–345

✎ "The Last of the Dragons" is a humorous fairy tale with characters that act in unexpected ways. The dragon is gentle, not frightening. The prince is not very brave. He is interested only in his studies. The princess, too, acts unexpectedly.

Pick a fairy tale or story that everybody knows. You could choose "Cinderella," "Little Red Riding Hood," or any other well-known tale. Rewrite the story, having the characters act in ways completely different from the ways they usually act. For example, the stepmother and the stepsisters in "Cinderella" could be kind and helpful. Cinderella, on the other hand, could be mean and selfish.

Try to make the story humorous. Have the characters do and say funny things. Feel free to change the plot of the story in unexpected ways, too.

📖 *Petronella* by Jay Williams (Parents' Magazine Press). Petronella is a very unusual princess who has unusual adventures.

The Street of the Flower Boxes, 350–365

✎ Before authors can write stories, they need to develop characters. One way to do this is to write a character profile. A character profile is a complete description of a character.

Write a character profile by following the steps below. You can base your character on a real person. Or you can make up the character. Write one paragraph for each numbered step.

1. Describe the character's face, hair, size, age, and clothing. Give him or her a name. Mention anything unusual about the way he or she looks.
2. Tell about something the character does well. What is so special about the way he or she does it?
3. Tell what the character thinks. A character's thoughts are often important in a story.
4. Now have the character take part in a conversation. Write the exact words of the character. Have the character talk about something that is important to him or her.

Now that you know the character a little better, think about and write a short story that he or she could be part of. The more you think about your character, the more real he or she will become.

📖 *The Spider Plant* by Yetta Speevack (Atheneum Publishers). Plants and flowers are important in cities. Sometimes, even one plant can make a difference, as Carmen Santos finds out in this story.

Minerva and Arachne, 368–373

✎ The story "Minerva and Arachne" is a myth. A myth explains something by telling a story. The people who made up myths were often trying to explain things in nature they didn't understand. The story about Arachne, for example, might explain why spiders spin webs.

Write a short myth that explains one of the following things in nature:
1. Why do leaves fall from trees in autumn?
2. Why do rainbows appear in the sky?
3. Why do giraffes have long necks?

📖 *Anansi, the Spider Man* by Philip Sherlock (Harper & Row Publishers, Inc.). Anansi, a spider who acts more like a person, is always up to something outrageous. More often than not, he's fooling others for his own profit.

The First Balloonists, 374–383

✎ Spiders were the first balloonists. But for the last two hundred years, people have been balloonists, too. Write a paragraph about balloonists or balloons. Choose one of these topic sentences for your paragraph:

1. The first hot-air balloons were built in the eighteenth century.
2. Today, balloons are used in scientific studies.

Use the encyclopedia to find out more about the topic you have chosen. Write at least four sentences that give details about the topic sentence.

📖 *Take a Balloon* by A. Harris Stone and Bertram M. Siegel (Prentice Hall, Inc.). You can do more than play with a balloon. The authors of this book show you how to find out the basics of jet propulsion, static electricity, sound, pitch, and elasticity— all with a balloon!

Charlotte's Web, 386–409

✎Suppose you and your friends wanted to put on a play based on "Charlotte's Web." You would have to rewrite the story in play form. Look at the play "7 Silly Simons" on pages 97–107 to find out how plays are written. Then choose the section of "Charlotte's Web" that you want to rewrite as a scene from a play.

First, list and describe the characters who will take part in the play. Next, describe the setting. The setting is the time and place in which the scene takes place. Then, write the words that each character says. You will also want to write stage directions. These words appear in parentheses. They tell how the character should say the lines. They also tell what the character should do.

📖*Stuart Little* by E. B. White (Harper & Row Publishers, Inc.). If you enjoyed Wilbur the Pig, you'll probably like Stuart Little, a mouse born into a human family. Like Wilbur, Stuart Little has a lot to learn about what people and animals think of each other.

SEVEN _____

The Fledgling, 414–438

✎ Different people view the world differently. What we see—our perspective—depends on who we are, where we are, and what we choose to look at.

Suppose, like Georgie, you were flying with the Goose Prince. If you flew over your neighborhood, what would your town, your home, and your school look like from several hundred feet up in the air? Write a paragraph describing your hometown or neighborhood from a bird's-eye view.

📖 *The Wayfarer's Tree* by Anne Colver and Stewart Graff (E. P. Dutton). Georgie grew up in Concord and had a bust of Henry Thoreau in her home. If you'd like to learn more about Concord and Thoreau, read this book. It's about a young boy who has Thoreau for a tutor while spending a year in the historic town of Concord.

Stories, Dreams, and Flying Machines, 439–448

✎ Look at the picture of Leonardo da Vinci's ornithopter on page 442. What does this strange machine have in common with the large jet airplanes that fly in and out of busy city airports? How is the ornithopter different from a modern airplane? Write a paragraph that lists three ways in which an ornithopter and a modern airplane are alike and three ways in which they are different.

Flying Paper Airplane Models by Frank Ross, Jr. (Lothrop, Lee & Shepard Books). This book has careful instructions for how to make paper models of jet and propeller airplanes in use today. It also shows how to make four flyers of the future, including a space shuttle!

The Web of Winter, 452–465

Normally, ducks fly to warm places once the winter winds begin to blow. Why do you think the young duck in "The Web of Winter" didn't fly away like other ducks? Why do you think it let the ice slowly freeze around it?

In a paragraph, tell how and why the little duck came to be trapped in ice. Then, in a second paragraph, tell where the duck flies once Bill and Thelma set him free.

The Duck by Angela Sheehan (Franklin Watts, Inc.). Did you know that ducks don't get wet? Read this book to find out all about what else ducks do and don't do.

Connie's New Eyes, 466–477

Connie David is a blind teacher. Pretend for a moment that you are a student in her class. How would having Connie for a teacher change the way that things are done in your classroom?

Think of four changes that would have to be made if Connie David were your teacher. List the changes on your paper. Be sure to write complete sentences.

Seeing Fingers: The Story of Louis Braille by Etta DeGering (David McKay Company, Inc.). Connie David used braille to write letters. Read about Louis Braille of France, who invented the system.

Animals on the Scent, 480–488

For writers, the sense of smell is the hardest sense to write about. Many people are not very aware of smells. There aren't too many words to describe smells. Yet smell can change your mood. It can bring back memories, make you think of spring, or make you hungry.

In your imagination, take a walk through your house or neighborhood. What smells do you remember? How would you describe the smells? Make a list of the smells, and then describe them in a paragraph.

📖 *The Natural History of the Nose* by Lisbeth Zappler (Doubleday & Company, Inc.). Read this book to find out more about how different animals' noses look and work.

Ginger Pye, 492–517

✎ Think of all the places you went yesterday. If a dog like Ginger Pye were to track your scent, what route would it follow? Describe the dog's route step by step. Make sure the steps are in order, beginning with when you left your house yesterday morning.

📖 *A Puppy for You* by Lilo Hess (Charles Scribner's Sons). If you're thinking about getting a dog, this book will help you choose the right one.

HELP WITH WORDS
(Glossary)

How to Use HELP WITH WORDS

HELP WITH WORDS is your glossary. It was written to help you understand certain words found in the stories and articles in this book. It is shorter than a full dictionary. However, it has many of the helps you will find in dictionaries.

Alphabetic Order

The words that begin with **a** come first in HELP WITH WORDS. Those that begin with **b** come next, and so on. You may need to check beyond the first letter of the word you want if another word begins with the same letter or letters. For example, in these words pairs, which word comes first in the dictionary:

1. **alert** or **agent**?
2. **embrace** or **embroider**?
3. **foreign** or **forgiveness**?
4. **responsibility** or **respect**?

Guide Words

Look at the words **ability** and **ambush** at the top of page 554. These two words are called "guide words," because they help you find the words you want. The left guide word on each page is the same as the first word explained on that page. The right guide word is the same as the last word explained on that page.

Entry Words

Find the word **accept** on page 554. Notice that it is printed in heavy black type. Such a word is called an "entry word." HELP WITH WORDS does not list entry words for names of people and places. It does list suffixes like **-al** and **-ence**.

Help with Spelling and Writing

Here is the entry for **accept:**

> **ac·cept** (ak sept′)   to re-
> ceive or take (She *ac-
> cepted* the gift with thanks.)

How is **accept** spelled? In HELP WITH WORDS, the centered dots show where you may break a word at the end of a line in writing. After what letters may you break the word **accept**?

All dictionaries give you help with forms of words if there is a spelling change before **-ed, -ing, -er, -est, -s,** or **-es.** Note the entry word **define** on page 559. Why do the forms **defined** and **defining** also appear?

Help with Meanings

A full dictionary gives all the meanings for a word. HELP WITH WORDS gives the meaning of the word as it is used in your book. For some words, it also gives other common meanings. The different meanings of a word are numbered so that you can find them quickly.

For help in understanding meanings, example sentences are sometimes given. For some entry words, pictures are used to help explain the meaning. A blue dot (●) appears after the meaning of each word that is pictured.

Help with Pronunciation

The pronunciation is given right after the entry word:

ac·cept (ak sept′)

The symbols after the entry word show how the word **accept** is pronounced or spoken. These symbols sometimes look a lot like the entry word:

draft (draft)

Often, however, they look different:

cour·age (kėr′ij)

When there is more than one way to pronounce a word, HELP WITH WORDS shows the pronunciations this way:

pe·tu·nia (pə tü′nyə *or* pə tyü′nyə)

Look once again at the pronunciation symbols for **courage:**

(kėr′ij)

Notice that (kėr′) is followed by a heavy mark called an "accent mark." This shows which part of the word **courage** is accented, or said more loudly. In some words a lighter secondary accent mark is also shown for a syllable that is said somewhat less loudly:

(ej′a kā′shən)

All the pronunciation symbols used in HELP WITH WORDS are shown on the opposite page. Some of these symbols are also shown in the key at the bottom of every right-hand page.

Study the symbols on page 553 carefully. Some look just like the letters of the alphabet: (a). Others have marks that make them look different from letters: (ā). The important thing to remember about both kinds of symbols is that they do not stand for letters; they stand for sounds.

Full pronunciation key

The pronunciation of each word is shown just after the word in this way: **ab·bre·vi·ate** (ə brē′vē āt): The letters and signs used are pronounced as in the words below. The mark ′ is placed after a syllable with primary or heavy accent, as in the example above. The mark ′ after a syllable shows a secondary or lighter accent, as in **ab·bre·vi·a·tion** (ə brē′vē ā′shən).

a	hat, cup	i	it, pin	p	paper, cup	v	very, save
ā	age, face	ī	ice, five	r	run, read	w	will, woman
ä	father, far			s	say, yes	y	young, yet
		j	jam, enjoy	sh	she, rush	z	zero, breeze
b	bad, rob	k	kind, seek	t	tell, it	zh	measure, seizure
ch	child, much	l	land, coal	th	thin, both		
d	did, red	m	me, am	ŦH	then, smooth		
		n	no, in			ə	represents:
e	let, best	ng	long, bring	u	cup, butter		a in about
ē	equal, be			ù	full, put		e in taken
ėr	term, learn	o	hot, rock	ü	rule, move		i in pencil
		ō	open, go				o in lemon
f	fat, if	ô	order, all				u in circus
g	go, bag	oi	oil, voice				
h	he, how	ou	house, out				

Grammatical key

adj.	adjective	*n.*	noun
adv.	adverb	*prep.*	preposition
conj.	conjunction	*pron.*	pronoun
interj.	interjection	*v.*	verb
sing.	singular	*pl.*	plural

Aa

abil·i·ty (ə bil'ə tē)
abil·i·ties the power to do something well

-a·ble a suffix that means **1** "capable of, fit for, or worthy of being" (an *enjoyable* trip) **2** "tending or liable to" (a *peaceable* person)

ac·cept (ak sept') to receive or take (She *accepted* the gift with thanks.)

ac·count (ə kount') a business relation or arrangement (I have a savings *account* at the Lincoln Bank.)

adapt (ə dapt') to make fit for, as for a new use (Many space products have been *adapted* for home use.)

ad·van·tage (ad van'tij) **1** a favorable feature **2** something that is of help (One *advantage* of living in the city is being near museums.)

ad·ven·tur·ous (ad ven'chər əs) daring; bold (My *adventurous* sister climbs mountains.)

agen·cy (ā'jən sē)
agen·cies **1** a person or company that acts or does business for another **2** the office of such a person or company (A travel *agency* got us our plane tickets.)

agent (ā'jənt) a person who acts for or in the place of someone else (The railroad *agent* signaled the train.)

aide (ād) a person who acts as an assistant (My mother is an *aide* to the museum director.)

-al a suffix meaning "having to do with" (All the characters in this book are *fictional*.)

al·der (ôl'dər) a tree that grows in cool, damp places (I can climb the *alder* near the brook.) ●

alert (ə lėrt') a danger signal; an alarm (The captain sounded a crash *alert*.)

al·fal·fa (al fal'fə) a plant with purple flowers and clover-like leaves grown as food for horses, cattle, sheep, and pigs (The farmer fed his horse *alfalfa*.) ●

al·i·bi (al'ə bī) the plea made by a person accused of a crime that he or she was somewhere else at the time of the crime (His *alibi* proved that he was not the hit-and-run driver.)

am·bush (am'bush) a trap in which hidden persons wait to attack by surprise (We set an *ambush* for the enemy.)

alder

alfalfa

an·aes·thet·ic (an'əs thet'ik) a drug or gas that causes entire or some loss of the feelings of pain and touch

anx·ious·ly (angk'shəs lē *or* ang'shəs lē) with fear of what may happen; with worry (We waited *anxiously* for the test results.)

apart·ment (ə pärt'mənt) **1** a room or set of rooms used as a dwelling (Our *apartment* has five rooms.) **2** a building made up of dwelling units (The *apartment* has an elevator.)

arc (ärk) part of a circle or curved line (The plane flew in a wide *arc*.)

ar·gue (är'gyü) **ar·gued; ar·gu·ing** to give reasons for or against something (My brother and I *argued* about whether to get a puppy.)

ar·ti·fi·cial (är'tə fish'əl) not natural; made by human labor (Those *artificial* roses look real.)

as·cend (ə send') **1** to come to take up or hold **2** to come next after (The prince will *ascend* the throne after his mother's death.)

as·sign·ment (ə sīn'mənt) a piece of work to be done (My *assignment* is to read three pages.)

-a·tion a suffix that means **1** "the act or process of" (the *exploration* of space) **2** "the result of something" (*civilization*)

at·mo·sphere (at'mə sfir) air that surrounds the earth (Clouds float in the lowest part of the *atmosphere*.)

at·tach·ment (ə tach'mənt) a connection (The *attachment* loosened, and the button fell off my coat.)

at·tack (ə tak') set upon forcefully (The guard dog will *attack* upon command.)

au·to·mat·ic (ô'tə mat'ik) moving or acting by itself (Our car has an *automatic* shift.)

aye (ī) yes ("*Aye*, I will help you," said the kind stranger.)

apartment (2)

Bb

balk (bôk) to stop short and refuse to go (The donkeys *balk* at the steep hill.)

a	hat	ō	open	sh	she
ā	age	ô	order	th	thin
ä	far	oi	oil	ŦH	then
e	let	ou	out	zh	measure
ē	equal	u	cup		a in about
ér	term	ù	put		e in taken
i	it	ü	rule ə =	i in pencil
ī	ice	ch	child		o in lemon
o	hot	ng	long		u in circus

bal·let (bal′ā *or* ba lā′) a form of dancing based on jumps, turns, poses, etc., all demanding great skill and grace of movement (Sometimes modern *ballet* tells a story.)

bar·ren (bar′ən) **1** not productive **2** having only poor or few plants

bel·low (bel′ō) to make a deep, loud noise (Carlos ran when he heard the bull *bellow.*)

be·tray (bi trā′) to be unfaithful to; to be false to (Why did the man break his promise and *betray* his friends?)

bil·low (bil′ō) a swelling or great wave (A *billow* of steam rose from the locomotive.)

bind (bīnd) **bound; bind·ing** to tie (Spiders catch and *bind* insects with silken threads.)

blub·ber (blub′ər) to weep noisily (The broken toy made the child *blubber.*)

blurt (blért) to say quickly without thinking (Try not to *blurt* answers to the questions.)

body·guard (bod′ē gärd′) a person or a group of people who protect another person (The President always has a *bodyguard* nearby.)

braille (brāl) a system of writing for the blind in which the letters of the alphabet are represented by raised dots, read by touching them (Connie has a machine that makes *braille* letters.)

brib·ery (brī′bər ē) **brib·er·ies** the giving, offering, or taking of a reward for doing something unlawful, dishonest, or distasteful (Not even *bribery* could make me jump off the high diving board.)

bul·ly (bul′ē) **bul·lies** someone who teases, frightens, threatens, or hurts smaller or weaker persons (When he saw the bigger boys and girls coming, the *bully* left the little kids alone.)

bunk (bungk) a narrow bed, built in or against a wall (The scouts all wanted an upper *bunk.*)

buoy (boi *or* bü′ē) a floating object anchored in water to mark a channel or warn of danger (Two *buoys* mark the entrance to the harbor.)

Cc

caf·e·te·ria (kaf′ə tir′ē ə) a restaurant in which people are served at a counter and take the food to tables on trays (The school *cafeteria* is crowded at lunchtime.)

can·o·py (kan′ə pē)
can·o·pies rooflike cover
(The *canopy* over the entry
to the restaurant is blue.) ●

cas·sette (ka set′) a con-
tainer for holding magnetic
tape for playing or record-
ing sound (This carrying
case holds twenty *cas-
settes.*)

cau·tious·ly (kô′shəs lē)
taking great care to be safe
(The tightrope walker
moved *cautiously* along
the rope.)

chal·lenge (chal′ənj)
chal·lenged;
chal·leng·ing   to dare
someone to take part in a
game or contest (They *challenged* us to a race.)

chi·tin (kīt′n) a hard growth
that forms part of the outer
body covering of shellfish
and some insects (The *chitin* protects the crab.)

cho·re·og·ra·pher
(kôr′ē og′rə fər) a person
who plans or creates dance
movements as for ballet or
modern dance

chute (shüt) a passageway
through which things slide
or are dropped (There is a
mail *chute* in the office
building.)

cinch (sinch) *slang*
something done with ease
(After many hours of prac-
ticing, it's a *cinch* to play
the drums.)

cit·a·del (sit′ə dəl)   a for-
tress that overlooks a city

clam·or·ous (klam′ər əs)
loud;   noisy (*Clamorous*
puppies crowded around
the woman holding their
food.)

col·o·ny (kol′ə nē)
col·o·nies a number of
animals or plants of the
same kind living or growing
together (I found an ant
colony in our yard.) ●

com·i·cal (kom′ə kəl)
funny,   amusing (The
clowns were *comical.*)

com·mu·ni·cate
(kə myü′nə kāt) give or
exchange thoughts, ideas,
information by speaking,
writing, signaling, etc. (We
can *communicate* with
out-of-town friends by mail
or telephone.)

com·mu·ni·ty (kə myü′nə tē)
com·mu·ni·ties 1 all the
people living in the same
place **2** the place where
people live, as a city or
town (Fire fighters protect
their *community* from fire.)

canopy

colony

a	hat	ō	open		sh	she
ā	age	ô	order		th	thin
ä	far	oi	oil		ŦH	then
e	let	ou	out		zh	measure
ē	equal	u	cup			a in about
ér	term	ủ	put			e in taken
i	it	ü	rule	ə =		i in pencil
ī	ice	ch	child			o in lemon
o	hot	ng	long			u in circus

com·pete (kəm pēt')
com·pet·ed; com·pet·ing
to take part in a contest
(Arachne *competed* against
the goddess Minerva.)

con·fess (kən fes') to admit
guilt (The robber *con-
fessed* to the crime.)

con·fi·dence (kon'fə dəns)
belief in oneself (Doing
something well builds *confidence.*)

con·spir·a·cy (kən spir'ə sē)
con·spir·a·cies a secret
plan with others to do
something unlawful (The
spies were in a *conspiracy*
to blow up the ship.)

con·tem·pla·tion
(kon'təm plā'shən) deep
thought (The lawyer sat in
contemplation of her case.)

con·tent·ed·ly
(kən ten'tid lē) in a very
pleased way (The cat
purred *contentedly.*)

con·vince (kən vins')
con·vinced; con·vinc·ing
to use arguments to
overcome objections (I
convinced Sue to join us.)

cords (kôrdz) thick string or
thin rope (When the *cords*
were cut, we opened the
box.)

cor·ral (kə ral') a fenced-
in area for horses or cattle
(The children led the pony
into the *corral.*)

crossties

cour·age (ker'ij) bravery;
the ability to face danger
without running away (He
faced the enemy with *courage.*)

cow·ard (kou'ərd) someone
who runs from danger or
trouble (The *coward* would
not stay to help anybody.)

cow·er (kou'ər) to draw
away or crouch down in
fear or shame (The kitten
cowered before the big
dog.)

crate (krāt) a large box or
frame usually made of
strips of wood for shipping
or storing fruit, vegetables,
or household goods (Mr.
Gomez shipped the
oranges in a *crate.*)

crea·ture (krē'chər) a living person or animal (There
are no *creatures* on the
moon.)

crept (krept) a past form of
creep meaning "moved
slowly on hands and knees;
crawled" (The baby *crept*
toward the TV.)

crin·kly (kring'klē) full of
wrinkles or ripples in a
normally smooth surface
(She crushed the paper,
and it was *crinkly.*)

cross·ties (krôs'tīz') the
cross supports to which
railroad ties are fastened
(The railroad track was
placed over *crossties* of
lumber.) ●

crude (krüd) **crud·er; crud·est** rough; not expertly planned or done (I drew a *crude* map of the area.)

cut·lass (kut′ləs) a short, heavy sword (The sailor slashed the rope with the *cutlass*.) ●

Dd

dairy (der′ē) **dair·ies** **1** a place where milk is stored or made into butter and cheese **2** a farm where milk is produced **3** a company or store that sells or distributes milk and milk products

dan·ger·ous (dān′jər əs) not safe; likely to cause harm (Riding a bicycle without obeying the rules of traffic is *dangerous*.)

dap·pled (dap′əld) marked with spots (My blue jeans are *dappled* from bleach.)

de·coy (dē′koi) a person or thing used to lead into a trap (The hunter used wooden ducks as *decoys*.)

de·fine (di fīn′) **de·fined; de·fin·ing** to explain the meaning of (The teacher *defined* the word for us.)

de·pend·a·ble (di pen′də bəl) able to be trusted

de·stroy (di stroi′) to ruin; break into pieces; wreck (The next storm will surely *destroy* that old house.)

de·test (di test′) dislike very strongly (I *detest* all wrongdoing.)

di·a·ry (dī′ər ē) **di·a·ries** a daily record of a person's thoughts and feelings about what has happened that day (Do you keep a *diary*?)

dif·fi·cult (dif′ə kult) hard to do or make (Some math problems are *difficult*.)

dim·ly (dim′lē) faintly; not clearly (I remember the trip *dimly*, because we went to Boston a long time ago.)

dis·dain (dis dān′) a feeling of scorn, as though something is unworthy or beneath one (Cinderella's stepsisters treated her with *disdain*.)

dis·ease (də zēz′) an illness (Smallpox is a deadly *disease*.)

cutlass

a	hat	ō	open	sh	she
ā	age	ô	order	th	thin
ä	far	oi	oil	₮H	then
e	let	ou	out	zh	measure
ē	equal	u	cup		a in about
ér	term	ù	put		e in taken
i	it	ü	rule	ə =	i in pencil
ī	ice	ch	child		o in lemon
o	hot	ng	long		u in circus

dis·guise (dis gīz′) **dis·guised; dis·guis·ing** to change one's appearance so as to look like someone else

dis·patch ri·der (dis pach′ rī′dər) a person who carries a message by horseback or motorcycle (The letter was delivered by a *dispatch rider.*)

doubt (dout) to be uncertain about the truth or reality of something (Do you *doubt* my word?)

down·stage (doun′stāj′) the part of a stage that is nearest the audience (The actors moved *downstage* to bow.)

draft (draft) **1** to make a sketch, plan, or chart **2** to select for a special purpose (During a war, a country usually *drafts* people into the army.)

dra·goon (drə gün′) a soldier on horseback (The *dragoons* rode two by two). ●

drought (drout) **1** a shortage of rain or water **2** a long period of dry weather (During the *drought,* our well was dry.)

dragoon

(to) embroider

Ee

ear·nest (ėr′nist) strong in purpose; serious (Let me give you some *earnest* advice.)

ease (ēz) **eased; eas·ing** to move with great care (He *eased* himself through the narrow opening.)

ea·sel (ē′zəl) an upright stand used to support or display something (a picture, blackboard, sign) (The artist placed her canvas on the *easel.*)

ed·u·ca·tion (ej′ə kā′shən) schooling; studying (My parents are saving now for my college *education.*)

em·brace (em brās′) to hold in one's arms; to hug (The father *embraced* his son.)

em·broi·der (em broi′dər) **em·broi·dered; em·broi·der·ing** to make a stitched design on cloth, leather, etc. with a needle (I used cotton thread to *embroider* flowers on the tablecloth.) ●

-ence a suffix that means **1** "example of an action or a process" (*residence*) **2** "state or quality" (*intelligence.*)

en·coun·ter (en koun′tər) **1** a face-to-face meeting, often by chance **2** a meeting of enemies; a fight

en·tice (en tīs′) **en·ticed; en·tic·ing** to attract or tempt (The feeder filled with sunflower seeds *enticed* the birds.)

en·vi·ous (en'vē əs)   being jealous or resentful of another (The Queen was *envious* of Snow White.)

ep·i·dem·ic (ep'ə dem'ik)   a rapid spread of a disease causing many people to have the illness at the same time (We had an *epidemic* of flu in town last winter.)

-er   a suffix that means "one who does something or has the job of" (*writer, teacher, farmer*)

event (i vent')   an important happening (The dream of people traveling to the moon became a historical *event* on July 20, 1969.)

ex·as·pe·rate (eg zas'pə rāt') **ex·as·pe·rat·ed; ex·as·pe·rat·ing**   to annoy or make angry (I was *exasperated* by the long wait.)

ex·cur·sion (ek skėr'zhən *or* ek skėr'shən)   a short trip (We went on an *excursion* to the shore.)

ex·pe·di·tion (ek'spə dish'ən)   a journey for a special purpose

ex·pose (ek spōz') **ex·posed; ex·pos·ing**   to be open to danger (Everyone in the class was *exposed* to measles.)

ex·ult (eg zult')   to feel great joy (The team *exulted* in its victory.)

Ff

fan·tas·tic (fan tas'tik)   strange; very odd or queer; unreal (That story is too *fantastic* to believe.)

fetch (fech)   bring; go and get (Some dogs can be trained to *fetch* the morning paper.)

flag·on (flag'ən)   a large bottle for holding liquids

flank (flangk)   the fleshy part of an animal between the ribs and the hip (The cowhand brushed the horse's *flanks*.)

flan·nel (flan'l)   a soft wool or cotton cloth (My *flannel* scarf keeps me warm.)

flat·ter (flat'ər)   to overpraise; to raise someone's hopes in order to get one's own way (You *flatter* me with your lovely words.)

fledg·ling (flej'ling   a young bird with newly grown feathers needed to fly (The *fledgling* fluttered from branch to branch.)

a	hat	ō	open	sh	she
ā	age	ô	order	th	thin
ä	far	oi	oil	ŦH	then
e	let	ou	out	zh	measure
ē	equal	u	cup		a in about
ėr	term	ů	put		e in taken
i	it	ü	rule	ə = { i in pencil
ī	ice	ch	child		o in lemon
o	hot	ng	long		u in circus

flue (flü) a pipe or tube, as in a chimney or dryer, through which smoke or hot air may pass (The *flue* was not clean, and the smoke backed into the house.)

flut·ing (flüt'ing) having a sound like that of a flute (The goose gave a soft, *fluting* call.)

ford (fôrd) a shallow place in a body of water that may be crossed by wading or driving (He waded through the *ford* in the river.)

for·eign (fôr'ən) outside one's own country (Have you ever visited a *foreign* country?)

fore·lock (fôr'lok') a piece of hair that grows above the forehead (His *forelock* kept falling into his eyes.)

for·give·ness (fər giv'nis) willingness to stop having hard feelings toward; pardon (to ask someone's *forgiveness*)

for·ma·tion (fôr mā'shən) something formed or shaped in a particular way (That cloud *formation* looks like an elephant.)

foun·da·tion (foun dā'shən) the part on which other parts rest (The *foundation* of a house is built first.)

fran·tic (fran'tik) very excited; wild with fear or pain

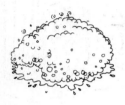

frothy

free-fall (frē'fôl) the part of a parachute jump before the parachute is opened

fren·zy (fren'zē) a frantic condition (She was in a *frenzy* when she lost her wallet.)

fric·tion (frik'shən) the rubbing of one object against another (The match was lighted by *friction*.)

frothy (frô'thē) foamy (The *frothy* soapsuds covered the sink.) ●

Gg

gal·lery (gal'ər ē) **gal·ler·ies** a room or group of rooms used for showing works of art (Mr. Hill bought his painting at a *gallery*.)

gape (gāp) **gaped; gap·ing** to stare with an open mouth (People come to *gape* at the air show.)

gear (gir) **1** to connect moving parts, such as interlocking wheels, so that they will work together **2** to adjust such moving parts (The mechanic *geared* the engine to run more quietly.)

ges·ture (jes'chər) a movement of the body to help express or emphasize a thought or feeling (My friend can't speak without using hand *gestures*.)

gland (gland) an organ in the body that produces a substance used in or discharged from the body (sweat *glands*)

gnu (nü *or* nyü) a large African antelope with a head like an ox, beard and mane, curved horns, and a long tail

gob·ble (gob′əl) **gob·bled; gob·bling** eat fast; swallow quickly in big pieces (The hungry cat *gobbled* the food.)

go·pher (gō′fər) a small rodent having large claws and big cheek pouches that lives in underground tunnels

gos·ling (goz′ling) a young goose

gouge (gouj) **gouged; goug·ing** to dig or chisel out (We *gouged* a hole in the ice for fishing.)

grad·u·ate (graj′ü it) a person who has finished a course of study at a school and has received a diploma

grate·ful (grāt′fəl) full of thanks because of a kindness (Tom was *grateful* for the favor.)

grey·hound (grā′hound′) a tall, slender dog with the ability to run very fast (The bus had a picture of a *greyhound* on it.)

grif·fin (grif′ən) an imaginary animal with the head, wings, and forelegs of an eagle and the body, hind legs, and tail of a lion

grog (grog) any strong drink

gy·rate (jī′rāt) **gy·rat·ed; gy·rat·ing** to spin (We watched the top *gyrate*.)

Hh

ham·ster (ham′stər) a small stocky rodent with large cheek pouches and a short tail, often kept as a pet ●

hand·i·cap (han′dē kap′) **hand·i·capped; hand·i·cap·ping** to put at a disadvantage or make more difficult (The runner was *handicapped* by a brace on his leg.)

hatch (hach) to come out of an egg (Those ducklings have just *hatched*.)

hearth (härth) **1** the stone or brick floor of a fireplace **2** a fireside (We sat by the *hearth* and told ghost stories.) ●

hamsters

hearth

a	hat	ō	open	sh	she
ā	age	ô	order	th	thin
ä	far	oi	oil	ŦH	then
e	let	ou	out	zh	measure
ē	equal	u	cup		a in about
ėr	term	ù	put		e in taken
i	it	ü	rule	ə =	i in pencil
ī	ice	ch	child		o in lemon
o	hot	ng	long		u in circus

her·i·tage (her'ə tij) something that is passed down from one generation to the next (Every country has its *heritage* of folk stories.)

hes·i·tate (hez'ə tāt) **hes·i·tat·ed; hes·i·tat·ing** to stop or hold back because one is not sure (The driver *hesitated* at a fork in the road.)

hitch (hich) to make a short, sudden move (I *hitched* over on the bench to make room for my friend.)

hith·er·to (hiŦH'ər tü') until now (This entrance to the cave was *hitherto* unknown.)

hoarse·ly (hôrs'lē) sounding rough and grating (We yelled *hoarsely* for our team to win.)

hogan

ho·gan (hō'gän') a Navajo single-room dwelling built with logs and covered on top with earth (The family sat by the fire in the *hogan*.) ●

hom·age (hom'ij *or* om'ij) honor or respect given or shown (People came to the meeting to pay *homage* to the great teacher.)

horse·hair (hôrs'her' *or* hôrs'har') cloth made from hair from the mane or tail of a horse (This *horsehair* sofa is very comfortable.)

hov·er (huv'ər) to stay in or near one place in the air (A helicopter *hovered* over the lifeboat.)

hur·tle (hér'tl) **hur·tled; hur·tling** to move in a violent, rushing way (The rocket *hurtled* into space.)

hys·ter·ics (hi ster'iks) a fit of laughing and crying that cannot be controlled

Ii

iden·ti·fy (ī den'tə fī) **iden·ti·fied; iden·ti·fy·ing** to say what something is (Can you *identify* this rock?)

im·age (im'ij) **1** a likeness or copy **2** a reflection

imag·i·na·tion (i maj'ə nā'shən) the power of forming an idea or picture of something not really there (The story shows that the writer has a strong *imagination*.)

im·plore (im plôr' *or* im plōr') **im·plored; im·plor·ing** to beg (The servant *implored* the king for mercy.)

in·can·ta·tion (in'kan tā'shən) special words or sounds recited or chanted as a magic spell (Some people think that the *incantation* "abracadabra" said three times is magic.)

in·de·pend·ence
(in′di pen′dəns) the state of not depending on others for control or help (The Colonists wanted their *independence* from England.)

in·fur·i·ate (in fyur′ē āt) **in·fur·i·at·ed; in·fur·i·at·ing** to fill with anger (Your habit of interrupting *infuriates* me.)

in·ner (in′ər) located farther in; inside (The nurse took me to an *inner* office.)

in·no·cent (in′ə sənt) **1** free from wrong or blame **2** not guilty (My cat is *innocent*; it did not scratch the chair.)

in·sert (in sėrt′) to put or place in (I need to *insert* a bookmark into my book.)

in·spec·tor (in spek′tər) a person who examines closely (The scale *inspector* was seen in the store.)

in·stant (in′stənt) a small space of time; moment (Sit down this *instant*!)

in·step (in′step) the upper part of the arch of a person's foot between the toes and the ankle

in·stinct (in′stingkt) a natural feeling or ability that doesn't have to be learned (*Instinct* guides some birds to fly south in the fall.)

in·sult (in sult′) to hurt or treat someone in a poor manner (I am *insulted* that I wasn't asked to join you.)

in·tense (in tens′) done with great effort, energy, or feeling (The contestant listened to the question with *intense* concentration.)

in·ter·na·tion·al
(in′tər nash′ə nəl) between or among nations (The peace treaty was an *international* agreement.)

ivo·ry (ī′vər ē) the hard, creamy-white, bonelike matter of which elephant tusks are made (*Ivory* is used for piano keys.)

Jj

jaun·ti·ness (jôn′tē nis) having a lively manner and appearance (The dog walked with *jauntiness* beside its owner.)

jest (jest) something said in fun; not serious (The matter was too important for anyone to *jest*.)

jit·tery (jit′ər ē) very nervous; upset

a	hat	ō	open		sh	she
ā	age	ô	order		th	thin
ä	far	oi	oil		ŦH	then
e	let	ou	out		zh	measure
ē	equal	u	cup		a	in about
ėr	term	ù	put		e	in taken
i	it	ü	rule	ə =	i	in pencil
ī	ice	ch	child		o	in lemon
o	hot	ng	long		u	in circus

Kk

know·ing·ly (nō′ing lē) in a way that suggests special knowledge ("That's not our bus," Tom said *knowingly.*)

Ll

lag (lag) **lagged; lag·ging** to fall behind; to move too slowly (My tired dog *lagged* behind us on the road.)

lank (langk) **1** long and thin **2** straight and flat (My sister twisted her *lank* hair into a ponytail.)

lat·tice (lat′is) a framework of crossed strips, usually of metal or wood, with open spaces between them (The cat peeked through the *lattice* on the gate.) •

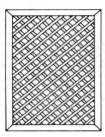

lattice

limb (lim) a tree branch (Several tree *limbs* broke during the storm.)

liq·uid (lik′wid) something that is not a solid or a gas and that flows freely (Water is a *liquid.*)

lit·ter (lit′ər) young animals born at one time (Our dog had a *litter* of six puppies last month.)

mandolin

loathe (lōŦH) feel a strong dislike for something; hate (I *loathe* dirty streets.)

-ly a suffix that means **1** "like in appearance or manner" (*ghostly, fatherly*) **2** "happening at regular periods of time" (*hourly, daily*) **3** "in some manner" (*cheerfully, slowly*)

Mm

mag·net (mag′nit)   **1** a piece of material that has the natural ability to attract iron **2** something that attracts (The circus is a *magnet* that draws children.)

ma·jes·tic (mə jes′tik) grand; noble

man·do·lin (man′də lin′ *or* man′dl ən) a musical instrument that has a pear-shaped body, four to six pairs of strings, and is played with a pick •

mar·ble (mär′bəl)   stone that can be highly polished, often used in architecture and sculpture (The stairs are made of *marble.*)

me·chan·i·cal (mə kan′ə kəl) made or worked by a machine or tool

mem·o·ry (mem′ər ē) **mem·o·ries 1** the ability to remember (a person with a good *memory*) **2** everything a person can remember (My grandfather has rich *memories* of his native land.)

-ment a suffix that means **1** "result or object of a certain action" (*equipment*) **2** "action or process" (*development*) **3** "state or condition" (*enjoyment*)

mere·ly (mir′lē) simply; only (It cost *merely* pennies.)

me·sa (mā′sə) a flat-topped hill with steep sides

mirth·less·ly (mėrth′lis lē) without joy (The victim of the prank laughed *mirthlessly*.)

mis·chief (mis′chif) an act or conduct, often playful, that can cause harm or annoyance (Much *mischief* is done at Halloween.)

mod·ern dance (mod′ərn dans) a dance that has less formal steps and movements than that of ballet

mole (mōl) a small animal with a thick body, tiny eyes, pointed nose, soft fur, hidden ears, and large front paws having long nails. (The *mole* lives underground most of the time.) ●

Morse code (môrs′ kōd) a communication system in which letters, numbers, and punctuation marks are represented by dots and dashes or by long and short sounds or beams of light (The message was tapped in *Morse code*.)

mourn (môrn) to feel or show sadness (They *mourn* their lost cat.)

mum·ble (mum′bəl) **mum·bled; mum·bling** to speak in a way that is hard to hear or understand (The shy children *mumbled* the poem.)

murky (mėr′kē) **murk·i·er; murk·i·est** dark and gloomy (I couldn't see anything in the *murky* hallway.)

mut·ter (mut′ər) to speak in a low, cross voice (The check-out line moved very slowly, and people began to *mutter*.)

Nn

na·tion·al (nash′ə nəl) belonging to a whole country (Every country has its *national* song of praise.)

nav·i·ga·tor (nav′ə gā′tər) a person in charge of steering or setting the course for a ship or an airplane (A *navigator* uses many instruments.)

mole

a	hat	ō	open	sh	she
ā	age	ô	order	th	thin
ä	far	oi	oil	ŦH	then
e	let	ou	out	zh	measure
ē	equal	u	cup		a in about
ėr	term	u̇	put		e in taken
i	it	ü	rule	ə =	i in pencil
ī	ice	ch	child		o in lemon
o	hot	ng	long		u in circus

ne·glect (ni glekt′)   to fail to give proper attention to (I sometimes *neglect* my chores.)

new·el·post (nü′əl *or* nü′əl pōst)   the upright post to which the railing of a stairway is attached (I sometimes hang my jacket on the *newel-post*.)

nudge (nuj)   **nudged; nudg·ing**   to push gently

Oo

parachute

ob·struct (əb strukt′)   to be in the way of; hinder (I hope that nothing will *obstruct* our plans.)

of·fi·cial (ə fish′əl)   authorized; approved; considered correct (The *official* rules of the contest were posted on the board.)

Olym·pics (ō lim′piks)   having to do with sports contests (People from many nations go to the *Olympics* to take part in sports events.)

or·di·nary (ôrd′n er′ē) **or·di·nar·i·ly;** *or* **or·di·nar·i·ness**   to be expected; normal; usual (We had an *ordinary* day in school.)

or·gan·dy *also* **or·gan·die** (ôr′gən dē′)   a thin, fine, crisp cotton cloth used for curtains, dresses, trimmings, etc.

orig·i·nal (ə rij′ə nəl)   **1** the first or earliest (the *original* homeowner)   **2** not copied (an *original* painting)   **3** creative (*original* idea)

-ous   a suffix that means "full of" or "having the qualities of" (*joyous; dangerous*)

Pp

par·a·chute (par′ə shüt)   an umbrellalike device made of lightweight fabric used for coming down gradually from great heights (That *parachute* is made of nylon.) •

par·a·sol (par′ə sôl)   a light umbrella used as a protection from the sun (The fluffy weed looked like a *parasol*.)

par·ti·cle (pär′tə kəl)   a very small bit of something (There were *particles* of soot on the windowsill.)

par·tic·u·lar (pər tik′yə lər)   considered by itself; apart from others (There was one *particular* story Rita liked best.)

par·tic·u·lar·ly (pər tik′yə lər lē)   especially (I *particularly* enjoy sports stories.)

ped·dler *or* **ped·lar** (ped′lər)   a person who goes from place to place or door to door selling things

peer (pir) to look closely in order to see better (to *peer* at something written in small print)

per·il·ous (per'ə ləs) dangerous (Driving on an icy road is *perilous.*)

per·i·win·kle (per'ē wing'kəl) a small sea snail that lives along rocky shores (We found some *periwinkles* on the beach.)

per·me·ate (pėr'mē āt) **per·me·at·ed; per·me·at·ing** to spread throughout (Smoke *permeated* the house.)

pes·ky (pes'kē) **pes·ki·er; pes·ki·est** annoying; troublesome (The *pesky* fly kept buzzing around my cake.)

pes·ter (pes'tər) **pes·tered; pes·ter·ing** to annoy; to bother; to make angry ("Stop *pestering* me!" Casey shouted at the barking puppy.)

pe·tu·nia (pə tü'nyə *or* pə tyü'nyə) a plant that has white, pink, red, or purple flowers shaped like funnels (*Petunias* are easy to grow from seeds.) ●

pho·ny *or* **pho·ney** (fō'nē) **pho·ni·er; pho·ni·est** not real; fake; a copy (The clerk would not accept the *phony* money.)

pho·to·graph·ic (fō'tə graf'ik) **1** having to do with the making of pictures with a camera (*photographic* supplies) **2** being able to remember clear impressions (a *photographic* memory)

pick·et (pik'it) to tie the reins of a horse to a post driven into the ground (Pam will *picket* the horse before she goes into the house.)

pin·ion (pin'yən) the wing or the end part of the wing of a bird (The goose curved its *pinions* to change the direction of its flight.)

pi·nyon *or* **piñon** (pin'yən *or* pē'nyōn) small pine tree found in the southwestern United States (The *pinyon* had shed a lot of its needles.) ●

plac·id·ly (plas'id lē) peacefully; calmly (The dog lay *placidly* by its owner's feet.)

plain (plān) a flat stretch of land (We traveled across a great *plain.*)

petunia

pinyon

a	hat	ō	open	sh	she
ā	age	ô	order	th	thin
ä	far	oi	oil	ŦH	then
e	let	ou	out	zh	measure
ē	equal	u	cup		a in about
ėr	term	u̇	put		e in taken
i	it	ü	rule	ə =	i in pencil
ī	ice	ch	child		o in lemon
o	hot	ng	long		u in circus

plane (plān) to smooth or shape wood with a plane (Have the carpenter *plane* the rough piece of wood until it is smooth.)

plead (plēd) **plead·ed** *or* **pled; plead·ing** beg; implore (The thirsty hiker *pleaded* for a drink of water from our canteen.)

pluck (pluk) **1** to pick (*pluck* berries) **2** to pull off (*pluck* feathers) **3** to grab suddenly (Lifeguards *plucked* the panicky swimmer from the pool.) **4** to pull at and let go (*pluck* guitar strings)

plum·met (plum′it) to drop or fall straight down (The injured bird *plummeted* to earth.)

por·trait (pôr′trit *or* pôr′trāt) a picture of a person (George Washington's *portrait* hangs in the lobby of our school.)

po·si·tion (pə zish′ən) the place where someone or something is (Radar charts the *position* of all air traffic.)

po·tion (pō′shən) a drink or dose used as medicine or poison, or in magic (The girl drank the *potion* and fell asleep.)

pre·cious (presh′əs) highly valued (This diamond ring is a *precious* possession of mine.)

quartz

prod·uct (prod′əkt) something that is manufactured (New *products* are tested thoroughly.)

prop (prop) **propped; prop·ping** to hold up; support (Tony *propped* himself up on an elbow.)

pro·to·type (prō′tə tīp) the original model of something (The *prototype* of a new airplane is tested before more planes are produced.)

pur·suit (pər süt′) the act of chasing (The dog ran off in *pursuit* of our neighbor's cat.)

pyr·a·mid (pir′ə mid) something having triangular sides meeting in a point (The tent looked like a *pyramid*.)

Qq

quartz (kwôrts) a very hard mineral that is found in certain kinds of rock, such as granite (A vein of *quartz* sparkled in the granite.) •

quest (kwest) a search or hunt (Settlers traveled to California in *quest* of gold.)

quiv·er (kwiv′ər) to tremble (I watched the leaves *quiver* in the breeze.)

Rr

ra·dar (rā′där)   an instrument for detecting and following the movement of distant objects by means of radio waves (The police often check traffic with *radar*.)

ra·di·al (rā′dē əl)   **1** arranged like rays **2** lines going straight from the center to the outside of a circle (Lita placed the sticks in a *radial* pattern.) •

reed (rēd)   a tall grass with a jointed stem that grows in wet places (A duck swam in and out among the *reeds*.)

re·fuse (ri fyüz′) **re·fused; re·fus·ing**   **1** to turn down an offer (He *refused* my help.) **2** to say no (He *refused* to return my book.)

reg·u·lar (reg′yə lər)   **1** usual; normal (his *regular* time for starting to school) **2** according to rule (The *regular* past form of *dive* is *dived*.)

re·lease (ri lēs′) **re·leased; re·leas·ing**   to let go; to set free (We were *released* early from school today.)

res·er·voir (rez′ər vwär *or* rez′ər vôr)   a place where water is collected and stored for use

re·sound (ri zound′)   to be filled with sound (The hallways *resound* with the children's footsteps.)

re·spect (ri spekt′)   a high regard (Congresswoman Tanaka has earned everyone's *respect*.)

re·spon·si·bil·i·ty (ri spon′sə bil′ə tē) **re·spon·si·bil·i·ties**   a duty that one is expected to perform (Getting to school on time is each pupil's *responsibility*.)

re·vive (ri vīv′) **re·vived; re·viv·ing**   **1** to bring back or come back to life or consciousness **2** to become fresh or strong again (After a good rest, you will *revive*.)

rev·o·lu·tion·ar·y (rev′ə lü′shə ner′ē)   of or dealing with a war or movement which causes a change in government

rick·et·y (rik′ə tē)   likely to fall apart or break down (The old rocking chair looked too *rickety* to sit in.)

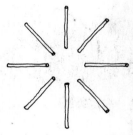

radial

a	hat	ō	open	sh	she
ā	age	ô	order	th	thin
ä	far	oi	oil	ŦH	then
e	let	ou	out	zh	measure
ē	equal	u	cup		a in about
ér	term	ů	put		e in taken
i	it	ü	rule	ə = { i in pencil
ī	ice	ch	child		o in lemon
o	hot	ng	long		u in circus

rid (rid) **rid** or **rid·ded; rid·ding** to make or get free from something (This collar will *rid* your dog of fleas.)

rip·ple (rip′əl) **rip·pled; rip·pling** to move in small waves

ri·val (rī′vəl) **ri·valed** or **ri·valled; ri·val·ing** or **ri·val·ling** to compete against; to try to be equal to or better than someone else (Arachne *rivaled* a goddess.)

ro·co·co (rō kō′kō) fancy; relating to the style of ornaments used to decorate buildings and furniture in the 1700's (The mirror is set in a *rococo* frame.)

ro·dent (rōd′nt) any of a group of related animals, such as rats, mice, squirrels, and beavers, with large front teeth especially suitable for biting and chewing

route (rüt or rout) the way to travel; road (Go by the northern *route* to the coast.)

rou·tine (rü tēn′) a regular or usual way of doing things (Playing the piano is part of my daily *routine*.)

rum·mage (rum′ij) **rum·maged; rum·mag·ing** to search by turning over or disarranging things (Lee *rummaged* through his desk for pencils.)

runt (runt) **1** an animal or a person smaller than the usual size **2** the smallest animal in a litter (My puppy was the *runt* of the litter.)

Ss

sad·dle (sad′l) a seat for the rider on a horse or on a bicycle (Before riding, Pat put a *saddle* on the horse.)

salt cel·lar (sôlt′sel′ər) a small dish or shaker for holding salt used at the table (When we have company for dinner, we use the silver *salt cellar*.) •

scat·ter (skat′ər) to throw here and there (In the winter we *scatter* bread crumbs on the ground for the birds.)

schol·ar·ship (skol′ər ship) aid, usually money, often given as an award to help a student continue his or her studies

scorn·ful (skôrn′fəl) showing dislike or disapproval (The manager gives slow workers a *scornful* look.)

scram·ble (skram′bəl) **scram·bled; scram·bling** **1** to climb on hands and knees **2** to struggle **3** to mix up

sedg·y (sej′ē) **sedg·i·er; sedg·i·est** having grass-like plants that grow in wet places (The geese flew toward the *sedgy* land.)

salt cellars

se·rum (sir′əm) a liquid used to prevent or cure an illness (This *serum* is used to treat snakebite.)

set·tle·ment house (set′l mənt hous′) a community center that provides services (counseling, recreation, adult education classes) to people in crowded parts of a city (Our drama club met at the *settlement house*.)

shield (shēld) to protect (Sunglasses will *shield* your eyes from harmful rays.)

shim·mer (shim′ər) to gleam faintly and unsteadily (When we fished at night, the moon would often *shimmer* on the water.)

shriv·el (shriv′əl) **shriv·eled** *or* **shriv·elled; shriv·el·ing** *or* **shriv·el·ling** to shrink and wrinkle; to dry up (The peach skin looked *shriveled*.)

sight·ed (sīt′id) having sight; able to see (Connie types letters to her *sighted* friends.)

sit·u·a·tion (sich′ü ā′shən) circumstances; conditions (Sitting in a stalled car on the highway can be a dangerous *situation*.)

snare (sner *or* snar) a trap to catch small animals or birds (They set up a *snare* to catch a rabbit.)

sog·gy (sog′ē) **sog·gi·er; sog·gi·est** thoroughly wet with water or moisture; soaked (My coat was *soggy* from the rain.)

so·lar sys·tem (sō′lər sis′təm) the sun and the nine planets and other bodies that move around the sun (We are studying the *solar system* now in school.)

sol·emn (sol′əm) showing deep thought; serious (Dad was *solemn* when he read my report card.)

so·lil·o·quize (sə lil′ə kwīz) **so·lil·o·quized; so·lil·o·quiz·ing** to talk to oneself (Jan sat in her room and *soliloquized* about her future.)

sought (sôt) a past form of *seek* meaning "hunted" or "tried to find" (I *sought* shelter from the rain.)

sou·ve·nir (sü′və nir′ *or* sü′və nir) something kept to remember a person or place by; a keepsake (These shells are *souvenirs* of my trip to the ocean.)

a	hat	ō	open	sh	she
ā	age	ô	order	th	thin
ä	far	oi	oil	ŦH	then
e	let	ou	out	zh	measure
ē	equal	u	cup		a in about
ér	term	ů	put		e in taken
i	it	ü	rule	ə =	i in pencil
ī	ice	ch	child		o in lemon
o	hot	ng	long		u in circus

573

span·i·el (span′yəl) a small or medium-sized dog with thick, silky hair, drooping ears, and usually short legs (My *spaniel* is a very gentle dog.)

spin·ner·et (spin′ə ret′) the organ spiders use to spin their threads (Most kinds of spiders have six *spinnerets*.)

spi·ral (spī′rəl) a winding and gradually widening coil (Each spring on my bed is a *spiral*.) •

spir·it·ed·ly (spir′ə tid lē) with great life and energy (The marchers paraded *spiritedly* for two miles.)

sta·ble (stā′bəl) a building where horses or cattle are kept

stam·mer (stam′ər) **stam·mered; stam·mer·ing** to speak haltingly, often repeating or changing one's mind about what to say next because of excitement, fear, or embarrassment

steely (stē′lē) **steel·i·er; steel·i·est** like steel in hardness or color (The captain's eyes were *steely* as she gave her orders.)

strand (strand) something twisted or bunched together, as thread, string, yarn (The *strand* of pearls is a gift.)

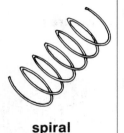

spiral

stra·te·gi·cal·ly (strə tē′jik lē) skillfully planned and managed (Sharon *strategically* placed signs pointing to her soft-drink stand.)

stri·dent (strīd′nt) having a harsh, shrill sound (We heard the *strident* calls of geese flying by.)

strut (strut) **strut·ted; strut·ting** to walk proudly (The cadets *strutted* in their new uniforms.)

stun (stun) **stunned; stun·ning** to daze or shock (I was *stunned* when I walked in on my surprise party.)

su·per·sti·tion (sü′pər stish′ən) **1** fear of the unknown or nature **2** beliefs resulting from lack of knowledge (One *supersition* considers standing under an open umbrella indoors unlucky.)

sur·face (sér′fis) the outside or any one side of something (We saw photographs of the *surface* of the moon.)

sur·vey (sər vā′) look over; examine (The horse *surveyed* its new stall.)

swag·ger (swag′ər) **swag·gered; swag·ger·ing** to walk with a rude air (The young sailor *swaggered* on the ship like a captain.)

Tt

tat·tered (tat'ərd) something torn and hanging; ragged (A *tattered* kite will never fly.) •

tav·ern tav'ərn) an eating house

ter·ri·er (ter'ē ər) a small, lively, courageous dog once used to force animals out of their burrows (My *terrier* can jump as high as that fence.)

tes·ti·ly (tes'tə lē) impatiently; showing annoyance (Leo *testily* helped his sister clean her room.)

this·tle (this'əl) a plant with a prickly stalk and leaves and usually purple flowers (The *thistle* is the national flower of Scotland.)

thrust (thrust) **thrust; thrust·ing** to push; to shove (Crowds *thrust* against the barricades to watch the parade.)

tin·der·box (tin'dər boks') a metal box for storing things needed for making fires, such as material that catches fire easily and flint for making sparks (The *tinderbox* needed some wood.) •

top·ple (top'əl) **top·pled; top·pling** to fall forward; to be thrown down or over (The building blocks *toppled* over on the floor.) •

tor·ment (tôr ment') to annoy or worry greatly (The cat *tormented* the chained dog by staying just out of the dog's reach.)

tra·di·tion (trə dish'ən) a custom that has been continued from one generation to another (A Thanksgiving feast is a *tradition*.)

trans·port (tran'spôrt *or* tran'spōrt) **1** the act of carrying from one place to another **2** a strong feeling (I was in a *transport* of delight when I heard that I had won the contest.) **3** a ship for carrying soldiers or military equipment **4** a vehicle used to carry persons or goods

trick·le (trik'əl) **trick·led; trick·ling** to fall in drops or flow in a thin stream (The glass tipped over, and the milk *trickled* to the floor.)

tattered

tinderbox

(to) topple

a	hat	ō	open		sh	she
ā	age	ô	order		th	thin
ä	far	oi	oil		ᴛʜ	then
e	let	ou	out		zh	measure
ē	equal	u	cup		a	in about
ér	term	u̇	put		e	in taken
i	it	ü	rule	ə =	i	in pencil
ī	ice	ch	child		o	in lemon
o	hot	ng	long		u	in circus

575

tri·umph (trī′umf) success, victory

tuck (tuk) **1** to put into a narrow place (to *tuck* something in a pocket) **2** to cover snugly (to *tuck* a child into bed)

twitch (twich) to move with a short, sudden, quick movement (The tired child's mouth *twitched* as if he were going to cry.)

ty·coon (tī kün′) a business person of great wealth and power (The *tycoon's* money was tied up in oil.)

Uu

uni·form (yü′nə fôrm) special clothing worn by members of a group (Our school band has ordered new *uniforms.*)

urge (ėrj) **urged; urg·ing** to request earnestly (I *urge* you to stay.)

use·less (yüs′lis) having no purpose; being of no use (A car without gas is *useless.*)

Vv

vac·u·um (vak′yü əm *or* vak′yûm) a space completely empty, even of air (People cannot live in a *vacuum* without air to breathe.)

van·ish (van′ish) to disappear suddenly from sight (We watched the jets *vanish* into the clouds.)

va·por (vā′pər) moisture in the air that can be seen, such as fog or mist (*Vapor* was rising from the pond.)

vast·ness (vast′nis) of very great size (The *vastness* of outer space is almost beyond understanding.)

ver·sion (vėr′zhən) an account or description from one point of view

vic·tim (vik′təm) someone who is injured in some way (Nick was a *victim* of a car accident.)

vig·i·lant (vij′ə lənt) watchful (A *vigilant* dog heard the burglar.)

Ww

waft (waft) to float or move lightly on water or in air (The feather *wafted* out the window.)

war·ble (wôr′bəl) **war·bled; war·bling** to sing with pleasing sounds that form a melody (A songbird was *warbling* outside my window.)

wary (wer′ē *or* war′ē) **war·i·er; war·i·est** being on guard against danger or trickery (The still mouse was *wary* of the cat.)

well-nigh (wel′nī′)   almost (It's *well-nigh* midnight.)

wham (hwam) **whammed; wham·ming**   to hit with a loud sound (A baseball *whammed* against the house.)

wheeze (hwēz) **wheezed; wheez·ing**   to breathe with difficulty, usually with a hoarse whistling or hissing sound (The thick smoke from the fire made people *wheeze*.)

whit·tle (hwit′l) **whit·tled; whit·tling**   to cut or pare chips from wood, etc., usually with a knife; to shape by cutting and trimming (Maria learned to *whittle* cats out of soap.) •

wis·dom (wiz′dəm)   good judgment based on experience; knowledge (I trust your *wisdom*.)

wit (wit)   power to reason and to figure out quick and clever solutions to problems (Thanks to her quick *wit*, Flora fooled the thief.)

wolf·hound (wŭlf′hound′)   a large dog once used to hunt wolves (Our neighbor owns a *wolfhound*.)

work·a·ble (wėr′kə bəl)   able to be done (Tim had a *workable* plan for putting the show together.)

wo·ven (wō′vən)   a past form of *weave* meaning "interlaced" (The place mats were *woven* from straw.)

Yy

yam (yam)   a sweet potato (Max ordered candied *yams* along with turkey.) •

yon·der (yon′dər)   at or in that place (Our campsite is *yonder*.)

Zz

ze·ro (zir′ō)   to focus attention on something (We must *zero* in on the problem.)

(to) whittle

yam

a	hat	ō	open	sh	she
ā	age	ô	order	th	thin
ä	far	oi	oil	ᴛʜ	then
e	let	ou	out	zh	measure
ē	equal	u	cup		a in about
ėr	term	u̇	put		e in taken
i	it	ü	rule	ə =	i in pencil
ī	ice	ch	child		o in lemon
o	hot	ng	long		u in circus

PHONICS HANDBOOK

VOWEL SOUNDS

The Long Sound /ā/a

THINK ABOUT THIS:

Say these words. Listen to the sound the underlined letters stand for.

day   name   rain   baby   eight

These words all have the long *a* vowel sound. Look at the words above to see some of the ways this vowel sound can be spelled.

DO THIS:

Say the first word in each row. Find and write the other word in the row that has the same vowel sound *and* spelling. Underline the letter or letters that stand for the vowel sound.

1. may   crayon   grant   year
2. change   patch   danger   genie
3. pail   leap   aside   afraid
4. weigh   eager   neighbor   ghost
5. shade   shall   dream   chase

The Short Sound /a/ a

THINK ABOUT THIS:

Say these words. Do all of these words have the same vowel sound?

ask   catch   apple   brand

All of these words have the short *a* vowel sound. How is the short *a* vowel sound spelled in each word? Notice where the letter *a* appears in each word.

DO THIS:

Read the words below. Find and write the words that have the short *a* vowel sound. Tell where the letter that stands for this vowel sound appears in each word. For example, you can write the following: The *a* in *damp* appears between the letters *d* and *m*.

1. damp   3. action   5. patch
2. plane   4. dragon   6. apron

The Long Sound /ē/ e

THINK ABOUT THIS:

Say these words. Listen to the sound the underlined letters stand for.

he   beat   need   city   chief   money

These words all have the long e vowel sound. Look at the words above to see some of the ways this vowel sound can be spelled.

DO THIS:

Say the first word in each row. Find and write the other word in the row that has the same vowel sound *and* spelling. Underline the letter or letters that stand for the vowel sound.

1. we   when   even   eight
2. happy   penny   yellow   try
3. each   meant   dream   heart
4. sleep   green   slow   steak
5. piece   pie   bright   field
6. valley yes   spread   chimney

The Short Sound /e/ e

THINK ABOUT THIS:

Say these words. Do both have the same vowel sound?
desk   head

Both *desk* and *head* have the short e vowel sound. How is the short e vowel sound spelled in each word? Notice where the letters e and *ea* appear in the words.

DO THIS:

Read the words below. Find and write the words that have the short e vowel sound. Tell where the letters that stand for this vowel sound appear.

1. meant   2. next   3. spread   4. well   5. funny   6. movie

The Long Sound /ī/ i

THINK ABOUT THIS:

Say these words. Listen to the sound the underlined letters stand for.

kite   my   climb   light   pie

These words all have the long i vowel sound. Look at the words above to see some of the ways this vowel sound can be spelled.

DO THIS:

Write the five words given on page 579 as headings on your paper. Then put each of the following words under the heading that has the same spelling for the long *i* vowel sound.

1. find   4. wild   7. shy
2. bright   5. might   8. ice
3. tie   6. hide   9. cry

The Short Sound /i/ *i*

THINK ABOUT THIS:

Say these words. Do all of these words have the same vowel sound?

si̲t   pi̲tch   i̲f   fi̲ll

All of these words have the short *i* vowel sound. How is the short *i* vowel sound spelled in each word? Notice where the letter *i* appears in each word.

DO THIS:

Read the words below. Find and write the words that have the short *i* vowel sound. Tell where the letter that stands for this vowel sound appears in each word.

1. fish   3. tiny   5. milk
2. night   4. rain   6. is

The Long Sound /ō/ *o*

THINK ABOUT THIS:

Say these words. Listen to the sound the underlined letters stand for.

bo̲ne   co̲ast   o̲pen   lo̲w   fo̲ld

These words all have the long *o* vowel sound. Look at the words above to see some of the ways this vowel sound can be spelled.

DO THIS:

Write the five words given above as headings on your paper. Then put each of the following words under the heading that has the same spelling for the long *o* vowel sound.

1. cold   4. know   7. grow
2. stone   5. wrote   8. yellow
3. most   6. go   9. float

The Short Sound /o/ o

THINK ABOUT THIS:
Say these words. Do all of these words have the same vowel sound?

    h<u>o</u>t   <u>o</u>x   st<u>o</u>p   r<u>o</u>ck

All of these words have the short o vowel sound. How is the short o vowel sound spelled in each word? Notice where the letter o appears.

DO THIS:
Read the words below. Find and write the words that have the short o vowel sound. Tell where the letter that stands for this vowel sound appears in each word.

    1. clock   2. frog   3. glow   4. odd   5. rob   6. coat

The Long Sound /yü/ u

THINK ABOUT THIS:
Say these words. Listen to the sound the underlined letters stand for.

    c<u>u</u>t<u>e</u>   p<u>u</u>pil

These words all have the long u vowel sound. Notice that there are only two common spellings for this vowel sound. What are they?

DO THIS:
Say the first word in each row. Find and write the other word in the row that has the same vowel sound *and* spelling. Underline the letter or letters that stand for the vowel sound.

1. c<u>u</u>t<u>e</u>	mule	none	cut
2. b<u>u</u>gle	unit	bone	tackle
3. h<u>u</u>g<u>e</u>	hug	hammer	use
4. p<u>u</u>pil	puppy	music	above

The Short Sound /u/ u

THINK ABOUT THIS:
Say these words. Listen to the sound the underlined letters stand for.

    c<u>u</u>p   s<u>o</u>n   t<u>ou</u>ch   c<u>o</u>me

These words all have the short u vowel sound. How many *different* spellings do you see for this sound? All of the other short vowel sounds you've worked with have only one or two common spellings. The short u vowel sound has four!

DO THIS:

Say the first word in each row. Find and write the other word in the row that has the same vowel sound *and* spelling. Underline the letter or letters that stand for the vowel sound.

1. t<u>u</u>g   who   hunt   book
2. t<u>ou</u>gh   young   through   rut
3. w<u>o</u>n   supper   sand   ton
4. d<u>one</u>   bone   some   do

Some Spellings for /ü/

THINK ABOUT THIS:

Say these words. Listen to the sound the underlined letters stand for.

t<u>o</u>   s<u>oo</u>n   bl<u>ew</u>   tr<u>ue</u>   r<u>u</u>d<u>e</u>

These words all have the same vowel sound. Your glossary uses the symbol /ü/ to show this sound. Look at the words above to see some of the ways this sound can be spelled.

DO THIS:

Write the five words given above as headings on your paper. Then put each of the following words under the heading that has the same spelling for this vowel sound.

1. who   4. crew   7. blue
2. roost   5. smooth   8. plume
3. glue   6. threw   9. rule

Some Spellings for /u̇/

THINK ABOUT THIS:

Say these words. Listen to the sound the underlined letters stand for.

b<u>oo</u>k   c<u>ou</u>ld   p<u>u</u>sh

These words have the same vowel sound. Your glossary uses the symbol /u̇/ to show this sound. Look at the words above to see the ways this sound can be spelled.

582

DO THIS:

Say the first word in each row. Find and write the other word in the row that has the same vowel sound *and* spelling. Underline the letter or letters that stand for the vowel sound.

1. t<u>oo</u>k   broom   foot   tone
2. w<u>ou</u>ld   should   wood   shout
3. p<u>u</u>t   pull   pink   pretty

Two More Vowel Sounds /ou/ and /oi/

THINK ABOUT THIS:

Say these words. Listen to the sound the underlined letters stand for.

l<u>ou</u>d   c<u>ow</u>

These words both have the same vowel sound. Your glossary uses the symbol /ou/ to show this sound. Look at the words above to see common spellings for this sound.

Now say these words. Again, listen to the sound the underlined letters stand for.

b<u>oy</u>   b<u>oi</u>l

These words both have the same vowel sound. It is NOT the vowel sound you hear in *loud* and *cow*. Your glossary uses the symbol /oi/ to show the vowel you hear in *boy* and *boil*.

DO THIS:

Write the symbols /ou/ and /oi/ as headings on your paper. Then put each of the following words under the symbol that stands for the vowel sound you hear in the word or in the accented syllable.

1. found   3. flower   5. enjoy   7. hound
2. voice   4. crown   6. oil   8. voyage

Some Spellings for /ô/

THINK ABOUT THIS:

Say these words. Listen to the sound the underlined letters stand for.

b<u>a</u>ll   l<u>o</u>ng   p<u>aw</u>   h<u>au</u>nt   b<u>ou</u>ght   c<u>augh</u>t

These words all have the same vowel sound. Your glossary uses the symbol /ô/ to show this sound. Look at all the different ways that this sound can be spelled. You must think: How AWful!

Letters are missing from certain words in the sentences below. The missing letters stand for the /ô/ sound. Write each word—spelled correctly—on your paper. Use a dictionary to help you.

1. If something is not true, then it must be f_lse.
2. A female child is a d_ _ _ _ter.
3. Some adults like tea; others prefer c_ffee.
4. The lion has a loud roar and sharp cl_ _s.
5. To write on the board, it's best to use ch_lk.
6. Please pass the s_lt and the pepper.
7. The team f_ _ _ _t hard to win a victory.
8. The c_ _se of that illness is not known.

Four Spellings for /ôr/

THINK ABOUT THIS:

Say these words. Listen to the sound the underlined letters stand for.

ho<u>r</u>n   m<u>ore</u>   f<u>our</u>   w<u>ar</u>n

Most people hear the same vowel sound when they say these words. Your glossary uses the symbol /ôr/ to show this sound.

The sound /ôr/ can be spelled *or*, *ore*, *our*, and *ar*. You know that the letter *r* is not usually thought of as a vowel letter. But when the letter *r* follows a vowel letter, it often influences the sound that the vowel letter stands for. For this reason, we sometimes call a sound like /ôr/ an "*r*-controlled" vowel sound.

DO THIS:

Say the first word in each row. Find and write the other word in the row that has the same *r*-controlled vowel sound *and* spelling. Underline the letters that stand for the *r*-controlled vowel sound.

1. ho<u>r</u>n	storm	turn	hear
2. m<u>ore</u>	most	store	pure
3. f<u>our</u>	round	flour	source
4. w<u>ar</u>n	term	warm	shore
5. p<u>our</u>	furry	court	yarn
6. dw<u>ar</u>f	quarter	wire	word
7. sc<u>ore</u>	sorry	scarf	before
8. bo<u>r</u>n	north	barn	bear

Another *r*-Controlled Vowel Sound /ėr/

THINK ABOUT THIS:

Say these words. Listen to the sound the underlined letters stand for.

b<u>ir</u>d　　w<u>or</u>d　　h<u>ur</u>t　　p<u>ur</u>r　　h<u>er</u>　　l<u>ear</u>n

All of these words have the same *r*-controlled vowel sound. Your glossary uses the symbol /ėr/ to show this sound. Look at the words above to see some of the ways this sound can be spelled.

DO THIS:

Write the six words given above as headings on your paper. Then put each of the following words under the heading that has the same spelling for the *r*-controlled vowel sound.

1. work　　4. turn　　7. furry
2. girl　　5. person　　8. heard
3. worm　　6. earth　　9. shirt

More *r*-Controlled Vowel Sounds /īr/, /er/, and /ir/

THINK ABOUT THIS:

Say these words. Listen to the sound the underlined letters stand for.

f<u>ire</u>　　h<u>ire</u>

Both of these words have the same *r*-controlled vowel sound. Your glossary uses the symbol /īr/ to show this sound. The letters *ire* are usually used to spell this sound.

Here is another *r*-controlled vowel sound. What letters are used to spell this sound?

m<u>erry</u>　　<u>err</u>and

Your glossary uses the symbol /er/ to show this sound.

Now say these words. Listen to the sound that the underlined letters stand for.

ch<u>eer</u>　　h<u>ear</u>　　p<u>ier</u>

These three words have the same *r*-controlled vowel sound. Your glossary uses the symbol /ir/ to show this sound. What letters can be used to spell this sound?

DO THIS:

Say the words in each row. Then find and write the two words in the row that have the same *r*-controlled vowel sound. Underline the letters that stand for the *r*-controlled vowel sound.

1. tire   read   wire   tear
2. merry   terrier   earth   more
3. reach   cherry   check   terrible
4. sneer   career   sneak   because
5. course   clear   certain   appear
6. find   earth   fierce   pierce

Still More *r*-Controlled Vowel Sounds /är/ and /ar/

THINK ABOUT THIS:

Say these words. Listen to the sound the underlined letters stand for.

p<u>ar</u>t   h<u>ear</u>t   s<u>er</u>geant

These three words have the same *r*-controlled vowel sound. Your glossary uses the symbol /är/ to show this sound. What letters can be used to spell this sound?

Now say these words. Again, listen to the sound the underlined letters stand for.

c<u>ar</u>ol   p<u>ar</u>rot

These two words have the same *r*-controlled vowel sound. Your glossary uses the symbol /ar/ to show this sound. What letters can be used to spell this sound?

DO THIS:

Say the words in each row. Then find and write the two words that have the same *r*-controlled vowel sound. Underline the letters that stand for the *r*-controlled vowel sound.

1. car   ear   dark   pear
2. sparrow   oar   purr   carry
3. party   art   cork   spare
4. harvest   hare   start   tore
5. marry   purr   wear   arrow

The Schwa Sound /ə/

THINK ABOUT THIS:
Say these words. First listen for the number of syllables in each word. Then listen for the vowel sound in the unaccented syllable.

allow   problem   conceit   fountain   focus

The underlined letter or letters in the unaccented syllable of each of these words stand for the same vowel sound. The dictionary and your glossary use the symbol /ə/ (called the *schwa*) to show this vowel sound.

DO THIS:
Copy and say the words below. Find the schwa sound in the unaccented syllable in each word and underline the letter or letters that stand for this sound.

1. scuba	4. bottom	7. circus	10. possess
2. captain	5. common	8. normal	11. mountain
3. agree	6. instant	9. person	12. alike

The *r*-Controlled Schwa Sound /ər/

THINK ABOUT THIS:
Say these words. Listen for the number of syllables in each word. Then listen for the *r*-controlled schwa vowel sound in the unaccented syllable or syllables.

murmur   percent   governor   beggar   mixture

Your glossary uses the symbol /ər/ to show this sound. Look at the words above to see some of the ways this sound can be spelled.

DO THIS:
Copy and say the words below. Find the /ər/ sound in the unaccented syllable or syllables in each word and underline the letters that stand for this sound.

1. actor	4. collar	7. error	10. measure
2. underside	5. doctor	8. border	11. sulfur
3. pasture	6. barber	9. dollar	12. cellar

CONSONANT SOUNDS

Clusters with *r*

THINK ABOUT THIS:

Say these pairs of words. Listen to the sounds the underlined letters stand for.

ring—bring	right—fright	ramp—tramp
raft—craft	round—ground	row—throw
rain—drain	ray—pray	rink—shrink

In the first word of each pair, you heard only one consonant sound at the beginning. But in the second word, you heard two consonant sounds together. We call such sounds *consonant clusters*.

DO THIS:

Copy and say the first word in each row. Then find and write the other word in the row that has the same beginning consonant sounds. Underline the letters in both words that stand for these sounds.

1. cream	dream	crust	clean
2. truck	rusty	twin	treat
3. proud	prove	please	pound
4. shrill	ship	shrug	threw
5. group	round	glove	green

NOW THINK ABOUT THIS:

Say these words. Listen to the sounds the underlined letters stand for.

    spring   scream   stroke

When you say these words, you hear three different consonant sounds together.

AND DO THIS:

Say the words in each row. Then find and write the two words in the row that have the same beginning consonant sounds. Underline the letters that stand for these sounds.

1. string	sprout	spin	sprinkle
2. scratch	school	stream	scramble
3. spring	straight	strap	store

Clusters with *l*

THINK ABOUT THIS:
Say these pairs of words. Listen to the sounds the underlined letters stand for.

lame—blame	lake—flake	lay—play
law—claw	lad—glad	late—slate

In the first word of each pair, you heard only one consonant sound at the beginning. How many consonant sounds did you hear at the beginning of the second word? What consonant letter stayed the same at the beginning of these words?

The letter *l* is also used in a three-letter consonant cluster, as in *spl*ash and *spl*it.

DO THIS:
Use each word below to make other words by writing a consonant letter before the letter *l*. For example, using the word *low*, you can make the words *slow*, *flow*, and *glow*.

1. link   3. lock   5. lot
2. lack   4. lump   6. lip

Some Other Beginning Clusters

THINK ABOUT THIS:
Say these words. Listen to the sounds the underlined letters stand for.

dwarf   swim   twin

These consonant clusters all use the letter *w*.

DO THIS:
Copy and say the first word in each row. Then find and write the other word in the row that has the same beginning sounds. Underline the letters in both words that stand for these sounds.

1. swam   smart   sweet   snake
2. twist   twinkle   tree   tiny
3. dwell   drop   dusk   dwindle

Clusters That Begin with s

THINK ABOUT THIS:

Here are some consonant clusters that you've already studied. What do these clusters have in common?

<u>sl</u>ate   <u>sw</u>im   <u>spr</u>ing   <u>scr</u>eam   <u>str</u>oke

These clusters all begin with the letter s. Here are some other clusters with the letter s:

<u>sc</u>ar   <u>sk</u>it   <u>sm</u>ile   <u>sn</u>ap   <u>sp</u>eak   <u>st</u>ack

And here is one more cluster that you should know:

squeak   square   squash

Can you think of some other words that begin with these clusters?

DO THIS:

Write each word below on your paper. Then write the letter s before the word. Say the new word, and write a sentence using that word.

1. care   2. kid   3. mart   4. nail   5. pace   6. tar

Clusters at the End

THINK ABOUT THIS:

A cluster can occur at the beginning of a word. It can also occur in the middle or at the end of a word. Here are some common final consonant clusters:

la<u>st</u>   ten<u>t</u>   raf<u>t</u>   mel<u>t</u>   fac<u>t</u>

What do these clusters all have in common?

Here are some other clusters you should know:

col<u>d</u>   han<u>d</u>   ba<u>nk</u>   ju<u>mp</u>   ra<u>nch</u>

DO THIS:

Say the words in each row. Then find and write the two words in the row that have the same final consonant sounds. Underline the letters that stand for the final consonant sounds.

1. colt	mart	halt	last
2. brand	skirt	spent	stunt
3. stomp	lamb	sand	camp
4. lost	blast	desk	plant
5. band	bold	melt	scold

Some Special Sounds at the Beginning

THINK ABOUT THIS:

Say these words. Listen to the sounds the underlined letters stand for.

<u>ch</u>in   <u>sh</u>ip   <u>th</u>in   <u>th</u>ese   <u>ph</u>one

In each word, you hear only one sound at the beginning. But two letters are used to spell each sound. What consonant letters stand for the beginning sound in each word?

DO THIS:

Say the words in each row. Then find and write the two words in the row that have the same beginning sound *and* spelling. Underline the letters that stand for this sound.

1. chop   crime   clean   child
2. shiver   shake   river   string
3. train   think   thank   twin
4. phase   photo   plane   pride

Some Special Sounds at the End

THINK ABOUT THIS:

Say these words. Listen to the sounds the underlined letters stand for.

ea<u>ch</u>   ru<u>sh</u>   tee<u>th</u>   rin<u>g</u>   gra<u>ph</u>   rou<u>gh</u>

In each word, you hear only one sound at the end. But two letters are used to spell each sound. What consonant letters stand for the final sound in each word?

DO THIS:

Say the words in each row. Then find and write the two words in the row that have the same final consonant sound *and* spelling. Underline the letters that stand for this sound.

1. much   back   flash   touch
2. thought   thing   bend   spring
3. rough   reach   tough   though
4. blast   wish   desk   crash
5. tooth   rough   push   booth
6. through   triumph   lamp   telegraph

ACKNOWLEDGMENTS
(continued)

To John Farquharson, Ltd., for "The Last of the Dragons" by E. Nesbit, on behalf of the E. Nesbit Estate.

To Grosset & Dunlap, Inc., for "A Voice from Below" by Felice Holman. From *The Cricket Winter* by Felice Holman. Copyright © 1967. Used by permission of Grosset & Dunlap, Inc.

To Harcourt Brace Jovanovich, Inc., for "Ginger on the Fire Escape" by Eleanor Estes. Abridged and slightly adapted from *Ginger Pye*, copyright 1951, 1979 by Eleanor Estes. Reprinted by permission of Harcourt Brace Jovanovich, Inc.

To Harper & Row, Publishers, Inc., for Chapter 6, "The Black Ponies," from *By the Shores of Silver Lake* by Laura Ingalls Wilder, copyright 1939, as to text by Harper & Brothers, renewed 1967, by Roger L. MacBride; for "Charlotte's Webb," Chapters VII and XIII, "Bad News" and "Good Progress," from *Charlotte's Web*, written by E. B. White, illustrated by Garth Williams, copyright 1952 by E. B. White; for "Ox on the Roof" from *On the Banks of Plum Creek* by Laura Ingalls Wilder, copyright, 1937, as to text, by Harper & Row, Publishers, Inc., renewed 1965 by Roger L. MacBride; and for an adaptation of "Georgie" and "Flyyyyyyyyyy!" from *The Fledgling* by Jane Langton; text copyright © 1980 by Jane Langton. All by permission of Harper & Row, Publishers, Inc.

To William D. Hayes and Kathryn H. Hayes for "Mr. Business Tycoon," and for "The Treasure Seekers," adapted from "The Lost Treasure of Thunder Mountain," copyright © 1973 by William D. Hayes and Kathryn Hitte, which originally appeared in *Vacation Fun,* a Scholastic magazine. Both by permission of the authors.

To Kathryn Hitte for "Minerva and Arachne." Used by permission.

To Holt, Rinehart and Winston, Publishers for "Talk" from *The Cow-Tail Switch and Other West African Stories* by Harold Courlander and George Herzog. Copyright 1947, © 1975 by Holt, Rinehart and Winston. Reprinted by permission of Holt, Rinehart and Winston, Publishers.

To Alfred A. Knopf, Inc., for "In Time of Silver Rain" by Langston Hughes. Copyright 1938 and renewed 1966 by Langston Hughes. Reprinted from *Selected Poems of Langston Hughes*, by permission of Alfred A. Knopf, Inc.

To Lantern Press, Inc., for "Crash Alert" by Clinton Pearl from *Teen-Age Outer Space Stories,* copyright © 1962. By permission of Lantern Press, Inc.

To J. B. Lippincott for selected photos and an adapted text excerpt from *Connie's New Eyes,* written and photographed by Bernard Wolf. Copyright © 1976 by Bernard Wolf. By permission of J. B. Lippincott, Publishers.

To Little, Brown and Co., for "Eletelephony" by Laura E. Richards from *Tirra Lirra* by Laura E. Richards, copyright 1930, 1932 by Laura E. Richards; and for "The Tale of Custard the Dragon" by Ogden Nash from *Verses From 1929 On* by Ogden Nash, copyright 1934 by Ogden Nash, copyright © renewed 1964 by Ogden Nash. Both used by permission of Little, Brown and Co.

To Esther MacBain Meeks for "The Web of Winter." Copyright © by Esther MacBain Meeks. Used by permission of the author.

To E. F. Moody for "The First Balloonists" from *The Pre-Man Aeronauts,* copyright © 1961, American Jr. Red Cross *News*. Reprinted by permission of the author.

To the Saturday Evening Post Company for "The Girl Who Saved the Train" by John Loveland. From *Golden Magazine* (now *Young World*) copyright © by Review Publishing Co., Inc., Indianapolis, Indiana. Reprinted by permission of the publisher.

To G. Schirmer, Inc., for "Wind" from *The Children* by Leonard Feeney. Copyright 1946 by G. Schi

To Scott, Foresman and Company for pronunciation key, grammatical key and reduced key, from *Thorndike-Barnhart Intermediate Dictionary* by E. L. Thorndike and Clarence L. Barnhart. Copyright © 1974 by Scott, Foresman and Company. Reprinted by permission.

To the State National Bank of Connecticut for "Dogs and Weather" by Winifred Welles, from her book *Skipping Along Alone,* published by Macmillan Publishing Co., Inc., © 1931. Reprinted by permission of the State National Bank of Connecticut, Agent for James Welles Shearer.

To Franklin Watts, Inc., for "Animal Riddles" from *Jokes and Fun* by Helen Hoke, copyright © 1973. Used by permission of Franklin Watts, Inc.

To Western Publishing Company, Inc., for "Beneath the Saddle" by Russell Gordon Carter and "Rococo Skates" by Marjorie Fischer, both from *Story Parade,* copyright 1936, copyright renewed 1964 by Story Parade, Inc. Both reprinted and adapted by permission of Western Publishing Company, Inc.